CANADIAN WOOD-FRAME HOUSE CONSTRUCTION

CMHC offers a wide range of housing-related information. For details, call 1 800 668-2642 or visit our home page at www.cmhc.ca

Cette publication est aussi disponible en français sous le titre :
Construction de maison à ossature de bois — Canada (61199)

The information contained in this publication represents current research results available to CMHC, and has been reviewed by a wide spectrum of experts in the housing industry. Readers are advised to evaluate the information, materials and techniques cautiously for themselves and to consult appropriate professional resources to determine whether information, materials and techniques are suitable in their case. The drawings and text are intended as general practice guides only. Project and site-specific factors of climate, cost, esthetics and so on must be taken into consideration. Any photographs in this book are for illustration purposes only and may not necessarily represent currently accepted standards.

Library and Archives Canada Cataloguing in Publication

Burrows, John, 1948-
    Canadian wood-frame house construction. -- Rev. ed.

"Second Combined Imperial/Metric Edition"--T.p. verso
Updated to conform to the 2005 National building Code of Canada and enhanced by John Burrows, JF Burrows Consulting Inc. Cf. Acknowledgements
Issued also in French under title: Construction de maison à ossature de bois — Canada.
Includes bibliographical references and index.
ISBN 0-660-19535-6
Cat. no.: NH17-3/2005

1. Wooden-frame houses--Canada--Design and construction. 2. Wooden-frame buildings--Canada--Design and construction. 3. House construction--Canada. I. Canada Mortgage and Housing Corporation II. Title.

TH4818.W6B87 2005   694   C2005-980262-6

© 1967 Canada Mortgage and Housing Corporation
Third edition 2006
Revised and reprinted 2006, 2007, 2008

Printed in Canada

Produced by CMHC

ACKNOWLEDGEMENTS

Canada Mortgage and Housing Corporation acknowledges the many individuals and their organizations for contributing to this latest edition of *Canadian Wood-Frame House Construction.*

The following people served as reviewers and performed the important role of ensuring the accuracy and usefulness of the publication for builders and educators, and its relevance to Healthy Housing™ initiatives at CMHC.

Joe Waugh, Canadian Home Builders' Association

Don Johnston, Canadian Home Builders' Association

Michael Nauth, Algonquin College

Wade Weaton, New Brunswick Community College

John Auld, University of Guelph

Peggy Lepper, Canadian Wood Council

Dan Uniat, City of Ottawa

Jim Bechthold, CMHC Prairie region

Bill Crawford, CMHC Ontario region

Brian Hudson, CMHC Atlantic region

Barry Craig, CMHC Policy and Research Division

CMHC also expresses its appreciation to John Burrows, of JF Burrows Consulting Inc., who updated this edition to conform to the 2005 National Building Code of Canada and enhanced this edition significantly by adding new, special features.

CMHC gratefully acknowledges the National Research Council and the Canadian Wood Council for the use of their information included in the tables of this publication.

TABLE OF CONTENTS

PREFACE

Since the first edition of Canada Mortgage and Housing Corporation's *Canadian Wood-Frame House Construction* appeared in 1967, this publication has been the primary means by which builders, carpenters and students of housing technology have learned about wood-frame house construction in Canada. This publication continues to be the most widely used reference in the field, in community colleges and in many university architecture programs.

This edition retains the convenient format of previous editions, reflecting the feedback from a broad cross-section of users across Canada. It is hoped that readers of this publication will continue to contribute their much-welcomed suggestions for future improvements.

The inclusion of *Healthy Housing*™ principles throughout this book represents a significant shift in awareness regarding the individual, social, environmental and economic impacts of the housing industry in Canada and around the world. Canadians continue to have good cause to be proud of their wood-frame house construction technology.

This latest edition is one among many continuing efforts toward the goal of providing choice in accessible, affordable and sustainable housing in Canada.

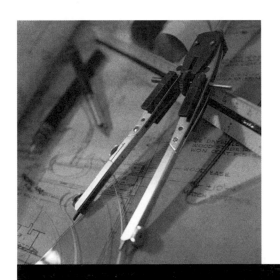

How To Use This Book

HOW TO USE THIS BOOK

This book presents a concise description of Canadian wood-frame house construction. It also references a number of publications, which can provide a greater depth of information. This book should not be considered to be a complete reference on wood-frame house construction. Instead, readers should consider it as the basic framework for learning about and appropriately applying wood-frame house construction technology and Healthy Housing principles.

Canadian Wood-Frame House Construction is based on the requirements of the 2005 edition of the National Building Code. This book is not a substitute for the National Building Code. Readers are encouraged to refer to the codes and standards pertaining to housing in their jurisdictions for a complete set of requirements.

The organization of *Canadian Wood-Frame House Construction* corresponds to the construction sequence for a typical Canadian house. The chapters are based on major aspects of wood-frame house construction and reflect typical practices. Actual practices may vary across Canada. Users of this publication are urged to consult with local building departments, trades and suppliers when designing and building a house.

Ideally, users of this book should gain an overview of its contents before exploring any of the topics in depth. Start at the beginning of the book and work forward through the stages of construction when planning and designing the house. However, if only specific information is required, each chapter has been developed as a stand-alone reference. It is expected experienced builders and tradespeople will continue to find this edition a convenient job-site guide—now enhanced with helpful new features.

In order to keep this book at a manageable size, a glossary of the numerous housing terms used in this book is not included. Most if not all of the housing terms used in this book can be found in CMHC's *Glossary of Housing Terms.*

The feedback and insights of readers is highly valued at Canada Mortgage and Housing Corporation (CMHC). Your views and suggestions on new or improved content are welcome. While every effort has been made to present accurate information, please point out any incorrect or incomplete information. Kindly take the time to help improve this publication. Forward your correspondence to:

Canadian Housing Information Centre
Canada Mortgage and Housing Corporation
700 Montreal Road
Ottawa ON K1A 0P7

NEW FEATURES

This edition of *Canadian Wood-Frame House Construction* has been updated to reflect the residential requirements of the 2005 National Building Code of Canada. In addition, many changes have been made to bring the book in line with current building science research, construction methods and construction materials. Sixteen new drawings have been added to further clarify wood-frame house construction and another 85 figures have been updated or improved. The design and nailing schedules for site-built trusses has been added in Appendix B.

Healthy Housing™ Insights

CMHC is committed to providing the Canadian housing industry with reliable information on appropriate housing technology that responds to people and the environment. Practical considerations derived from CMHC's Healthy Housing initiatives have been included in this edition.

Healthy Housing Insights, conveniently identified throughout this publication, are presented in the format depicted below.

Planning Ahead and *Checking Back* Notes

The *Planning Ahead* and *Checking Back* notes have valuable pointers for builders. The *Planning Ahead* notes tell

HEALTHY HOUSING INSIGHTS

Healthy Housing Insights are presented throughout this book to enable users to consider and practically apply the following elements of healthy housing to wood-frame house construction:

→ Occupant Health

→ Energy Efficiency

→ Resource Efficiency

→ Environmental Responsibility

→ Affordability

Healthy Housing Insights are intended to help users make appropriate choices that will sustain the health of the house occupants, and the environment. They deal with issues that have not yet found their way into building code requirements, but which are recognized as practical options for building more-sustainable housing.

you about factors that affect later stages of construction. The *Checking Back* notes remind you about problems that need to be solved before continuing with building.

The format for these notes is depicted below. Further information on how they may be used to plan and properly construct a dwelling is provided.

Examples for Using the Sizing Tables

Examples have been provided for sizing typical structural components of the house.

PLANNING AHEAD

Planning Ahead notes are intended to identify important factors that may affect later stages of construction. Options for dealing with these related aspects of construction are also presented.

It is recommended that you review all of the *Planning Ahead* notes during the design stage of the house. Resolving conflicts on paper is much easier than on site, and generally less expensive.

➡ Points like this identify key factors to consider when using *Planning Ahead* notes.

Planning Ahead notes are cross-referenced with *Checking Back* notes to ensure that critical aspects are appropriately resolved at every stage of construction.

CHECKING BACK

Checking Back notes are intended to flag aspects of earlier stages of construction that may affect a present stage of construction. They are conveniently referenced to *Planning Ahead* notes.

In case a *Planning Ahead* note has been overlooked, *Checking Back* notes are helpful reminders of the need to resolve potential problems during the early stages of planning and design, prior to construction.

➡ Points like this identify items to review when *Checking Back* notes are encountered.

Checking Back notes may also be used as a concise checklist when reviewing plans to avoid construction problems.

Imperial and Metric Dimensions

This edition of *Canadian Wood-Frame House Construction* contains imperial as well as metric units. The National Building Code of Canada uses metric units, and these govern when strict interpretations of Code requirements are required. However, imperial units of measure (feet and inches) dominate most of wood-frame house construction technology. For this reason, the imperial units are provided first in this publication, followed by the actual Code requirements in metric units.

For lumber, the imperial dimensions are nominal sizes. Nominal means the rough sawn size before planing and dimensional changes resulting from drying. For example, a wood member with a nominal size of 2 in. by 4 in. has a finished size of about 1-1/2 in. by 3-1/2 in. The metric dimensions for lumber are actual sizes.

Every reasonable effort has been made to provide accurate conversions of metric dimensions to imperial equivalents; however, it remains the responsibility of designers and builders to comply with building code requirements in their jurisdictions. In addition, conversion factors are given in Table 1.

Note: Consult your local building department on the units of measurement required for house plans.

SIZING TABLE

Examples using the sizing tables found in the Appendix A have been developed to assist users in their proper application. They may be found in the sections dealing with the actual framing of the house.

By reviewing these examples, readers may correctly apply the tables when sizing structural components of the house. Readers should consult their local building departments to ensure that the sizing of basic structural components has been done properly.

When encountering situations not covered by any of the tables, it is advisable to consult a structural designer.

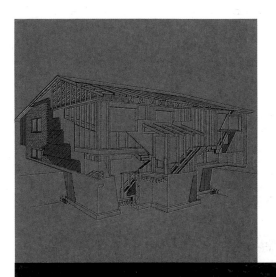

Introduction

INTRODUCTION

Wood-frame construction has been used millions of times in North America in the last century to provide one of the world's most affordable and comfortable housing standards. From the earliest trial-and-error efforts of early settlers to use abundant forest resources as a housing material, wood-frame construction has become a sophisticated construction method supported by in-depth technical research and capable of meeting or exceeding all building science challenges. This book will be useful to students, builders, homeowners and to foreign housing professionals seeking solutions to global housing needs.

ADVANTAGES OF WOOD-FRAME CONSTRUCTION

Wood-frame construction combines dimension lumber, engineered wood products and structural wood panel sheathing to make wall, floor and roof assemblies that are robust, economical and fast to build. Wood-frame has a long history of satisfactory performance in North America with millions of houses in service. Current wood-frame technology is the result of many years of development and improvement and extensive research by the National Research Council, Canada Mortgage and Housing Corporation and others.

Like any other building system, wood-frame construction requires reasonable care in its design and construction to provide lasting shelter, comfort and safety. When well-designed and constructed, wood-frame construction can be expected to provide the following advantages:

➜ Wood-frame construction is fast, easy to renovate, and durable.

➜ Wood is a renewable resource and Canada is a world leader in forest conservation, protection and sustainable use.

➜ Wood is a natural insulator, relative to other structural materials, and wood-frame construction is easy to insulate to minimize heating and cooling costs.

➜ Normal construction readily withstands typical wind and snow loads found throughout Canada.

➜ Construction techniques can be easily adapted to withstand extreme wind and earthquake loads.

➜ Wood-frame construction can be adapted to suit all climate ranges from hot, humid climates to cold, arctic climates.

➜ Wood-frame construction is easily learned. The tools are basic, the techniques are proven, and years of experience have resulted in tricks of the trade that save time. The building materials are strong, light, and easy to use.

→ Wood-frame construction will meet or exceed code-established levels of fire safety and sound control.

Depending on the level of economic activity, about 2 million new homes are constructed annually in Canada and the United States. Because of these advantages, the vast majority of these residential units are wood-frame construction.

DESIGN PRINCIPLES

There are many house designs and plans available for wood-frame housing. Regardless of whether a stock design is selected or a custom design is created, there are basic requirements that must be met, like code provisions, and design principles that should be respected, not only for the durability of the house, but also for the benefit of the occupants and the environment. Building design should provide easy access to people of diverse physical capabilities and be adaptable to meet the occupants' changing needs. The design should be simple and intuitive to use. It should minimize hazards and adverse consequences of accidental or unintended actions. The design should be comfortable and easy to use. The building should be sized appropriately. In cases where there are special requirements, such as barrier-free access for people with disabilities, professional design assistance should be sought.

STRUCTURAL DESIGN

The building code requirements for wood-frame housing are based on a combination of calculated designs and solutions based on performance history. The calculated solutions in the building codes are based on gravity loads, dead loads, occupancy loads and balanced snow loads.

The building code for residential construction does not explicitly include prescriptive requirements for wind and earthquake resistance. However, elements such as roof rafters and roof trusses that are designed for gravity loads may also withstand wind and earthquake loads, up to a certain magnitude, without being explicitly designed for that purpose. Some jurisdictions with potentially high wind or earthquake loads may require engineering design for houses. The Canadian Wood Council's *Engineering Guide for Wood Frame Construction* specifies lateral loads and lateral design solutions for these situations.

FIRE SAFETY

Wood-frame construction is capable of meeting the fire safety provisions of the National Building Code of Canada. Fire safety is a combination of many factors, some of which can be minimized by building requirements, and others that can only be controlled by the occupants. Examples of building code fire safety measures include:

→ Limiting the area of unprotected openings (windows) in buildings close to property lines to reduce the chance of a fire spreading from one house to another.

→ Requiring the provision of smoke alarms.

→ Setting minimum door and exit route widths and requiring window egress routes from bedrooms to help occupants escape in the event of fire.

Examples of ways occupants can minimize their exposure to fire risk are:

→ Maintaining smoke alarms in working order.

→ Ensuring all occupants are aware of escape routes and an outdoor gathering point in the event of fire.

→ Exercising care with all cooking and heating operations and appliances.

ROOM HEIGHT

Building codes establish minimum ceiling heights for living area rooms. In general, the minimum ceiling height is 7.5 ft. (2.3 m), but this can be reduced to 6.9 ft. (2.1 m) in localized areas such as bathrooms and laundry rooms on the main floors. Unfinished basement areas need to have a minimum ceiling height of 6.4 ft. (1.95 m).

MATERIAL COMPATIBILITY

Many types of building materials are needed to construct a house. Occasionally, one material can have a detrimental effect on an adjacent material, resulting in premature material degradation. Experience shows that sealants and metals are two groups of materials that may cause material incompatibility. In the case of metals, builders may not be aware that connecting different metals can lead to premature failure. There is a large number of sealant products to suit a wide range of applications, and there is no simple and universal product labelling system to help avoid improper selections, leading to problems such as paint failure or finish damage to window frames. Other cases of premature failure result from job-site-imposed conditions or deadlines. For example, in the rush to apply paint in unheated conditions as winter approaches, the painter might ignore the temperature application ranges recommended for a product. While ignoring the product limits may get the project completed in time, it also brings a fairly high likelihood of recalls at a later date, often at higher cost than doing the work according to instructions in the first place.

✳ CONSTRUCTION SAFETY

Construction is a process that requires care to avoid personal injury. Based on stages of construction, here are factors to consider:

1. Site work: The use of chainsaws for site clearing requires care. Wear appropriate safety equipment and get professional help if necessary.

✳2. Excavation: Steep excavations in unstable soils can cave in suddenly. Ensure that excavations are adequately back-sloped to prevent slope failure.

3. Foundation: Concrete formwork must be strong enough to restrain the weight of the concrete while it is being placed.

4. Framing: Care is required to control the placement of wall sections that have been framed and sheathed on the floor platform. Wood trusses are unstable until they have been braced. Placement of the trusses and other framing assemblies involves working well above ground level. Fall protection and securing of ladders and scaffolding are important steps to safe construction.

5. Exterior finishes and roofing: This stage also involves working at heights well above ground and care and protection is required.

6. Electrical and mechanical: The installation of wiring, and heating and electrical appliances needs to be done by qualified personnel to ensure safety both during construction and during the service life of the house.

7. General: The use of hand tools and power tools requires concentration and experience. Eye and hearing protection are required when using most tools. Follow manufacturer's instructions for all equipment and tools.

RELATED PUBLICATIONS

Housing for Persons with Disabilities
Canada Mortgage and Housing Corporation

Housing Choices for Canadians with Disabilities
Canada Mortgage and Housing Corporation

Healthy Housing™

HEALTHY HOUSING

A growing awareness of the relationship between the health of people, the environment and the economy has fostered the Healthy Housing concept in Canada. Wood-frame construction continues to dominate the Canadian residential market and offers many opportunities to explore and incorporate Healthy Housing principles. In fact, wood-frame house construction continues to represent an environmentally responsible choice. Wood is a renewable resource that, if properly managed and utilized, can enhance our quality of life, sustain our natural environment and contribute to the economy.

Healthy Housing principles are presented throughout this publication to make readers aware of the many options available to them at the various stages of house construction—from siting the building through to interior finishes and landscaping. Before any of these specific topics are discussed, an overview of Healthy Housing principles has been provided.

Healthy Housing represents a collaborative effort supported by CMHC that enables researchers, the building industry and interested groups to engage in an ongoing exploration of environmentally and economically sound design and development techniques.

PRINCIPLES OF HEALTHY HOUSING

Healthy Housing is founded on five fundamental principles: occupant health, energy efficiency, resource efficiency, environmental responsibility and affordability.

The principles of Healthy Housing each consist of a number of related elements (Figure 1). Each should be considered at the design stage before beginning house construction. Decisions are easiest to reconsider and revise appropriately at this stage. Incorporating these elements during construction is equally important, and makes the difference between a healthful idea and a healthy house.

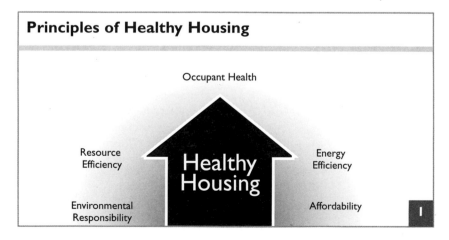

Principles of Healthy Housing

Occupant Health

Resource Efficiency

Energy Efficiency

Healthy Housing

Environmental Responsibility

Affordability

I

Occupant Health

Indoor Air Quality: The reduction of the level of contaminants built into the building (material selection), and the removal of any contaminants at the source, coupled with the dilution of house air with fresh outside air (ventilation).

Water Quality: The selection of a safe supply of potable water, and where this is not possible, appropriate home treatment to remove bacteria, chemical contaminants and unpleasant tastes or odours.

Light, Sound and Radiation: The provision of adequate natural light throughout the house, the isolation of internal and external noise sources, and the avoidance of exposure to electromagnetic fields.

Energy Efficiency

Building Thermal Performance: The reduction of building envelope area (compact design), the improvement of the building envelope through better insulated and more airtight assemblies, and the installation of high performance windows and doors.

Energy for Heating, Cooling and Ventilation: The selection of appropriate house energy sources and the provision of high-efficiency equipment having the proper capacity.

Renewable Energy Technologies: The orientation of the building and the placement of windows to capture solar gains during cold months and to enhance natural ventilation and cooling of the house during hot months.

Electrical Consumption and Peak Demand: The use of controls to avoid or minimize electrical power consumption during peak periods, typically mornings and early evenings, and the selection of efficient domestic appliances and lights.

Resource Efficiency

Embodied Energy: The selection of renewable, recycled or reused materials where possible and consideration of the environmental impacts associated with manufactured materials.

Management of Construction Waste: The intelligent use of materials to reduce waste, to enable their reuse and to recycle waste materials into useful products.

Water: The installation of water-efficient plumbing fixtures and appliances indoors and the careful planning of landscaping and natural drainage to minimize water consumption outdoors.

Durability and Longevity: The construction of a durable building structure, thermal envelope and finishes.

Environmental Responsibility

Emissions and Combustion By products: The selection of appropriate materials made from environmentally responsible manufacturing processes and the installation of high-efficiency, low-emission equipment and appliances.

Waste water and Sewage: The reduction of waste-water, and sewage through water conservation and the provision of an appropriate treatment technique for private septic systems.

Community Planning and Site Planning Issues: The design of viable communities that are properly sited to minimize ecological damage and to take better advantage of the sun and the wind.

Hazardous Materials—Landfill and Disposal: The avoidance of hazardous materials during construction and in the home, combined with a facility for composting and recycling.

Affordability

Affordability: The availability of suitable housing having both an affordable purchase price and affordable, long-term operating costs.

Viability for the Construction Industry: The reliance on simple but effective technologies that are adaptable across the range of Canadian climates and markets and exportable abroad.

Adaptability: The flexibility of design and construction to enable cost-effective renovation and reuse long into the future.

Marketability: Catering to the real needs of people and accounting for shifts in demographics and consumer perceptions about housing.

HEALTHY WOOD-FRAME HOUSE CONSTRUCTION

There are many Healthy Housing practices to be considered when designing and building a home. The preceding outline is the basis for a number of suggestions, presented within the chapters to follow as *Healthy Housing Insights.* Refer to the previous chapter, "How to Use this Book" for a guide on how to consider and incorporate Healthy Housing alternatives into your house construction.

RELATED PUBLICATIONS

Building Materials for the Environmentally Hypersensitive Canada Mortgage and Housing Corporation

Healthy Housing Renovation Planner Canada Mortgage and Housing Corporation

PLANNING AHEAD

4 Rs of Wood-Frame Construction

Many of the chapters contain Healthy Housing Insights on the appropriate use of wood to minimize waste and to make the most efficient use of this valuable resource. These are presented according to an approach which the building industry has adopted as the 4 Rs:

➜ **Review** conventional procedures and practices;

➜ **Reduce** the wastes being generated;

➜ **Re-use** materials; and

➜ **Recycle** what traditionally has been conventionally seen as waste.

Refer to the Healthy Housing Insight on applying the 4 Rs of Wood-Frame Construction in the "Framing the House" chapter.

Typical House
Construction Process

TYPICAL HOUSE CONSTRUCTION PROCESS

Due to the wide variety of house styles and sizes, and the differences between professional builders and do-it-yourselfers, it is difficult to say exactly what is a typical house construction process. Many factors apply, such as whether a single house or an entire subdivision is being built, weather, site conditions and the availability of labour and materials.

The description of the typical house construction process which follows is based on common wood-frame house construction techniques. It assumes that a typical two- or three-bedroom house is being built by a builder employing subtrades. Special features, such as a sunroom, swimming pool or detached garage or workshop, are not included in this description. Before proceeding, it is interesting to review how Canadian wood-frame house construction has changed in the past 30 years. The first observation is that it takes less time than ever to build a wood-frame house.

The steady decline in construction time is due largely to the introduction of panel products like plywood, oriented strandboard (OSB) and gypsum board; factory-built components, such as roof trusses, windows and cabinets; versatile power tools; plastic piping for sanitary plumbing; and, specialized work crews. While it may have taken 10 weeks in 1970 to complete a given house, the same work can typically be completed in eight weeks today, provided all the materials and subtrades are available. Construction time depends on many factors, especially size and complexity. For average-sized houses, about 16 weeks is required from start to finish (see chart on next page). For very large or highly detailed building, 18 or more weeks may be needed. On the other hand, completing a small, simple dwelling may only require eight to 10 weeks. This does not account for delays due to inclement weather, inspections, material shortages, custom-ordered items or busy sub trades during construction. Prior to construction, delays may be incurred while financing and a building permit are being obtained. Shorter construction time has taken place even as the average size of houses has increased. In 1970, the average house was 1,100 sq. ft. (102 m²) and today the typical new Canadian home is in the 2,000 sq. ft. (185 m²) range. The traditional need to set aside late spring, all summer and part of the fall for construction has not changed significantly for the single-house builder. At the same time, advances in Canadian homebuilding have made construction an efficient, year-round activity in many parts of Canada.

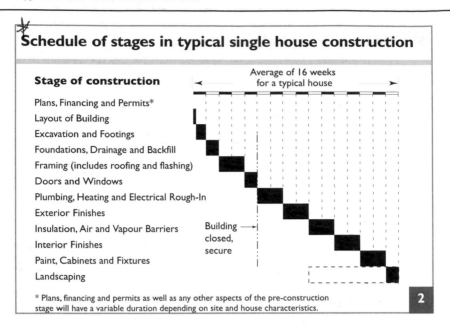

Schedule of stages in typical single house construction

Stage of construction	Average of 16 weeks for a typical house
Plans, Financing and Permits*	
Layout of Building	
Excavation and Footings	
Foundations, Drainage and Backfill	
Framing (includes roofing and flashing)	
Doors and Windows	
Plumbing, Heating and Electrical Rough-In	
Exterior Finishes	
Insulation, Air and Vapour Barriers	Building closed, secure
Interior Finishes	
Paint, Cabinets and Fixtures	
Landscaping	

* Plans, financing and permits as well as any other aspects of the pre-construction stage will have a variable duration depending on site and house characteristics.

2

STAGES OF CONSTRUCTION

There are a number of stages in constructing a house that must be properly planned, coordinated and executed by the builder (Figure 2). A short description of these has been provided following the typical construction sequence. It should be noted that the chapters that follow are presented according to this sequence.

Plans, Financing and Permits

This stage is also referred to as the pre-construction stage. The amount of time needed to develop a complete set of plans, estimate the cost of the dwelling, arrange for financing and obtain a building permit and all other required approvals, will vary considerably across the country. Providing access to the building site and arranging for temporary power may also take place during this stage. Because the time required for these factors is unpredictable, it has not been shown in Figure 2, but it should be taken into account.

Site drainage in typical construction

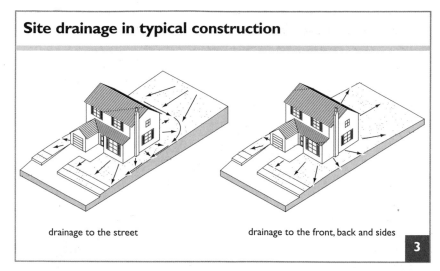

drainage to the street   drainage to the front, back and sides

3

Site Planning

Careful planning is required to ensure the house is well situated in relation to property lines, sunshine and shading, and trees and other natural features. The elevation of the house should take into consideration storm and wastewater disposal and site drainage (Figure 3).

Layout of Building

The first stage of construction involves layout of the building on the property. To properly observe the bylaws for setbacks to property lines, the services of a land surveyor may be required. Accurately laying out the excavation for the depth and placement of foundations is critical. Layout can usually be performed in a single day provided property boundaries do not need to be established. On the other hand, site planning to take advantage of the sun and wind, to manage drainage (runoff) and snow accumulation, and to afford a pleasing view, may require considerably more effort.

Excavation and Footings

Once the building layout is complete, excavation for the foundations may proceed. A single day is often all that is needed, provided appropriate equipment is employed and there is easy access to the excavation area. Another few days are needed to trench for and rough-in services, form and place footings, remove footing formwork, lay out the foundation walls and columns, and prepare to construct the foundations.

Foundations, Drainage and Backfill

Foundations can be installed in several days by a skilled subtrade, allowing time for concrete curing and formwork removal. Dampproofing, foundation drainage systems and backfill will usually require another day or two. In some cases, unusual site conditions in unserviced areas may require additional measures for foundation drainage, such as waterproofing, sump pumps, ditching or dry wells. Properly storing topsoil and excavated material suitable for backfilling can eliminate the need to import fill and topsoil. Placement of the granular layer and basement floor slab usually occurs later when the basement plumbing rough-in is completed.

Framing

Generally, about two weeks is needed to complete the framing and install roofing to provide weather protection during subsequent stages of construction. This assumes that temporary power is available for tools and equipment. Chimney installation and the building of stairs or the installation of pre-manufactured stairs is generally considered part of the framing stage. Typical arrangements with carpentry sub trades vary across Canada. Where window and exterior door installation is included, another day or two is needed to complete this stage. Deck framing is usually performed later.

Doors and Windows

Installing doors and windows, usually after framing is completed, requires a few days to a week to complete. Complete installation generally includes flashing and installing locks and related hardware. Jamb extensions and trim are typically part of the finishing carpentry work. The interior air sealing of gaps around window and door openings is commonly performed by the insulation and vapour-retarder contractor.

Plumbing, Heating and Electrical Rough-in

This stage usually does not start until all framing is completed. Plumbing is brought from the service connections and roughed-in to the fixtures. Bathtubs and shower enclosures are generally installed at this time, but may need to be situated earlier if their size means framing will interfere with later installation. The furnace and ductwork or piping is installed, along with ductwork for exhaust fans and mechanical ventilation equipment such as heat recovery ventilators (HRVs). Electrical wiring, smoke and carbon monoxide alarms, telephone and computer lines, and cable TV is roughed-in throughout the dwelling. The work requires about two weeks to complete, but does not include items such as wood stoves and fireplaces that are usually installed by the suppliers.

Exterior Finishes

Depending on the type of exterior finish being applied to the dwelling, between one and two weeks is needed to complete this stage. If an exterior air barrier, such as a sheathing membrane, is being used, it is usually applied at this time; however it may also have been installed during the framing stage. Brick, siding and stucco, soffit, fascia, eavestroughing, downspouts and window and door caulking are all part of the exterior finishes stage. Exterior trim and millwork, staining and painting may also be carried out at this stage.

Insulation, Air and Vapour Barriers

This stage may be performed at the same time as exterior finishes, provided the insulation is protected against moisture damage, such as that caused by wind-driven rain. Installing insulation, air barriers and vapour retarders requires a few days to complete when all of the detailing around penetrations, fixtures and outlets is included.

Interior Finishes

This stage typically begins with installing ceiling, wall and floor finishes. Finishing carpentry for interior doors, frames, shelving and trim along with stair balusters and handrails is generally carried out immediately after the floor, wall and ceiling finishes are prepared for painting and varnishing. The interior finishes stage normally requires about two weeks to complete, but significantly more time may be required depending on the type of finishes selected.

Paint, Cabinets and Fixtures

Painting and varnishing are usually performed at the beginning of this stage. Cabinets and items such as ceramic tile backsplashes are then installed. While this is proceeding, plumbers complete the installation of the plumbing fixtures and electricians finish connecting circuits, receptacles, switches, light fixtures and smoke alarms. Connections to equipment such as furnaces, water heaters, mechanical ventilation systems, stoves and clothes dryers are also performed at this time. The heating contractor will install all grilles and registers for forced-air systems and radiators for hydronic or electric baseboard systems. In some cases, appliances such as refrigerators, dishwashers, stoves and dryers will also be installed at this time. All of the trades should ensure that their installations have been inspected and function properly and then hand over any operating instructions and warranties to the builder or owner. A final cleanup of the dwelling concludes all work. About two weeks is normally required to complete this stage of construction.

Landscaping

This final stage includes finish grading, driveways, steps, walkways, ground cover, shrubs and trees. Carpentry work associated with decks and fences, and plumbing work for items such as underground sprinkler systems is also carried out at this time. Approximately one week is needed to carry out this final stage; however, the time will vary depending on the nature of the landscaping, the time of year and any special features, such as decks and pools.

A summary of the stages of house construction, showing their sequence and duration, is shown in Figure 2. Again, this should be viewed as a guide. It is important for do-it-yourself and less-experienced builders to obtain advice on local conditions and practices. It is also important to add in several weeks time to allow for unavoidable delays.

APPROVALS, PERMITS AND INSPECTIONS

The system of approvals, permits and inspections for house construction can be quite complex for both inexperienced and do-it-yourself builders. Practices differ among localities. However, the most important consideration before proceeding with house plans and specifications is to ensure that the property is zoned for residential use. Properties located in areas under the jurisdiction of a conservation authority may have many restrictions and requirements that apply to dwellings. Some properties may have development regulations, covenants or restrictions, governing the size, location and finishes of the house. Without knowing the zoning and environmental guidelines for construction, it is not prudent to proceed with the house design.

Requirements for plans, permits and inspections vary across Canada; this means that special provisions may be required to suit local climatic and geological conditions. For example, the wet climates of both the east and west coasts require special attention to rain penetration; varying snow loads across Canada result in the different structural capacities for roof members; and houses in areas subject to earthquake risk require additional strengthening. Most municipalities will require that the basic requirements described in the National Building Code of Canada be met. Plans should be drawn to scale and provide sufficient detail to enable a plans examiner to confirm that the house conforms to Code requirements. Most building departments will indicate the preferred format for house plans and the minimum information needed to obtain a building permit. Good plans also enable suppliers and subtrades to properly supply and install materials and equipment. A complete set of plans and specifications should be prepared by a competent designer, the cost of which is often more than recovered through avoided extras and unforeseen problems.

This book has been updated to incorporate the requirements of the 2005 National Building Code of Canada (NBCC). However, it is not meant to replace the NBCC. Consultations with municipal building officials during the design, plan approval, and construction stages are suggested to ensure that problems are avoided. The 2005 NBCC, includes *prescriptive* requirements and, for the first time, *performance* functional statements that form the basis for an *objective-based code.* Previously, the NBCC was used to determine what was required and what materials could be used. An objective-based code states the outcome that must be achieved and provides latitude for users to determine the solution. For example, while the traditional code might dictate how thick a concrete foundation wall must be, the objective code explains the need for the wall to resist forces and allows the user to submit an alternate design that will work at least as well as the prescribed wall. The objective-based code will be used mostly by engineers, architects and other design professionals seeking economic solutions for building challenges.

Figure 4 shows the process of approvals, permits and inspections which may apply to a new house. It is recommended that readers consult their local building departments to obtain a complete list of forms and procedures. In some areas, it may be necessary to observe additional registration and inspection requirements by warranty programs for new houses. The scheduling of inspections to avoid lengthy delays is very important. It is advisable to determine exactly what work must be completed prior to calling for a particular inspection, as well as the amount of notice required. This is most critical in remote communities where inspectors must travel long distances to perform inspections.

The many approvals, permits and inspections in Canada are intended to maintain minimum levels of health and safety in new houses. It's important to understand the local requirements and plan ahead, so that the legal and administrative aspects of house building do not interfere with the actual construction of the house. Builders and their subtrades can focus solely on the quality of their work when the paperwork associated with approvals, permits and inspections is handled properly. The following chapters present aspects of these stages of house construction in greater detail.

ESSEX REGIONAL CONSERVATION AUTHORITHY
ALL ABOUT NATURE

Approvals, permits and inspections process for new houses

1 stop permit. ERCA

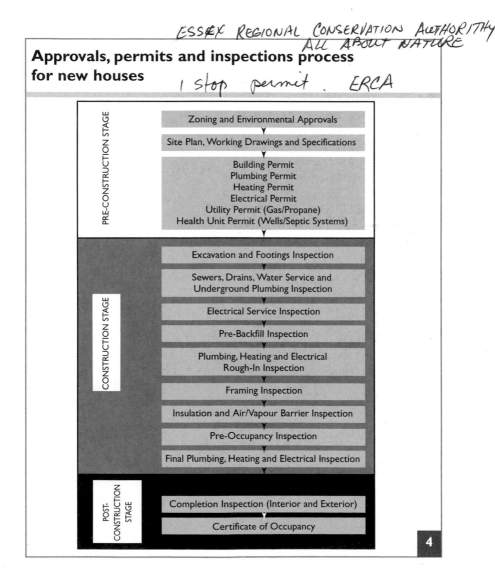

PRE-CONSTRUCTION STAGE

Zoning and Environmental Approvals

Site Plan, Working Drawings and Specifications

Building Permit
Plumbing Permit
Heating Permit
Electrical Permit
Utility Permit (Gas/Propane)
Health Unit Permit (Wells/Septic Systems)

CONSTRUCTION STAGE

Excavation and Footings Inspection

Sewers, Drains, Water Service and Underground Plumbing Inspection

Electrical Service Inspection

Pre-Backfill Inspection

Plumbing, Heating and Electrical Rough-In Inspection

Framing Inspection

Insulation and Air/Vapour Barrier Inspection

Pre-Occupancy Inspection

Final Plumbing, Heating and Electrical Inspection

POST-CONSTRUCTION STAGE

Completion Inspection (Interior and Exterior)

Certificate of Occupancy

4

Location and Excavation

LOCATION AND EXCAVATION

MARKING THE EXCAVATION AREA

Before the exact location of the house on the site is decided, it is important to check with the municipality or township for minimum setback and side yard requirements, because these can be determining factors in placing the house.

Always check with local utility companies prior to digging to ensure that the excavation will not interfere with buried services. Inadvertently cutting

---

Establishing the lines of a house

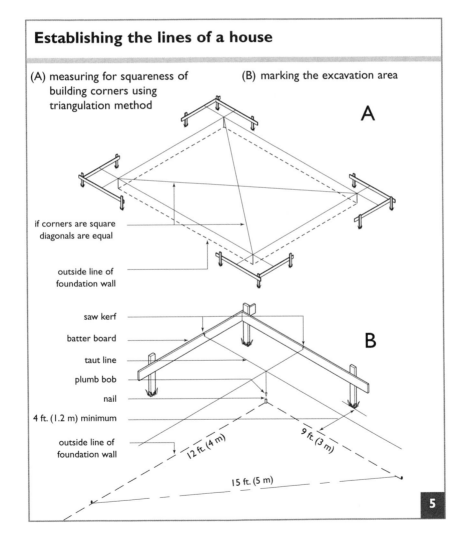

(A) measuring for squareness of building corners using triangulation method

(B) marking the excavation area

A

if corners are square diagonals are equal

outside line of foundation wall

saw kerf

batter board

taut line

plumb bob

nail

4 ft. (1.2 m) minimum

outside line of foundation wall

B

12 ft. (4 m)

9 ft. (3 m)

15 ft. (5 m)

5

---

telephone, gas or power lines can prove costly and can result in personal injury.

After the site is cleared, the perimeter of the house is marked using the exact location of the corners of the lot as a reference. These are usually determined by a certified survey. The corners of the house are marked by small wooden stakes, accurately located at each corner, with nails driven into their tops indicating the outside line of the foundation walls.

Because these stakes will be eventually lost during excavation, additional markings are needed. Offset markings may be located by extending the lines of the foundation walls from the established corners, and fixing these offset markings either with stakes on the ground or marks on surrounding, but permanent, objects. These markings are used after the excavation to set up an arrangement of batter boards (Figure 5). However, if the foundation shape is simple, the site area unconstrained and the excavation carefully done, the batter boards can be erected before excavation.

The area to be excavated is staked out, usually 24 to 28 in. (600 to 700 mm) wider than the corners of the house. This extra width is needed for easy handling and erection of the formwork, placement of the drain tile, application of damp-proofing, and placement of the exterior insulation, if applicable. Allow for a slope on the sides of the excavation where the depth exceeds 4 ft. (1.2 m). This makes the slope more stable and ensures the safety of the workers.

An alternative approach to marking the perimeter of the excavation, especially when the foundation shape is not a simple rectangle, is to spray fluorescent paint directly on the ground.

EXCAVATION SIZE AND DEPTH

In most cases, the quickest and least expensive way to excavate is to use a bulldozer or excavator. Before this is done, however, all topsoil should be stripped and stored for reuse. The subsoil from the excavation is usually carried away for disposal unless grading requirements allow its use on the site. The depth of the excavation and, consequently, the elevation of the foundation usually depend on the elevation of the street, sewer and water services, the profile of the lot and the level of finished grade around the perimeter of the house. The elevation of adjoining houses and surface drainage patterns must also be considered.

The basement headroom and the elevation of the floor above grade also affect the depth of the excavation. Basement headroom should be at least 6 ft. 5 in. (1.95 m) to the underside of beams or joists, but a headroom of 6 ft. 7 in. (2 m) is preferable. If the basement is to be used as a living space, however, the minimum headroom should be 7 ft. 7 in. (2.3 m), the same height as the other finished floor areas. The elevation of the first floor should allow for a minimum distance from finished grade to the beginning of exterior finishing (normally starting at the foundation top) of 6 in. (150 mm) for masonry and metal siding, and 8 in. (200 mm) for wood siding, plywood, hardboard and stucco (Figure 6). This is

Intended to minimize damage to siding caused by melting snow and rainwater splashing on the ground.

At times, the type of soil encountered will also affect the depth of the excavation. The excavation may be deepened until suitable soil is encountered. Similarly, the depth of the water table or encountering bedrock can affect the depth of the excavation.

The rough grade around the house should be kept at least 4 in. (100 mm) below the line established for the finished grade to allow for subsequent placing of topsoil or paving material.

If a granular base is to be used under the basement floor slab, the excavation should be made deep enough to accommodate this base. Normally, this depth is also sufficient to accommodate the thickness of the footings. If the site is well-drained and only a damp-proofing

membrane is used without the granular base underneath, the excavation is stopped at the elevation established for the top surface of the footings. When this is done, the footings are formed by trenching. Adequate space must be provided for the drainage pipe beside the footing.

The steepness of the excavation's back slope is determined by the type of subsoil encountered. With clay or other stable soils, and depending on the depth of the excavation, the back slope can be nearly vertical. When sand is encountered, the banks must be cut back.

Be sure that the excavation does not affect the foundations of adjacent buildings. Care must always be taken when excavating below the level of footings of adjacent houses. Local building departments should be contacted in these situations.

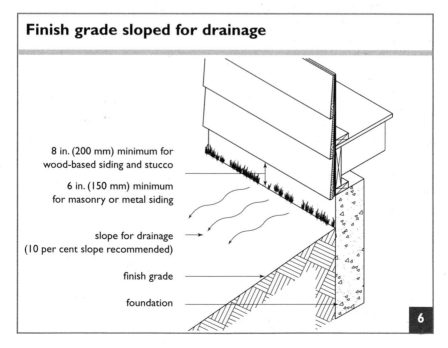

Finish grade sloped for drainage

8 in. (200 mm) minimum for wood-based siding and stucco

6 in. (150 mm) minimum for masonry or metal siding

slope for drainage (10 per cent slope recommended)

finish grade

foundation

6

HEALTHY HOUSING INSIGHT

Siting for Sun, Wind and Water

In addition to local requirements for the location of the dwelling on the lot, such as setbacks from property lines, consideration should be given to solar access, wind effects and water runoff. Careful consideration of these factors can minimize environmental impacts, save energy and promote healthy housing. Here are some important points that should be considered when siting and orienting the dwelling.

Solar Access

→ To take advantage of passive solar heating, the preferred orientation for windows is within 15° west of south and 20° east of south. Plan the layout of the house and its solar orientation to take advantage of the sun's free energy.

→ Today's high performance windows allow for good natural light and generous views while saving energy and promoting occupant well-being. Passive solar heating opportunities are attainable.

Principal Wind Direction

→ The wind can be harnessed to provide natural ventilation through operable windows on the windward and leeward sides of the house if they are aligned with principal wind directions.

→ Proper landscaping and site grading can minimize uncomfortable winds in outdoor living areas and reduce snow removal. The local weather office can provide information on principal wind directions during the different seasons.

Water Runoff and Site Drainage

→ Attempt to maintain natural runoff patterns when draining the site of rainwater and snowmelt. Do not site the building in low spots or where it obstructs the natural path of water runoff.

→ Convey water from roofs and driveways to areas where it may infiltrate the soil and replenish groundwater. Avoid connecting downspouts from eavestroughs to weeping tiles or sumps.

→ Collect and store rainwater in rain barrels or cisterns to use for watering gardens or washing vehicles.

Remember to always protect the excavation in winter. Building on frozen soils can cause a number of problems that are costly and very difficult to remedy.

PLACEMENT OF THE HOUSE

After the excavation is completed, the next step is to establish the lines and elevation for the footings and foundation walls. Figure 7 shows a convenient arrangement of batter boards for this purpose.

Using the previously established location of the foundation walls, three stakes of suitable length are placed at each corner at least 4 ft. (1.2 m) beyond the lines of the excavation. Boards are then nailed horizontally, as shown in

Figure 7, so the tops of all the boards are level and at the same elevation. Wire or stout string, called carpenter's dryline, is stretched across the tops of opposite boards at two corners and adjusted exactly to follow the line of the outside edge of the foundation wall. By cutting saw kerfs 1/4 to 3/8 in. (6 to 8 mm) deep or driving nails where the lines touch the boards, the position of the lines is recorded so that they may be replaced if broken or disturbed. After similar cuts are made in all of the batter boards, the perimeter of the house foundation will be established.

Two methods determine whether the building corners are square. The first is to measure the diagonals. If the diagonals are equal, the building corners are square (Figure 5). Another method, called triangulation, measures

Method of setting batter boards and establishing corners for excavation

- batter board
- dryline
- plumb line which represents the foundation-wall corner line
- back slope
- workspace for tradespeople
- wall-footing junction
- footing on undisturbed soil using formboards
- subsoil

7

along one side of the corner a distance in multiples of 12 in. (300 mm) and along the adjacent side the same number in multiples of 16 in. (400 mm). The diagonal, or hypotenuse, will have an equal number of multiples of 20 in. (500 mm) when the corner is square (Figure 5).

RELATED PUBLICATIONS

Glossary of Housing Terms
Canada Mortgage and Housing Corporation

2005 National Building Code of Canada
National Research Council of Canada

Landscape Guide for Canadian Homes
Canada Mortgage and Housing Corporation

Concrete Work

CONCRETE WORK

Concrete, both non-reinforced and reinforced, is used for a variety of purposes in houses, such as concrete foundations and basement and garage slabs-on-ground. Concrete for columns, fireplaces and chimneys and foundation walls, must have a minimum strength of 2,200 psi (15 MPa). Basement floors must have a minimum strength of 3,000 psi (20 MPa). Garage and carport floors, exterior steps and driveways must have a minimum strength of 4,600 psi (32 MPa), and air-entrained concrete must be specified. Air entrainment for exterior applications must be between 5 and 8 per cent. Air entrainment will produce a concrete that contains a system of minute air bubbles that make the concrete more workable and more easily placed than plain concrete. Most important, when cured, air-entrained concrete is many times more resistant to damage from frost action. In areas where soils are sulphate reactive, cement types 20, 40, 50 or equivalent must be used to protect the concrete.

Whether concrete is delivered from a plant or mixed on site, additional water should not be added at the construction site to make concrete easier to place. Additional water will lower strength, increase permeability and decrease freeze-thaw resistance. If more workability is required, the concrete supplier should be asked to adjust the mix, possibly by adding a plasticizer to improve workability and placement.

Slump is a standard concrete test that is an indication of the workability and potential strength of the concrete (water-to-cement ratio). Concrete with too little slump is difficult to handle and finish. Concrete with too much slump may not develop sufficient strength.

READY-MIX CONCRETE

Ready-mix concrete is available in most locations. Manufactured in plants to established mix designs, the quality of ready-mix concrete can be tailored to meet strength, durability, and workability requirements.

ON-SITE MIXING

When mixing must be done on site, water and aggregate should be clean and free of organic material or other substances that might damage the concrete. The aggregates should also be well-graded.

The air-entraining admixture should be added strictly according to the manufacturer's recommendations, because too much admixture will decrease the strength of the concrete. Contact the manufacturer's representative, if possible, for advice about the proper proportion for a specific use. Air-entraining admixtures should be used only if the concrete is mixed in a motorized mixer.

On-site mixing can use pre-mixed bags of cement and aggregate. In such cases, the manufacturer's instructions must be followed to obtain the desired strength and durability. If site-mixed concrete is to be proportioned on site, the ratios of fine and coarse aggregates, cement and water should be properly adjusted to produce a mixture that will work readily into angles and corners without allowing the material to segregate or free water to collect on the surface. The concrete mixes in Table 2 (p. 356) are considered acceptable for site-mixed concrete if the water to cement ratio is: 0.70 for columns, fireplaces and chimneys, and foundation walls; 0.65 for basement floors; and 0.45 for garage and carport floors and exterior steps. Aggregate used in these mixes must not be larger than one-fifth the distance between vertical forms or one-third the thickness of the flatwork. The slump for mixes in Table 2 must not exceed 6 in. (150 mm) for footings and foundation walls, and 4 in. (100 mm) for slabs-on-ground.

PLACING CONCRETE

Concrete should be placed into the forms continuously in horizontal lifts not exceeding 48 in. (1,200 mm) in depth. Concrete should not be allowed to fall into the forms from a height of more than 8 ft. (2.5 m) as this causes the concrete to segregate. For higher drops, the concrete should be deposited through a suitable vertical pipe. Buggies, wheelbarrows, chutes or pumping may be used to move the concrete if all locations in the forms are not accessible to ready-mix trucks. The chutes should be metal or metal-lined with round bottoms and sloped with a rise-to-run inclination between 1:2 and 1:3.

The concrete should not be deposited in a pile but should be spread out and leveled by raking or shoveling. Vibrators may be used to consolidate the concrete, but should not be used to assist placement. Concrete can also be placed by pumping, if proper equipment is available.

If it is necessary to interrupt the placing operations, the surface of the concrete placed in the forms should be levelled off and the concrete allowed to partially set. The surface should then be roughened to provide a good bonding surface for the next lift. When work resumes, the surface should be cleaned and slightly dampened prior to placing in the concrete. Bonding agents or grout of 1 part cement to 2 parts sand should be spread about 1/2 in. (12 mm) thick over the roughened surface to provide a good joint between the two lifts. The new lift should be placed immediately after the application of the grout.

When being placed, the concrete should be uniformly compacted by means of tamping hand tools (puddling sticks) or, preferably, by a vibrator.

When mixing and placing concrete (in all temperature conditions), ensure that its temperature is maintained between 50°F (10°C) and 77°F (25°C). It must be maintained at a temperature of not less than 50°F (10°C) for a minimum of 72 hours while curing. The concrete should not be placed against frozen soil and any ice and snow should be removed from the formwork.

CURING CONCRETE

Curing involves keeping newly placed concrete damp for several days after placing to allow it to develop its full strength. The cracking of concrete walls and floors can often result from improper curing. Proper procedures for curing must be followed to ensure concrete is able to achieve its potential strength, water tightness and durability. For proper curing and strength development, wall forms should be left in place for at least three days, and longer if possible.

The curing of walls should be carried out after the forms are removed for at least another day if the temperature of concrete is kept above 70°F (21°C), and for another three days if the temperature of concrete is kept between 50°F (10°C) and 70°F (21°C).

A good method of curing is to place a soil-soaker hose around the top of the wall allowing water to run down the wall. When water curing is not practical, spray-on curing compounds that inhibit evaporation may be used. If a damp-proofing compound is applied to the wall, curing can progress without the need for spraying.

In hot weather, concrete should be protected from rapid drying. Wood forms should be sprinkled with water while they are in place in order to prevent excessive drying.

In freezing weather, freshly placed concrete may be protected with a thick layer of straw or other insulating material. In addition, it may be necessary for the concrete to be protected by an enclosure and the space heated with fuel-burning heaters to ensure appropriate temperatures during the curing period.

Concrete slabs-on-ground can be cured by use of water sprays, by covering with burlap kept continuously moist, or by covering with polyethylene sheeting or other means to prevent moisture loss. Unless curing is carried on for about a week after placing the concrete, the exposed surface of the slab may show unsightly cracking or be otherwise weakened.

Allowing concrete to cure properly is an important step in the construction process. Attention to this step helps to avoid costly problems.

RELATED PUBLICATIONS

Concrete Construction for Housing and Small Buildings
Canadian Standards Association

Footings, Foundations
and Slabs

FOOTINGS, FOUNDATIONS AND SLABS

FOOTINGS

Footings receive the house loads through posts or foundation walls and then transmit these loads to the soil. The type and size of footings should be suitable for the soil conditions and located far enough below ground level to be protected from frost action. Frost action can also be avoided by providing good drainage around the foundation to direct water away from the building. In some cases, insulation can be used to provide frost protection for shallow foundations. Competent design is normally called for when using this approach.

Footings should rest on undisturbed soil, rock, or compacted granular material. The granular material should not contain pyritic shale, a type of material peculiar to the St. Lawrence lowlands and subject to swelling.

The distance between the base of the footings and the finished grade should usually be at least the depth of frost penetration. Table 3 (p. 356) shows the minimum depths for several soil conditions. Where fill has been used, the foundation should extend below the fill to undisturbed earth or be designed to suit the condition of the fill.

Wall Footings

The size of the wall footings should comply with building code requirements. Table 4 (p. 357) presents the size of concrete footings on average stable soil. However, if the distance of the water table from the bearing surface is the same as the width of the footings, the footings sizes listed in Table 4 should be doubled. Unless soil conditions and design allow for sharply cut trenches, side forms should be used for footings.

Size of footings

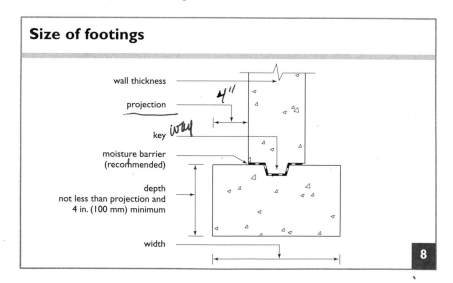

wall thickness

projection 4"

key

moisture barrier (recommended)

depth not less than projection and 4 in. (100 mm) minimum

width

8

Footings should project beyond each side of the wall at least 4 in. (100 mm), and without reinforcement their thickness should be no less than the projection beyond the wall. Footings must never be less than 4 in. (100 mm) thick (Figure 8). If the soil has low loadbearing capacity, wider reinforced footings may be required. Local building officials are often in a position to provide useful advice on local conditions.

A key formed into the top of the footings is a good practice that helps the foundation wall resist the lateral pressures from the earth pushing against it.

If the footings excavation is uneven and in places too deep, a compacted granular mat can be used to level the excavation. Excavated material should not be used as a base.

Pipe trenches directly under wall footings should be backfilled with concrete.

Wood Footings

For preserved wood foundations, continuous wood footings are usually more practical and economical than concrete footings. Wood footings and the granular drainage layer act together to distribute loads from the structure to the undisturbed soil. Sizes of interior and exterior footings and construction practices are given in the Canadian Wood Council publication *Permanent Wood Foundations.*

Column Footings

Footings for posts or columns (Figures 9 and 10) should be placed so that the members they are supporting will be centered. Footings vary in size depending on the allowable soil pressure and the load they support. On average stable soil, common sizes are 4.3 sq. ft. (0.4 m²) — about 25 x 25 in. (640 x 640 mm)— for one-storey houses and 8 sq. ft. (0.75 m²)—34 x 34 in. (870 x 870 mm)

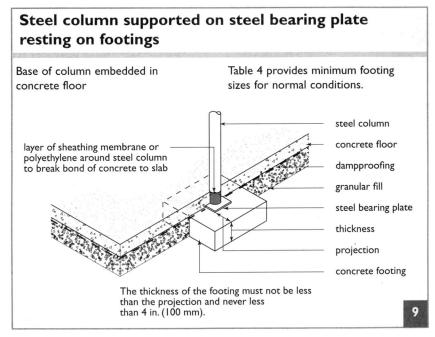

Steel column supported on steel bearing plate resting on footings

Base of column embedded in concrete floor

Table 4 provides minimum footing sizes for normal conditions.

layer of sheathing membrane or polyethylene around steel column to break bond of concrete to slab

steel column
concrete floor
dampproofing
granular fill
steel bearing plate
thickness
projection
concrete footing

The thickness of the footing must not be less than the projection and never less than 4 in. (100 mm).

9

Wood column supported on concrete footings

Polyethylene layer separates wood from concrete. Base of column may be soaked in wood preservative for additional moisture protection.

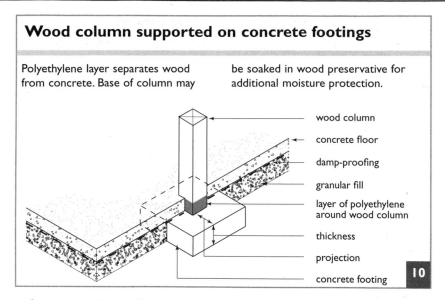

- wood column
- concrete floor
- damp-proofing
- granular fill
- layer of polyethylene around wood column
- thickness
- projection
- concrete footing

10

— for two-storey houses. The minimum thickness of column footings without reinforcement must be at least 4 in. (100 mm). The thickness must also never be less than the column footings pad projection measured from the edge of the column base plate to the edge of the footings pad. Footings for fireplaces and chimneys are usually placed at the same time as other footings.

Stepped footings

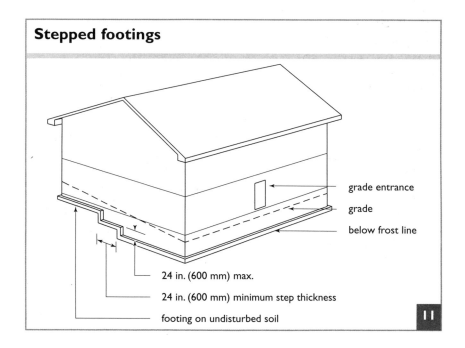

- grade entrance
- grade
- below frost line

24 in. (600 mm) max.

24 in. (600 mm) minimum step thickness

footing on undisturbed soil

11

Stepped Footings

On steeply sloping sites, or where an unstable soil is encountered in part of the excavation, stepped footings may be required. They may also be required in split-level houses. The vertical part of the step should be placed at the same time as the footing. The bottom of the footing is always placed on undisturbed soil or compacted granular fill with each run level.

The vertical connection between footings at the step should be of concrete at least 6 in. (150 mm) thick and the same width as the footings (Figure 11). On steep slopes, more than one step may be required. Except in rock, the vertical distance between steps should not exceed 24 in. (600 mm), and the horizontal distance between steps should not be less than 24 in. (600 mm). For sand or gravel, a vertical distance between steps of no more than 16 in. (400 mm) is recommended. For very steep slopes, where these limitations cannot be maintained, special footings may be required.

FOUNDATIONS

The foundation wall carries the floor, wall, roof and other building loads (including snow and occupant loads) down to the footings. The four most common types of foundations are cast-in-place concrete, concrete blocks, insulated concrete forms (ICF) and preserved wood. Precast concrete or steel foundations may also be used.

Wall thickness of concrete and concrete block walls may vary from 6 to 12 in. (150 to 300 mm) depending upon their depth below grade and the lateral support provided by the floor-framing system. Table 5 (p. 357) shows minimum foundation wall thicknesses for solid concrete and concrete masonry units in stable soils.

Where unstable soils are encountered, construction of foundation walls should follow proven local practices or be specifically designed by an engineer.

Formwork for Foundations

Crushed stone or a coarse granular mat is used around the perimeter and under the basement slab for drainage, and for radon mitigation should it be discovered to be a problem. It is advantageous to spread the layer of stone around the footings in advance to provide a clean, dry surface on which to work.

Formwork for concrete walls must be tight, well-braced and tied to withstand the pressure of the concrete. Reusable forms are made of plywood or steel, and use steel form ties to hold the two sides of the formwork together (Figure 12). The ties are usually broken off to remove the forms after the concrete has cured. If these forms are not available, the formwork may be made with lumber (tongue-and-groove or shiplap) or plywood, together with the necessary framing members. They can be built in sections and then erected.

Combination steel form ties and spreaders are generally used to hold the forms together and to maintain the necessary width. Where wire ties are used, wood spacer blocks, whose length equals the finished thickness of the wall, are placed between the faces of the form and removed as the concrete reaches their level. Wire ties hold the forms rigidly against the spacer blocks.

Concrete formwork and combination form ties

wall thickness

break point

reusable forms —
plywood or other
facing

waler

horizontal
bracing

diagonal brace
if required

form tie

stake

block

anchor bolt

cast-in-place
concrete wall

strip footing

12

Chalklines, pour strips or nails may be used on wood forms to show the elevation to which the concrete will be placed.

New insulated form products (insulated concrete forms) are being used increasingly in Canada. These provide both the formwork and the insulation for the concrete wall. They eliminate the need for form stripping and in some situations provide real advantages.

Frames for basement windows, doors and other openings, along with the boxes that will form notches for the ends of floor beams, are set into place

when the formwork is built. Framing and bracing are used to keep the forms vertical and in place until the concrete has set (Figure 13). It is important to check the diagonals of the frames to ensure that the frames are square.

If wood beams at or below grade are not treated with preservative to prevent decay, the wall notch or pocket for such beams must allow at least 1/2 in. (12 mm) of clearance at the sides and ends of the beam for air circulation (Figure 14). These air circulation requirements do not apply to steel beams.

Concrete frames and braces

(A) window installed in
   cast-in-place concrete wall

(B) framing/bracing
   around door frame

A

B

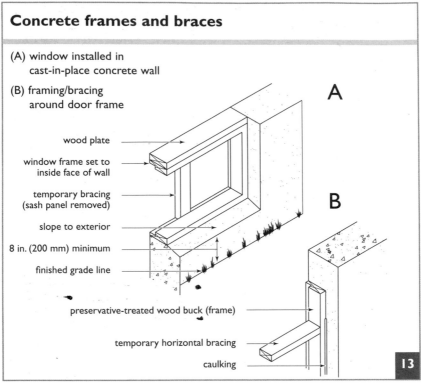

wood plate

window frame set to
inside face of wall

temporary bracing
(sash panel removed)

slope to exterior

8 in. (200 mm) minimum

finished grade line

preservative-treated wood buck (frame)

temporary horizontal bracing

caulking

13

Notches or beam pockets in foundation walls

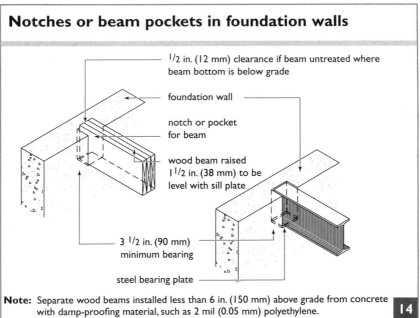

$1/2$ in. (12 mm) clearance if beam untreated where
beam bottom is below grade

foundation wall

notch or pocket
for beam

wood beam raised
$1 1/2$ in. (38 mm) to be
level with sill plate

$3 1/2$ in. (90 mm)
minimum bearing

steel bearing plate

Note: Separate wood beams installed less than 6 in. (150 mm) above grade from concrete
with damp-proofing material, such as 2 mil (0.05 mm) polyethylene.

14

Where a masonry chimney is to be incorporated in the outside walls, provision should be made for it at this stage.

Forms should not be removed until the concrete has acquired sufficient strength to support loads imposed during early construction. At least three days are required, but a week is preferable, particularly in cold weather.

After the forms have been removed, all holes and recesses from the form ties must be sealed with cement mortar or damp-proofing material.

Cast-in-place Foundation Walls

Concrete should be placed continuously without interruption. During the placing operation, it should be tamped or vibrated to remove air pockets and to work the material under window frames and other blocking.

Anchor bolts for sill plates should be placed while the concrete is in an unhardened condition. Anchorage is commonly accomplished by using 1/2 in. (12.7 mm)-thick anchor bolts spaced not more than 8 ft. (2.4 m) apart (Figure 15). Anchor bolts should be embedded at least 4 in. (100 mm) into the foundation wall. The end of the anchor bolt embedded in the concrete should be deformed or bent to provide good secure anchoring. Also ensure that the bolts are free from oil and that the concrete has cured to minimize the possibility of withdrawal of the bolt.

Control Joints

Uncontrolled cracking can occur in concrete slabs and walls. If this is to be avoided or controlled, steel reinforcing rods or properly located and formed vertical control joints should be used (Figure 17). Wall-crack control joints are formed by nailing strips of wood

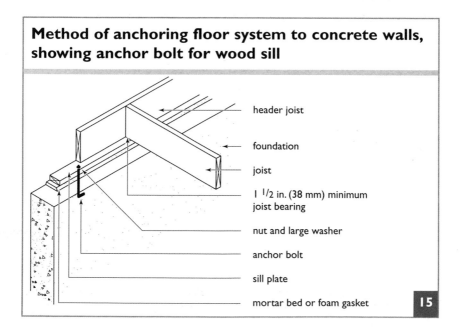

Method of anchoring floor system to concrete walls, showing anchor bolt for wood sill

header joist

foundation

joist

1 1/2 in. (38 mm) minimum joist bearing

nut and large washer

anchor bolt

sill plate

mortar bed or foam gasket

15

Different combinations of slab/footing and slab/wall isolation joints

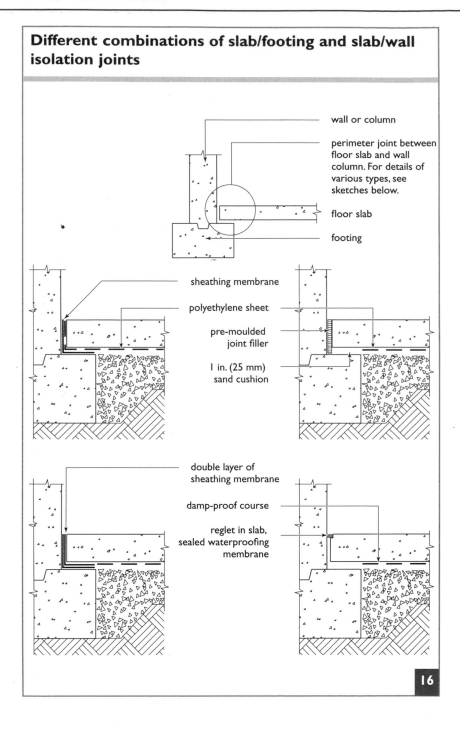

- wall or column
- perimeter joint between floor slab and wall column. For details of various types, see sketches below.
- floor slab
- footing
- sheathing membrane
- polyethylene sheet
- pre-moulded joint filler
- 1 in. (25 mm) sand cushion
- double layer of sheathing membrane
- damp-proof course
- reglet in slab, sealed waterproofing membrane

16

Control joint in basement wall

caulk outside face
of wall at joint

control crack

1/2 in. (12 mm)

3/4 in. (19 mm)

3/4 in. (19 mm)

bevelled 3/4 in. (19 mm) strip
nailed to inside and outside form
face to make grooves

Note: The combined thickness of inner and outer strips should equal approximately
one-fifth of the wall thickness. This example is for an 8 in. (200 mm)-thick
foundation wall.

17

about 3/4 in. (19 mm) thick, bevelled from 3/4 to 1/2 in. (19 to 12 mm) in width, to the inside of both interior and exterior wall forms. The purpose of these is to make grooves in the wall that will predetermine the location of shrinkage cracks. Control joints are necessary in walls longer than 82 ft. (25 m). Shorter walls are also susceptible to cracking. Control joints in these walls are also recommended.

Control joints should be located first at the natural planes of weakness, such as windows and doors, and then within 10 ft. (3 m) from the corners, and 20 ft. (6 m) apart. The sides of windows or door openings, if present, should be chosen as joint locations. After removal of the wall forms, the groove in the exterior face of the wall should be carefully caulked with a good-quality joint sealer (Figure 17). The damp-proofing material, applied after the caulking operation, should be compatible with the caulking material

used. A supplier should be contacted for advice regarding the compatibility of caulking materials.

Insulated Concrete Form Foundations

Insulated concrete form (ICF) walls are concrete walls that are cast into flat-faced polystyrene forms that remain in place for the service life of the foundation. For housing applications (foundations not supporting more than two floors with a maximum floor-to-ceiling height of 10 ft. (3m)), typical concrete thickness ranges from 5-1/2 to 9-1/2 in. (140 to 240 mm). The reinforcing required is dependent on the wall thickness and the height of the backfill supported by the wall. The connection of the ICF foundation wall to the wood-frame floor (Figure 18) is similar to that of the cast-in-place concrete wall without polystyrene forms. Where an ICF foundation supports a masonry wall, the top of the ICF is flared and reinforced to accommodate the masonry (Figure 89, p. 189).

Concrete-block Foundation Walls

Concrete blocks are available in various sizes and shapes, but the most widely used come in modular sizes 8 in. (200 mm) high, 16 in. (400 mm) long, and 6, 8, 10 or 12 in. (150, 200, 250 or 300 mm) wide. The actual size is 3/8 in. (10 mm) less than the modular size to allow for the mortar joint.

Block courses (rows) start at the footings and are laid up with 3/8-to-1/2 in. (10-to-12 mm) mortar joints. No joint should exceed 3/4 in. (20 mm). All joints should be tooled smooth to resist water seepage. Full bed-and head-joints should be used in the bottom course. Succeeding courses may be laid with mortar applied to the contact surfaces of the block. Depending on the height of the wall, it may be necessary to add steel reinforcement to a concrete block foundation wall. Pilasters are column-like projections that normally protrude into the basement space. They are sometimes required by building codes to strengthen a wall or support a beam. Ensure that they are placed at a height where they can properly support beams if necessary. In these situations, they will often need to be at a height lower than the top of the foundation.

Special concrete blocks, such as universal, pier or sash blocks, should be used to frame the sides of openings for basement doors and windows. For example, sash blocks (Figure 19) have a keyed face or recess into which the frames are

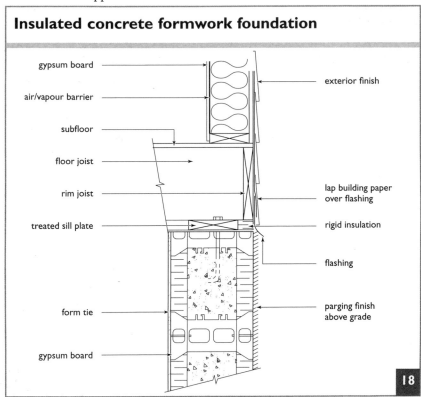

Insulated concrete formwork foundation

gypsum board

air/vapour barrier

subfloor

floor joist

rim joist

treated sill plate

form tie

gypsum board

exterior finish

lap building paper over flashing

rigid insulation

flashing

parging finish above grade

18

connected, thus providing rigidity and helping to control air infiltration. Proper sill and lintel details should also be used to achieve the same effect.

Block walls should be capped either with 2 in. (50 mm) of solid masonry or concrete, or with a mortar filling in the top course of blocks. Alternatively, where termites are not a problem, a wood plank 2 in. (nominal) (38 mm) thick and the same width as the wall may be used. At grade, another separation should be introduced to prevent convection currents in the cores of hollow masonry walls. This separation can be achieved with a strip of polyethylene between the top two courses, by filling the top course with mortar, or by using a solid masonry unit.

In all cases, the siding should overlap the foundation wall by at least 1/2 in.

(12 mm) so that rainwater cannot reach the top of the foundation. Pilasters supporting beams should be capped with 8 in. (200 mm) of solid masonry.

Freshly laid block walls should be protected from below-freezing temperatures. Freezing of the mortar before it is set will result in low adhesion, low strength and joint failures. Mortar mix proportions should conform to those shown in Table 6 (p. 358).

Concrete-block walls should be parged on the outside with at least 1/4 in. (6 mm) of Portland cement plaster. A cove should be formed on the outside perimeter joint between the footings and the wall (Figure 20). The wall should then be damp-proofed by applying at least one heavy coat of bituminous material over the parging up to the

Concrete blocks for foundation construction

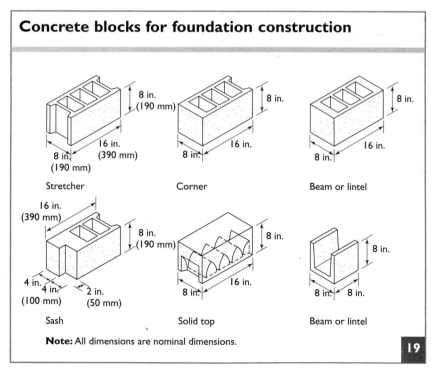

Stretcher

Corner

Beam or lintel

Sash

Solid top

Beam or lintel

Note: All dimensions are nominal dimensions.

19

PLANNING AHEAD

Minimum Foundation Wall Thickness for Exterior Insulated Masonry Veneer Walls

When determining the minimum thickness of foundation walls required in (Table 5, p. 357), it is important to consider:

→ how the exterior walls will be framed;

→ the thickness of exterior insulation materials;

→ the width of the air space; and

→ the thickness of masonry veneer, such as brick or stone.

Review the "Wall Framing" chapter for framing options and details. Check the "Wall Sheathing and Exterior Finishes" and "Thermal Insulation" chapters when calculating the required thickness for foundation walls supporting masonry veneer.

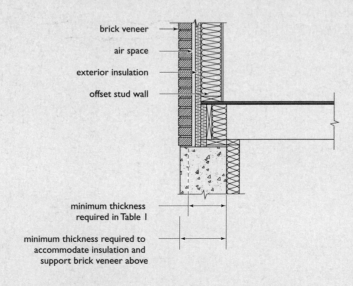

PLANNING AHEAD

Sill Anchors in Concrete and Masonry Foundations

Before pouring a concrete foundation or completing the final courses of a masonry foundation, it is necessary to determine how the floor joists will be anchored and supported. The two most common options are illustrated below. If a sill plate is going to be employed, then its location on top of the wall must be known in order to establish the centreline for sill anchor bolt placement. Refer to the "Floor Framing" chapter for sill-anchor bolt placement and use.

➡ When building in high wind and earthquake areas, additional measures for anchoring the floor framing to the foundation may be considered.

➡ Consult a competent structural designer for specific details in such cases.

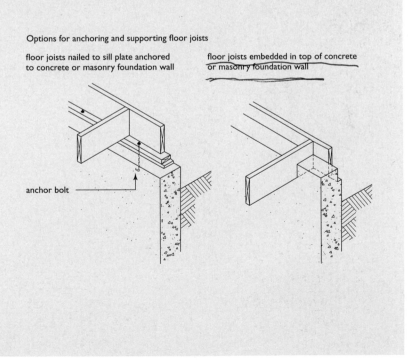

Options for anchoring and supporting floor joists

floor joists nailed to sill plate anchored to concrete or masonry foundation wall

floor joists embedded in top of concrete or masonry foundation wall

anchor bolt

proposed ground level. For added protection where quantities of water accumulate in the soil, two layers of bitumen-saturated membrane may be mopped on and covered overall with a heavy coating of bituminous material. This covering will prevent leaks if minor cracks develop in the blocks or joints between the blocks.

Preserved Wood Foundations

Preserved wood foundations are constructed by the same methods employed in house framing with some additional bracing requirements, special fasteners and adhesives. The foundations usually consist of a pressure-treated wood footing plate resting on a granular drainage layer, with pressure-treated bottom and top plates, studs and blocking and pressure-treated plywood

as outside cladding, covered with a polyethylene sheet for damp-proofing. The space between the studs may be filled with insulation and the interior finished to provide a well-insulated living space, partly or entirely below ground level. A polyethylene sheet ground cover is required under preserved-wood foundation floors. In addition, a polyethylene strip should be placed between the bottom plate and the footing to keep the plate dry and to prevent moisture from getting into the wall cavity.

In preserved wood foundations, all wood used in the foundation system must be pressure-treated with chemical preservatives in accordance with Canadian Standards Association (CSA) Standard O80.15. The chemicals permanently impregnate the wood cells to levels of

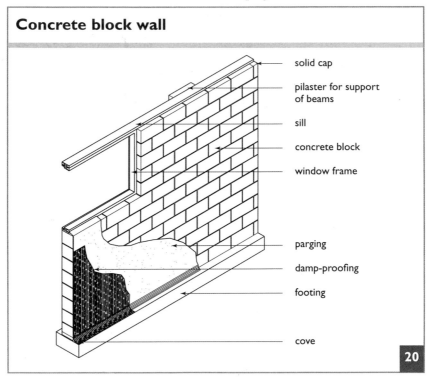

Concrete block wall

- solid cap
- pilaster for support of beams
- sill
- concrete block
- window frame
- parging
- damp-proofing
- footing
- cove

20

penetration and concentration that make the wood highly resistant to attack by decay organisms and insects such as termites. The dried wood is odourless and is only slightly coloured. Properly treated lumber and plywood can be identified by a certification mark showing that the material has been treated by a plant certified according to CSA Standard 0322 (Figure 21).

Wood foundations are suitable for low-rise or multiple dwellings. They can be built with a conventional concrete slab floor, a wood floor on sleepers resting on a granular drainage layer, or a suspended wood floor (Figure 22). They must be designed to carry not only the vertical load of the house and its floor and roof loads, but also the horizontal loads of the backfill material. The required size, species and grade of studs and thickness of plywood depend on stud spacing and backfill height and the number of storeys supported.

SLABS

Concrete slabs are used for basement floors and for houses or portions of houses constructed at grade. In small buildings, they are generally supported by the ground below and not by the structure at the perimeter.

Facsimile of certification mark

Company name and logo

CSA CERTIFIED 0322
CERTIFIÉ
PWF — FBT
L/B·P/C CCA 2577

The certification mark contains the following information:

CSA - identifies the certifying agency

0322 - identifies the standard, CSA 0322, under which the material is certified

PWF and FBT - identifies the intended use of the material

L/B and/or P/C - the plant is licensed for lumber and/or plywood inspection

CCA (or ACA) - identifies the preservative used

2577 - the first two digits identify the treating plant, the last two the year of treatment

21

Preservative-treated wood foundations

(A) with concrete floor slab and wood footings

(B) with wood sleeper floor

(C) with suspended wood floor

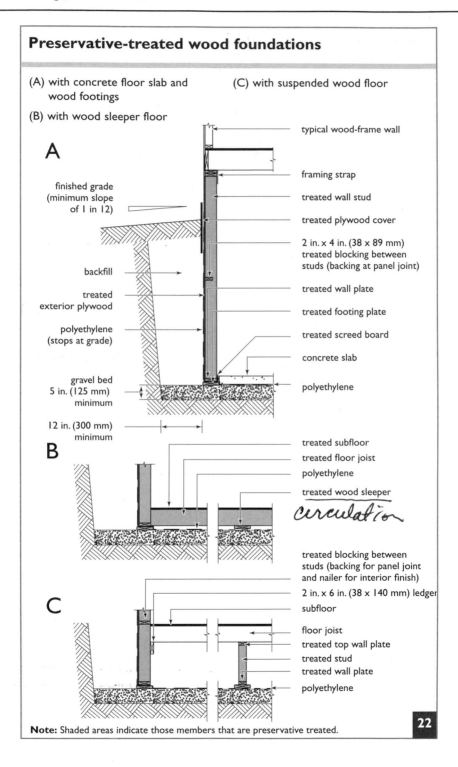

A

finished grade (minimum slope of 1 in 12)

backfill

treated exterior plywood

polyethylene (stops at grade)

gravel bed 5 in. (125 mm) minimum

12 in. (300 mm) minimum

B

C

typical wood-frame wall

framing strap

treated wall stud

treated plywood cover

2 in. x 4 in. (38 x 89 mm) treated blocking between studs (backing at panel joint)

treated wall plate

treated footing plate

treated screed board

concrete slab

polyethylene

treated subfloor

treated floor joist

polyethylene

treated wood sleeper

circulation

treated blocking between studs (backing for panel joint and nailer for interior finish)

2 in. x 6 in. (38 x 140 mm) ledger

subfloor

floor joist

treated top wall plate

treated stud

treated wall plate

polyethylene

Note: Shaded areas indicate those members that are preservative treated.

22

Preservative-treated wood foundations (cont'd)

(D) on concrete strip foundation

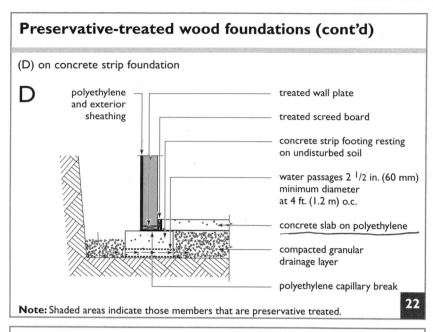

D

- polyethylene and exterior sheathing
- treated wall plate
- treated screed board
- concrete strip footing resting on undisturbed soil
- water passages 2 1/2 in. (60 mm) minimum diameter at 4 ft. (1.2 m) o.c.
- concrete slab on polyethylene
- compacted granular drainage layer
- polyethylene capillary break

Note: Shaded areas indicate those members that are preservative treated.

22

Concrete footings resting on granular drainage layer

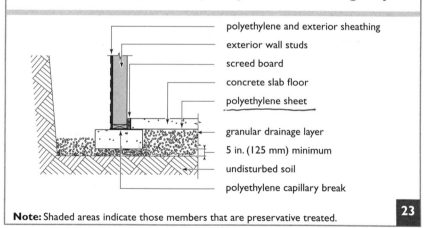

- polyethylene and exterior sheathing
- exterior wall studs
- screed board
- concrete slab floor
- polyethylene sheet
- granular drainage layer
- 5 in. (125 mm) minimum
- undisturbed soil
- polyethylene capillary break

Note: Shaded areas indicate those members that are preservative treated.

23

Basement Floor Slabs

Basement floors are usually installed after the roof construction is completed, the building enclosed, sewer and water lines installed and the basement floor drain is in place. While curing, concrete gives off moisture that can seriously affect finish flooring, drywall or millwork.

The basement should be ventilated to allow moisture to escape before finish flooring or millwork is installed.

Basement-floor slabs should be at least 3 in. (75 mm) thick and sloped toward the floor drain. There should be at least one drain (or sump pit) located near the laundry area if provided.

The following summarizes the requirements, the good practice and the sequence of events in the construction of concrete basement-floor slabs.

1. Complete the installation of sewer lines and other subsurface work before the slab is placed. Compact backfill in trenches.

2. Place at least 4 in. (100 mm) of crushed rock or coarse gravel under the floor slab to restrict the passage of moisture by capillary action from the ground to the slab and to facilitate soil gas remediation if necessary.

3. Apply a layer of 6 mil (0.15 mm) polyethylene sheet or Type S roll roofing below the slab to damp-proof the floor. Damp-proofing is especially desirable when a finish floor will be attached later to the slab by an adhesive. Where the water table is high, waterproofing the slab, as explained below, will be necessary to avoid problems. To prevent the entry of soil gas, polyethylene that is lapped at least 4 in. (100 mm) at the joints can be used (Figure 23).

4. In order to allow for slight movement due to shrinkage of the slab during drying and settling of the subbase, a pre-moulded joint filler or double layer of sheathing paper (Figure 16) between floor slab and wall or column should be provided.

5. After the concrete has been placed and consolidated, it should be struck off with a straightedge to the proper elevation. This can be determined by measuring down from the bottom of properly levelled floor joists. In order to eliminate local high or low areas and to embed large aggregate particles, the surface is then immediately smoothed using a large float of either the darby or bull type or by using other appropriate means. Tools used for air-entrained concrete should have a magnesium surface. Care must be taken not to overwork the concrete, because this will result in a less-durable surface.

6. After the water sheen has disappeared and the concrete has stiffened slightly, edging, jointing and floating operations can begin. Any of these operations performed while bleed water is present will cause serious dusting or scaling.

7. If minor random cracking in the slab is to be avoided, proper control jointing or grooving may be necessary. Control joints should be placed on line with interior columns and at changes in width of the floor slab (Figure 24). The maximum spacing of control joints should be between 15 and 20 ft. (4.5 and 6.0 m) in either direction. Joints may be formed in the freshly placed concrete by cutting grooves by hand with a jointing tool as soon as the concrete is firm enough. The depth of joints should be about one-quarter the thickness of the floor slab.

Location of control joints MUST KNOW

1. control joints within 10 ft. (3 m) of corners
2. spacing of joints 20 ft. (6 m) maximum
3. joints incorporate side of opening
4. control joint in floor slab
5. floor slab joint spacing of 20 ft. (6 m) maximum
6. control joint around column footings
   (see note)

Note: The diamond-shaped joints (6) may be omitted if column footings are below floor level and the column is wrapped with two layers of sheathing membrane or joint filler to break the bond.

24

8. As soon as the floor surface has been finished, curing should begin. Curing should continue for at least five days at air temperature of 70°F (21°C) or higher, or for seven days at temperatures of 50°F (10°C) to 70°F (21°C). Curing may be carried out by ponding water on top of the slab (by temporarily plugging all floor drains), or by covering with burlap, which is kept continuously wet. If this is not practical, liquid, membrane-forming, curing compound may be spread on the concrete surface. If the finish is to be tile, caution should be used, because curing compounds may not be compatible with adhesives.

Slabs-on-ground

Because the requirements for slabs-on-ground are similar to basement slabs (Figure 25), the steps and precautions described above apply here as well. An important difference is the need to establish the finish floor level at a sufficient height above the natural grade so that the finished grade will provide good drainage away from the house. The top of the slab should be at least 8 in. (200 mm) above finished grade.

It is important to remove all debris, stumps and organic matter from the area below the slab and fill voids with compacted granular material to provide a smooth surface free of soft pockets.

Independent concrete floor slab and foundation wall

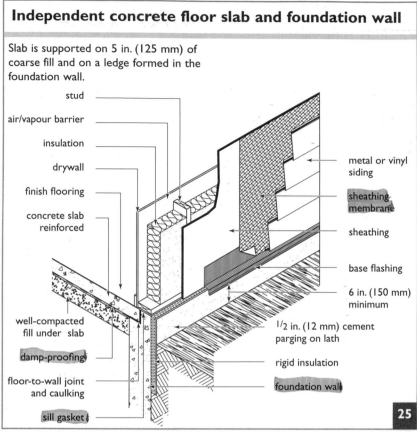

Slab is supported on 5 in. (125 mm) of coarse fill and on a ledge formed in the foundation wall.

stud
air/vapour barrier
insulation
drywall
finish flooring
concrete slab reinforced
well-compacted fill under slab
damp-proofing
floor-to-wall joint and caulking
sill gasket

metal or vinyl siding
sheathing membrane
sheathing
base flashing
6 in. (150 mm) minimum
1/2 in. (12 mm) cement parging on lath
rigid insulation
foundation wall

25

A water-repellent type of rigid insulation should be installed around the perimeter of the slab. Rigid insulation should be protected from physical or ultraviolet damage by using parging or a board finish. To resist cracking, the slab should be reinforced with approximately 3/8 in. (9.5 mm) thick reinforcing steel bars spaced 2 ft. (600 mm) on centre in both directions. (The steel bars have a metric product designation of 10M.) Alternatively, a welded wire mesh can be used that forms a grid of 6 in. (152 mm) squares in which the thickness of the steel is 0.15 in. (3.4 mm). (The metric product designation of this grid is 152 x 152 MW 9.1 x MW9.1.)

A topping is generally not needed since the finished surface resulting from mechanical trowelling is very smooth. When a topping is used, it should consist of 1 part cement to 2 1/2 parts well-graded sand. A layer 3/4 in. (20 mm) thick is placed after the concrete slab has set. The layer should be trowelled to a smooth level finish.

Footings and foundations for houses with slabs-on-ground have similar requirements as those for crawl spaces and are constructed in the same manner. If the slab is a structural slab and supports loads from the walls above, it must be designed by an engineer.

FOUNDATION DAMP-PROOFING AND WATERPROOFING

Damp-proofing on the exterior face of the foundation is intended to control the movement of soil moisture into the wall. On the interior face of the foundation, it is also used to prevent the movement of moisture from the concrete or unit masonry into interior wood framing that supports insulation or interior finishes. Damp-proofing takes many forms. Most commonly, a heavy coat of bituminous material, polyethylene or other sheet material is used.

Waterproofing, on the other hand, is intended to deal with severe water problems normally associated with high water tables. Whereas damp-proofing is necessary for all foundations that contain habitable space, waterproofing is required only for foundations that are subject to hydrostatic pressures. Special attention of a qualified professional is normally recommended for these buildings. Often measures need to be taken to deal with the water and the forces that are superimposed onto the foundation.

Concrete and unit masonry walls below grade should be damp-proofed with a heavy coat of bituminous material applied on the exterior surface from the footings to the finished grade line. Such a coating is usually sufficient to make the wall watertight against ordinary seepage that may occur after a rainstorm or from soil dampness. Insulated concrete form (ICF) foundations must also be damp-proofed and the material used must be solvent free and be compatible with the foam formwork/insulation.

Added protection from moisture can be provided by special, dense, glass-fibre insulation or by other commercially available drainage layers, which will be discussed later.

In poorly drained soils, waterproofed walls may be necessary and should consist of an impermeable membrane, such as two layers of bitumen-saturated felt. The layers of felt should be attached to the wall and each other, and covered with liquid bitumen. ICF foundations must also be waterproofed where hydrostatic pressure is a possibility. The waterproofing materials must be compatible with the foam formwork/insulation.

Where hydrostatic pressures exist, waterproofing the foundation involves more than the impermeable wall membrane as noted. It also requires that the floor slab be waterproofed with a membrane sandwiched between two layers of concrete, each not less than 3 in. (75 mm) thick. The floor membrane must extend to the wall membrane, forming a complete seal. In many cases, foundations subjected to hydrostatic pressure are also equipped with a means of relieving the water pressure, in order to prevent structural damage.

Foundations that are waterproofed do not need to be damp-proofed. Waterproofing can provide all of the protection that damp-proofing normally provides.

Care must be taken when backfilling walls to prevent damage to the damp-proofing, waterproofing, insulation or drainage layer.

Damp-proofing is also required on the interior of concrete or unit masonry walls that come into contact with interior wood framing supporting insulation or interior finishes. The damp-proofing, installed between the foundation wall and interior framing, prevents moisture in the foundation wall from coming into contact with the wood framing. The damp-proofing must extend from the basement floor and terminate at the exterior finish grade level.

FOUNDATION DRAINAGE

In most locations, it is necessary to drain away any subsurface water to prevent damp basements and wet floors. Foundation drainage is required unless it can be shown that natural, free-draining soil makes it unnecessary. Foundation drainage normally consists of a drain tile installed around the perimeter of the basement and, usually, a wall drainage layer. A layer of granular material can often substitute for the perimeter drain tile as noted below.

Drain tile should be laid on solid undisturbed soil around the footings, making sure that the top of the tile is below the level of the basement floor or

crawl space, with a slight slope to the outlet. The tile is then covered with a minimum of 6 in. (150 mm) of coarse, *CLEAR* clean gravel or crushed rock (Figure 26). Pyritic shale and materials finer than 5/32 in. (4 mm) should be avoided.

The drain tile should be connected with a tight joint pipe to a storm sewer or other satisfactory outlet. Adequate drainage to prevent the infiltration of water into the basement is essential. A sump may be necessary in some cases.

On wet sites, special drainage features, such as lateral drain tiles under the floor slab, may be needed to avoid hydrostatic pressures on basement walls and slab. Note that foundation drainage is not intended to deal with high water tables. A professional engineer or architect should be involved in the design of buildings sited on high water tables.

If a preserved wood foundation is used, a granular layer must be employed in combination with a sump. The bottom of the excavation is sloped so that it drains to the sump, which is subsequently drained by gravity or mechanical means to a sewer, ditch or dry well. The granular layer should extend at

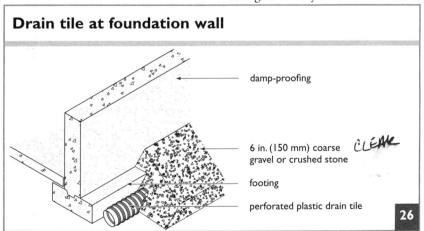

Drain tile at foundation wall

damp-proofing

6 in. (150 mm) coarse *CLEAR* gravel or crushed stone

footing

perforated plastic drain tile

26

least 12 in. (300 mm) beyond the footings and, if thicker than 8 in. (200 mm), should be compacted.

This granular layer technique is applicable to any type of foundation that includes a sump pump. With concrete footings placed on undisturbed soil, water passages of 2.5 in. (60 mm) in diameter and at regular 4 ft. (1.2 m) intervals should be put in the footings to permit draining water to the sump (Figure 27).

Wall drainage layers are required by building codes in some regions of the country. Consult the local building department in your area. Drainage layer materials are normally applied to the outside of the basement wall. They are intended to direct infiltrating rainwater that comes into contact with the foundation wall, down to the drain tile, and prevent the water from entering the basement through cracks or poorly sealed tie-rod holes that might exist.

Wall drainage layers normally consist of 3/4 in. (19 mm) or thicker mineral-fibre insulation with a density of at least 3.6 lb./cu. ft. (57 kg/m³) or other commercially available wall drainage materials. Alternatively, free-draining granular material may be used as backfill. It is important that the drainage layer directs water to the drain tile avoiding any possible ponding of water at the base of the foundation wall. The granular fill that surrounds the drain tile should also cover the base of the wall drainage layer.

As with foundation walls, surface drainage should be directed away from basement windows. Basement windows that extend below ground level require window wells (Figure 28). Galvanized sheet steel, corrugated for added strength, is commonly used for this purpose. This type of window well is available in a variety of sizes to suit various window openings. For concrete window wells, forms are installed and the concrete placed after the backfill has been compacted.

Concrete footing resting on undisturbed soil

undisturbed soil

polyethylene and exterior sheathing
exterior wall studs
treated wall plate
treated screed board
concrete strip footing resting on undisturbed soil
concrete slab floor
polyethylene sheet
compacted granular drainage layer
polyethylene capillary break
water passages 2 1/2 in. (60 mm) minimum diameter at 4 ft. (1.2 m) o.c. around perimeter

Note: Shaded areas indicate those members that are preservative treated.

27

Window well at basement wall

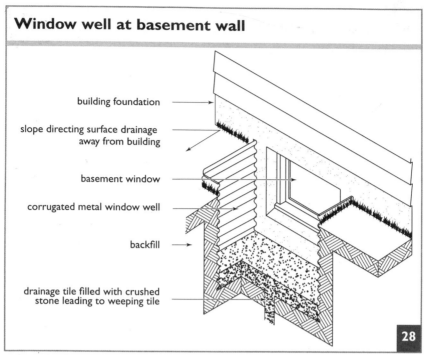

building foundation

slope directing surface drainage away from building

basement window

corrugated metal window well

backfill

drainage tile filled with crushed stone leading to weeping tile

28

When the backfill is not a granular material, the bottom of the window well should be drained by a tube or hole 6 in. (150 mm) in diameter drilled down through the backfill material to the drain tile and filled with crushed stone.

BACKFILLING

Backfilling foundation walls should not be carried out until the floor joists and subfloor are in place. This applies to concrete, masonry and preserved wood foundation walls. Table 5 (p.357) shows the maximum height from basement floor to finished grade for both laterally supported and laterally unsupported foundation walls.

Backfill material within 2 ft. (600 mm) of the foundation should be free-draining granular material (not subject to ice-lensing). It should be free of large rocks, clay clumps, construction wastes and pyritic shales. These materials can cause undue pressure on the foundation wall, damage to the damp-proofing or water-proofing membranes, and can impair proper drainage around the foundation.

Sudden pressures against foundation walls brought about by loads of backfill material may cause the walls to move, resulting in damage such as cracking in the wall. It is important, therefore, that backfill material be deposited gradually and uniformly around the perimeter in small lifts, with each lift being compacted to the appropriate density before the next lift is placed. Care must also be taken to ensure that externally mounted insulation, drainage material, damp-proofing or waterproofing membranes are not damaged.

PLANNING AHEAD

Weeping Tiles, Sumps and Sewage Ejectors

The means by which the foundation and basement plumbing will be drained requires careful planning, particularly in areas without sewers.

Foundation drainage may consist of weeping tile or a granular drainage layer, or both. When the house is located on a site where gravity drainage of the foundation is possible, a sump pump is not required. However, in flat or low-lying areas without storm sewers, a sump pump will be required to pump the water to a ditch or dry well. In areas with storm sewers, it may also be required when the foundation drainage lies below the storm sewer.

When plumbing fixtures are installed in the basement of a house located below the sanitary sewer, or without municipal sewer services, a sewage ejector is required to pump sewage up to the sewer or septic system. Some key factors to consider include:

➜ Always check with the building department for local requirements for foundation drainage and basement plumbing.

➜ Avoid leading water from roofs and driveways into the foundation drainage

system. Drain this water away from the house.

➜ Use gravity drainage of foundations and basement plumbing in areas without municipal sewer services whenever possible. Plan the location of the building and septic system accordingly.

➜ Plan site drainage to divert water away from wells and septic systems.

➜ Only use sump pumps and sewage ejectors with tight seals to avoid odours and soil gases from entering the dwelling.

➜ Never discharge a sump pump into a septic system. The water will dilute the effluent in the septic tank and impair its proper digestion.

➜ Consider the location of any other services entering at or beneath the foundation to avoid conflicting interference.

Refer to the "Eavestroughs and Downspouts" chapter for more information on dealing with roof drainage. The "Surface Drainage, Driveways and Walkways" chapter discusses options for draining runoff.

FOUNDATION INSULATION

Foundation insulation provides a means of reducing the heat loss of the building. Depending on the approach taken, foundation insulation can also provide other benefits, such as acting as an exterior wall-drainage layer. The requirements for basement insulation vary from province to province and should be checked with the local municipality.

Foundations can be insulated on the interior or the exterior of the building. Interior insulated basements may be partially insulated to 2 ft. (600 mm) below grade or full depth. Interior basement insulation often requires framing to support the insulation and the interior finish. This approach creates a finished basement space that often adds to the habitable area of the house.

Insulating the basement from the outside has advantages. The insulation often can also provide wall drainage, offering additional protection while reducing heat loss. Exterior basement insulation also reduces the temperature swing that the foundation wall experiences, which reduces thermal stresses and the cracking that sometimes results. The disadvantage of this system is that the insulation often requires protection when it extends above grade.

FOOTINGS AND FOUNDATIONS FOR CRAWL SPACES

Houses with a crawl space are supported on a foundation wall that is carried at least 6 in. (150 mm) above the exterior finished grade.

Trenches are dug for the foundation walls and the footings placed at a depth below grade determined by soil conditions and frost penetration (see Table 3, p.356). The sizes of the footings are generally the same as those used to support basement walls. The foundation walls may be built of concrete, concrete masonry units or preserved wood, but since the inside grade is never much lower than the outside grade, the thickness of the foundation walls is usually less than those enclosing a basement. Table 5, p. 357, shows minimum foundation wall thickness for stable soils.

Footings for columns supporting the floor beams should be placed on solid undisturbed ground, and this may require some excavation. Concrete, masonry or preserved wood columns are generally used to support the beams. The excavated area is backfilled around the base of the columns and footings when the crawl space floor is leveled. Crawl space insulation, which can be installed either at the perimeter of the foundation or in the floor frame under the living space, is discussed and illustrated in the chapter on "Thermal Insulation."

Crawl Space Ventilation and Ground Cover

Where the crawl space floor is below the level of the outside finished grade, the foundation walls should be damp-proofed. Drain tile is then installed around the footings and connected to a sewer, ditch or dry well. The floors of the crawl space and access trenches are graded toward the drain, and a ground cover of 6 mil (0.15 mm) polyethylene or Type S roll roofing is installed over the surface with the joints lapped at least 4 in. (100 mm). The ground cover prevents ground moisture from entering the crawl space area. The crawl space should also be ventilated. See the chapter on Ventilation.

FOUNDATIONS FOR DECKS AND CONCRETE STEPS

Frost action can cause supports for exterior decks, balconies and stairs to shift. Movement can cause structural damage and can change the direction of drainage, thereby reversing the desired removal of water away from the building envelope. For this reason, balconies with roofs, concrete steps with more than three risers, and decks more than 2 ft. (600 mm) above the ground require their supports to be founded on rock, on coarse-grained soil with good drainage, or, for other types of soils, must extend below the frost line (Figure 151, p. 332).

GARAGE FOUNDATIONS

Foundations for garages are usually concrete or masonry, though concrete slab-on-grade or preserved wood foundations are also used. The minimum depth below grade for a garage foundation attached to a house should not be less than that shown in Table 3, p. 356.

If fill is required below the floor, a granular material is preferable and should be well compacted to avoid settlement after the floor is laid. The concrete floor should be at least 3 in. (75 mm) thick with a base of 6 in. (150 mm) of crushed stone or gravel. Unless a floor drain is installed, the floor should be sloped toward the entrance.

Detailing, placing and curing of concrete garage floors should be carried out as described for basement floor slabs. Control joints should be used to produce panels as nearly square as possible. For a single car garage, one control joint should be sufficient.

The foundation walls should not be less than 6 in. (150 mm) thick and should extend at least 6 in. (150 mm) above grade.

Sill plates should be anchored to the foundation wall or slab with anchor bolts spaced about 8 ft. (2.4 m) apart and with at least two bolts in each sill piece. Extra anchors may be required at the side of the main door.

RELATED PUBLICATIONS

Construction of Preserved Wood Foundations
Canadian Standards Association

Building Solutions: A Problem Solving Guide for Builders and Renovators
Canada Mortgage and Housing Corporation

Protection and Care of Materials
on the Building Site

PROTECTION AND CARE OF MATERIALS ON THE BUILDING SITE

The protection of building materials on the site and their storage before use is very important. If materials are stored without protection in inclement weather, damage may be caused that could result in wastage of material and troublesome construction defects.

When possible, material should be delivered to the site just before it is to be used. This is especially true of windows and doors and exterior trim materials. Interior finishing materials may be stored in the house once the roof is on.

In the normal staging of construction, the framing lumber and sheathing materials are delivered to the job after the foundation is complete. Structural and framing materials in place before the house is enclosed will be subject to weather. Vertical wood members can dry relatively quickly after wetting. Horizontal wood components need more time to dry.

Lumber stored in close piles may soak up and retain water, causing very slow drying. This condition should be avoided because it may lead to staining and decay. Lifts of lumber should be placed on skids raised off the ground and covered with sheets of waterproof material to shed water. If the wrapping is damaged, the bundles should be re-covered using a waterproof tarpaulin. Sheets of polyethylene may also be placed on the ground, under the skids, to prevent ground moisture from wetting the lumber.

After the framing is started, the roof shingles may be delivered. Asphalt shingles should be stored so that the bundles can lie flat without bending. Using curved or buckled shingles will result in an unattractive roof.

Windows and doors are usually the next items to be installed after the roofing. If they are delivered before they can be installed, they should be protected from the weather. Doors and windows are costly items and exposure to the weather may nullify their good construction.

Insulation, interior wall and ceiling finish, wood siding and similar items can be stored in the house. Heavy materials such as gypsum wallboard should be distributed over the floor area in order not to overload the floor joists. Heavy loads, concentrated on one spot for any appreciable time, may cause permanent deflection in the floor joists.

Hardwood flooring, interior trim and millwork should not be stored in the house until the basement floor has been completed and allowed to dry. The curing of the slab gives off moisture that may cause the kiln-dried material to swell, resulting in shrinkage after the materials are installed.

Lumber and Other Wood Products

LUMBER AND OTHER WOOD PRODUCTS

The primary component of wood-frame construction is dimension lumber. It forms the structural shell that encloses and divides spaces and to which finishes are applied. In addition to lumber, other wood products are frequently used in the construction of the structure and in the interior and exterior finishes. All of these products are intended for specific uses and are manufactured to meet certain standards.

Lumber is commonly referred to by its nominal dimension although actual dimensions may be smaller. For example nominal 2 by 4 in. lumber is actually about 1-½ by 3-½ in. The lumber that is commonly used for framing is 2 to 4 in. (nominal) (38 to 89 mm) thick and is called dimension lumber. Timber is the name given to lumber nominally thicker than 5 in. (114 mm); there are also decking, boards and finish lumber groupings. Table 7, p. 358 presents the grades, common grade mixes, principal uses and grade categories for the various sizes of dimension lumber.

GRADE MARKS

Lumber used in construction is grade-stamped in Canada with identifying markings to show that it conforms to the National Lumber Grades Authority (NLGA) grading rules for Canadian lumber. The grading and grade marking of lumber must also conform to CSA Standard 0141, "Softwood Lumber." Grade stamps show the name or symbol (or both) of the grading agency, the species or species combination designation, the grade, the moisture content at the time of manufacture, and the mill number.

"S-GRN" in the grade mark signifies that the lumber was surfaced at a moisture content higher than 19 per cent to a size that would allow for natural shrinkage during seasoning. "S-DRY" in the mark indicates the lumber was surfaced at a moisture content not exceeding 19 per cent. "MC 15" indicates a moisture content not exceeding 15 per cent.

Facsimiles of Canadian grade marks are shown in Table 8, p. 360.

LUMBER GRADES

Each piece of lumber is examined and assigned a grade depending on its physical characteristics. In addition to visually graded lumber, machine-stress-rated (MSR) lumber is available in Canada. MSR lumber is identified in grade stamps by its structural properties and, for most wood-frame construction purposes, is independent of species.

Many softwood lumber species in Canada are harvested, milled and marketed together. Those having similar properties may be combined into a single-species combination and marketed under a group designation. The Canadian commercial species combinations and their characteristics are shown in Table 9, p. 363.

The top grade is Select Structural, which is used only where high strength,

Machine Stress Rating

stiffness and good appearance are required. Lumber marked No. 1 grade may contain some percentage of Select Structural material, but permitted knots are slightly larger.

Tests have shown that No. 1 and No. 2 grades of lumber have the same strength. These grades are popular for most general construction uses. No. 3 grade lumber is used in general construction where appearance is not a factor.

Nominal 2 x 4 in. (38 x 89 mm) and 2 x 6 in. (38 x 140 mm) lumber is available as Stud grade. Stud grade is stiff, straight lumber suitable for vertical wall members. Finger-jointed studs are an alternative to solid lumber studs. Nominal 2 x 4 in. (38 x 89 mm) is also available as Construction, Standard, Utility and Economy grades. Construction and Standard grades are used for structural purposes. Construction grade lumber has strength properties similar to No. 3 grade, and Standard grade is lower. Utility and Economy grades are not used for structural purposes. Economy is the lowest grade.

Minimum grades for various uses of lumber in wood-frame construction, such as stud wall framing, plank-frame construction, posts and beams, sheathing and subflooring are set forth in the National Building Code of Canada. Tables giving maximum allowable spans for visually graded lumber and for MSR lumber when used as joists and rafters are available from the Canadian Wood Council. In this publication, a number of tables have been provided that present the maximum allowable spans for structural components using various grades of lumber.

Metric sizes of softwood lumber are the same as those in use in Canada under the imperial system of measurement, but their sizes are expressed in millimetres of actual thickness and width after surfacing. The concept of "nominal size" is not used with metric dimensions. Table 10, p. 364, relates the current metric dimensions to the imperial equivalents actual and nominal.

ENGINEERED WOOD PRODUCTS

In addition to dimension lumber, a wide variety of engineered wood products (EWPs) are manufactured for use in wood-frame house construction. These products can provide equivalent or superior strength compared to dimension lumber, and are typically manufactured using less wood fibre. EWPs include products such as glue-laminated timber, wood I-joists and structural composite lumber. A description of the various types that are available follows.

Dimension lumber and other wood products are often combined in the manufacture of EWPs using glue or mechanical fasteners or both. The most common example is the engineered pitched-roof truss. Less common, but of increasing application, is the parallel-chord truss with metal or wood webs. Wood I-joists consisting of lumber flanges and plywood, or oriented strandboard webs are also being used frequently (Figure 29).

All these products provide greater flexibility in design by virtue of their larger spans. In addition, when used for the roof structure, they can accommodate higher insulation levels.

Parallel-chord trusses and wood I-joist

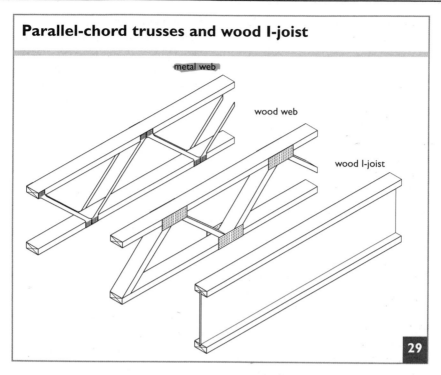

metal web

wood web

wood I-joist

29

Structural Composite Lumber

Structural composite lumber (SCL) is a sub-set of EWPs that includes products such as laminated veneer lumber (LVL) and parallel-strand lumber (PSL).

Laminated veneer lumber consists of thin veneer panels laid parallel to each other, coated with a waterproof adhesive, and bonded by heat and pressure. Available in a wide variety of sizes and strengths, LVL may be cut into desired lengths for use as beams, columns, headers (lintels), joists and as flanges for wood I-beams.

Parallel-strand lumber is manufactured using thin veneer panels cut into narrow strips and then bonded together using a process similar to LVL. Members are available in a variety of widths, depths and lengths, and are primarily used as beams, columns and headers.

SHEET OR PANEL PRODUCTS

In addition to dimension lumber, other wood products in the form of sheets and panels are used in wood-frame construction. Plywood, oriented strand board (OSB) and waferboard, for example, are used to add stiffness to the structural components of the roof, wall and floor, apart from forming a uniform surface for the application of other materials. Fibreboard, particleboard and hardboard are also used in many aspects of interior and exterior finishing.

Plywood, one of the most commonly and extensively used wood products, is used in constructing the shell (subfloor, roof sheathing), exterior finishing, some interior finishing and cabinetry.

Plywood is made of thin layers or plies of wood glued together with the grain of alternate plys running in counter directions. Common thicknesses range from 1/4 to 3/4 in. (6.0 to 18.5 mm). Like dimension lumber, plywood is graded for particular uses. Douglas fir plywood (DFP) and Canadian softwood plywood (CSP) are the two most common softwood plywoods produced. All sheathing grade plywood, waferboard and oriented strand board is made with an exterior grade glue. Overlaid plywood is used for concrete formwork.

Oriented strand board (OSB) is a structural panel made from wood strands mechanically oriented in layers, with the outer layers running parallel to the long dimension of the sheet, and the inner layers having a random or cross alignment. This orientation of layers makes OSB similar to plywood in performance. OSB is primarily used for roof or wall sheathing, sub-flooring, siding and the webs of wood I-joists.

Waferboard is made of wood wafers glued together and has the same uses as OSB and plywood (e.g., subflooring, roof sheathing and wall sheathing). The availability of waferboard is limited.

Fibreboard is made of wood fibres bonded together under pressure. It is available both in a plain and an asphalt-impregnated form. The impregnated version is used primarily for wall sheathing.

Particleboard is generally used in underlay or interior finishing such as shelving and other cabinetry. Often covered with a plastic laminate or other protective and decorative material, it is used to manufacture cabinet doors. The same material is often used as the base for plain or preformed kitchen countertops.

Hardboard is made of wood fibre, like fibreboard, but is denser and harder. It is present in many furniture and cabinetry products. Hardboard siding with a prefinished colour is an alternative to wood, vinyl or aluminum siding. Large panels with prefinished and textured surfaces are often used to create special effects inside or outside the building.

RELATED PUBLICATION

Wood Reference Handbook
Canadian Wood Council

Framing the House

FRAMING THE HOUSE

Wood-frame construction combines repetitive framing elements, such as wall studs, floor joists and roof trusses, with floor, wall and roof sheathing to produce rigid building assemblies capable of resisting wind, earthquake, snow, occupant and construction loads. The repetitive framing members may be dimension lumber or engineered wood products, such as roof trusses or wood I-joists. For housing applications, the repetitive framing members are spaced no more than 24 in. (600 mm) apart, the span of the horizontal members does not exceed 40 ft. (12.2 m), and the design load due to occupants and contents does not exceed 50 psf (pounds per square foot) (2.4 kPa).

The structural shell of a one- or two-storey house must be erected before any other work can begin. The shell consists of the foundation, floors, walls and roof (Figure 30). In some cases, interior walls may be load-bearing, so they must be erected at the same time as the exterior walls. The shell must be framed and sheathed to provide its rigidity. Temporary bracing and cross bracing may also be required to allow construction to proceed without accidents or damage.

Before starting the framing of the house, it is important to consider the levels of insulation to be used in the different elements of the structural shell, because framing dimensions may have to be increased to accommodate higher levels of insulation. Refer to the chapter on "Thermal Insulation" for more information.

The platform and balloon methods of framing are two ways of constructing a wood-frame house. Balloon framing was the most common method of wood-frame construction in the latter

Cutaway of a wood-frame house

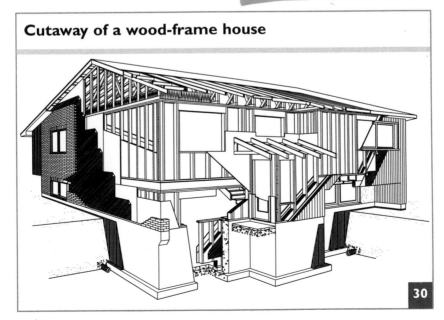

30

part of the 19th century, and early part of the 20th century. Platform framing has dominated since the late 1940s, and today is conventional practice in Canada.

provide fire stops at the floor and ceiling and also nailing support for wall sheathing and interior finish.

PLATFORM CONSTRUCTION

The most commonly used method for framing a house is platform construction. The chief advantage of this approach is that the floor system, assembled independently from the walls, provides a platform or working surface upon which walls and partitions may be assembled and erected. Since the studs are one storey high, walls can easily be prefabricated off the site or assembled on the subfloor in sections and erected one storey at a time without using heavy lifting equipment. The bottom and top plates, which are an integral part of the wall framing,

BALLOON CONSTRUCTION

Balloon framing differs from platform framing in that the studs used for exterior and some interior walls are continuous, passing through the floors and ending at the top plates that support the roof framing. Since the connections between the floor joists and studs in balloon framing do not lend themselves to prefabrication or easy assembly on the site, this method of framing houses is rarely used. However, some of the techniques involved in balloon framing may be used with the platform framing method. For example, ceiling joists or a dropped ceiling may be supported on a 1 x 4 in. (19 x 89 mm) ribbon let

HEALTHY HOUSING INSIGHT

Applying the 4 Rs of Wood-frame Construction

Wood-frame construction has the potential to remain one of the most environmentally appropriate building choices, provided optimum use is made of wood resources. Currently, about 20 per cent of the volume of materials used in a typical new house is wood, yet some 40 per cent of construction waste is made up of dimension lumber and manufactured wood products. Clearly, there is a significant opportunity to waste less of this valuable resource. Canada's building

industry has responded to this challenge and taken the 4 Rs approach to wood-frame construction: Review, Reduce, Reuse, and Recycle. Here are some important 4 Rs considerations.

Review

Wood-frame house construction follows traditional practices that evolved when wood was abundant and waste management was not an issue. It now makes economic and environmental sense to review how the house will be designed and built.

Continued on page 87

Continued from page 86

→ Review current trade practices and to see if these pose a barrier to the efficient use of wood, as well as any other building materials.

→ Check plans to ensure that standard sizes and maximum spans are used wherever possible–get more house for less cost and waste.

→ Identify more efficient framing practices.

Reduce

Lumber represents the greatest component of the waste stream for new housing. Better use of our natural resources is possible by reducing inefficient and wasteful practices.

→ Cut all wood in one area on the site. Most waste is generated by poor cutting practices. Organize offcuts so that short lengths are easily visible and readily accessible–use up warped or twisted full length pieces first when a shorter piece is needed.

→ Order materials in packages corresponding to the stage of construction. Avoid having all materials shipped at once. Only order what is needed—make adjustments with each order.

→ Store materials properly to avoid damage. Damaged wood is the second-highest cause of wood waste, after poor cutting practices.

→ Use simplified framing techniques, such as constructing walls at 24 in. (600 mm) on centre, wherever possible.

→ Reduce the inefficient use of space in the house. Permit fees and property taxes that are computed on the basis of the building size prove that bigger is not necessarily better.

Reuse

In some cases, materials may be reused, while in other cases, used materials may be purchased or obtained free of charge.

→ Plan ahead to reuse lumber wisely. For example, reuse footing formwork lumber as bracing or strapping.

→ Check with demolition contractors for used building materials. In many cases, these materials will provide acceptable service at a fraction of the cost.

→ Buy recycled rather than new materials.

Continued on page 88

Continued from page 87

Recycle

When it is not possible to eliminate waste entirely, consider recycling.

➜ Sort and securely store materials for recycling—avoid using a single waste bin without dividers.

➜ Offer waste products to schools or community groups that may have a use for these in shops and crafts.

➜ The Healthy Housing principle of resource efficiency applies not only to wood, but to all building materials. Additional and more specific insights on the 4 Rs of wood-frame construction are provided in a number of the sections that follow.

into the studs. Floor joists may also be supported in this manner where the level of the floors is offset at an adjoining wall in split-level houses. In some two-storey houses, the centre load-bearing wall in an otherwise platform-framed house is balloon-framed to provide convenient passage for heating ducts and pipes.

STRUCTURAL STRENGTH

The attachment of dimension lumber or engineered wood products and structural wood panel sheathing to make wall, floor and roof assemblies provides wood-frame construction with inherent strength to resist vertical loads (snow, occupants and contents) and horizontal loads (wind and earthquake). In addition, finishes like drywall (gypsum board), partitions,

and closets add rigidity. The primary rigidity for a wood-frame building comes from the wall sheathing that provides shear-wall resistance against racking, and roof and floor sheathing that provides the lateral resistance. Where additional strength is required due to exposure to earthquake or high-wind risk, the floors, walls and roofs can be made stronger by using heavier sheathing materials and closer fastening patterns. In addition, the floors, walls and roofs of wood-frame buildings are meant to act as a structural unit. This is why the floor must be bolted to the concrete foundation. Additional connections may also be required between the roof or floors and walls and between the walls and the foundations.

Floor Framing

FLOOR FRAMING

In a wood-frame house, the floor framing consists of sills, headers, beams and joists. In the interior, load-bearing stud walls are sometimes used instead of posts and beams to support the floor joists and the centre-bearing partition. All framing lumber should be well-seasoned and have a moisture content not exceeding 19 per cent at the time of installation, as required by the National Building Code of Canada.

SILL PLATES AND ANCHORS

The sill plate should be levelled carefully. If the top of the foundation is level, the sill plate may be laid directly on the foundation and the junction caulked. Alternatively, the sill plate may be placed on a closed-cell foam gasket or other air-impermeable material of the same width as the sill plate. If the top of the foundation is uneven or not level, the sill plate may be laid in a full bed of mortar. All sill plates must be anchored to the foundation wall with 1/2 in. (12.7 mm) minimum diameter bolts or other approved anchors.

CHECKING BACK

Requirements for Sill Anchors

Before selecting a floor-framing system, it is important to check to determine how the floor system will be connected to the foundation wall.

When the sill-plate method of foundation wall and joist connection is employed, the sill plate must be securely anchored to the foundation wall. This is normally done using sill anchors embedded in the top of poured concrete walls or in the top course of concrete blocks having their voids filled with concrete. The method of connecting the floor system to the foundation wall should be determined at the time the foundation wall is being constructed

because considerable time and expense is involved in providing sill anchors after the concrete has set.

The following requirements for sill anchor bolt size and placement apply:

→ Anchors must have a diameter no less than 1/2 in. (12.7 mm).

→ Anchors must be fastened to the sill plate with nuts and washers, and embedded no less than 4 in. (100 mm).

→ Anchors must be provided at a maximum spacing of 8 ft. (2.4 m), with no less than 2 anchors per sill plate.

COLUMNS AND BEAMS

Wood or steel columns are generally used in the basement to support the beams, which in turn support the inner ends of the first-floor joists as well as loads from upper floors transferred through walls and posts.

Round, adjustable, structural-steel columns fitted with plates at both ends are commonly used. The top plate should be as wide as the beam it supports and either be bolted to the flange where a steel beam is used or nailed to the wood beam. Columns may be adjusted to length after installation to compensate for movement in the soil or settling caused by shrinkage in the framing members.

Wood columns at least 6 x 6 in. (140 x 140 mm) may be solid or built-up of 2 in. nominal (38 mm) lumber. Generally, 3 in. (76 mm) nails spaced at 12 in. (300 mm) on centre are used to fasten the built-up members together. Wood columns should be the same width as the beam they support and cut to ensure even bearing at top and bottom. Each column is nailed to the beam at the top and separated from the concrete base at the bottom by damp-proofing material such as 6 mil (0.15 mm) polyethylene or Type S roll roofing.

Columns are usually spaced 8 to 10 ft. (2.4 to 3.0 m) on centre, depending on the loading and strength of the beam they support.

Either wood or steel beams may be used in house construction. One advantage of steel is the absence of shrinkage. For steel beams, the I-beam is the commonly used shape. Wood beams can be solid or built-up. The built-up wood beam (Figure 31) is usually made of three or more pieces of 2 in. nominal (38 mm) thick lumber set on edge and spiked together from each side with 3 1/2 in. (89 mm) nails. The nails are driven not more than 18 in. (450 mm) apart in each row, with the end nails located 4 to 6 in. (100 150 mm) from the end of each piece. Butt joints

Built-up wood beam

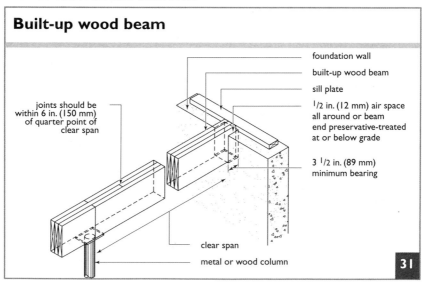

joints should be within 6 in. (150 mm) of quarter point of clear span

foundation wall

built-up wood beam

sill plate

1/2 in. (12 mm) air space all around or beam end preservative-treated at or below grade

3 1/2 in. (89 mm) minimum bearing

clear span

metal or wood column

31

PLANNING AHEAD

Accommodating Ductwork and Piping

An important consideration when designing the beam and joist layout is accommodating ductwork and piping. Ductwork for heating and mechanical ventilation systems, unlike electrical wiring, is not very flexible. To minimize sharp bends and long runs, consider how ducts will be concealed when designing the beam and floor joist layout. Piping is somewhat more flexible than ductwork, however, plumbing components such as soil stacks are usually required to run vertically with few, if any, horizontal offsets. Bathroom plumbing may also be made more difficult if bathrooms are not grouped around a common soil stack. The following items should be considered when beam and joist layouts are being designed:

→ Review the house design with a knowledgeable plumbing and heating contractor at the preliminary stage for an idea of what is required and how it may be accommodated. Consider a higher basement to conceal services above a finished ceiling.

→ Avoid the use of flush beams where floor joists are tied into the sides of beams. Resting joists on top of beams provides a continuous chase over the beam for ductwork and piping.

→ Keep joist spans running in the same direction over the entire floor plan, whenever possible. This minimizes situations where ducts or piping must pass beneath the joists.

→ Use blocking, rather than additional floor joists, under non-load-bearing partition walls running parallel to floor joists. This permits ductwork and piping to enter the partition wall from underneath.

→ Always provide a 2 x 6 in. (38 x 140 mm) wall when it contains a plumbing stack. Alternatively, strap the wall out to conceal the stack and accommodate any potable water piping.

→ Where possible, align wall studs in partitions with floor joists so that the full width of a stud space may be accessed from beneath.

→ If, in following all of the above points, it appears that it will still be difficult to accommodate ductwork and piping, consider using parallel-chord floor trusses that will permit passage of services between the webs.

→ Be prepared to revise your framing plan to accommodate ductwork and piping.

in each member are located over a supporting post or within about 6 in. (150 mm) of the quarter points in the span. (See Tables 11, 12 and 13, p. 365-p. 369). Joints are not permitted in the end spans and joints are permitted in not more than half the members at any one location.

Alternatives to built-up wood beams and columns include steel (Table 14, p. 371) or glue-laminated (glulam) (Table 15, p. 372) laminated veneer lumber (LVL) beams, and parallel strand lumber (PSL) beams and columns.

Ends of beams should bear at least 3 1/2 in. (89 mm) on concrete or masonry walls or columns. There is a decay hazard, however, where beams are tightly set into wall notches, such that moisture cannot escape readily. Therefore, the ends of wood beams, located at or below grade and framed into masonry or concrete walls, should be treated to prevent decay or have a 1/2 in. (12 mm) air space at the ends and sides. Untreated wood beams should also be separated from the concrete with an impermeable membrane where they are at a level of 6 in. (150 mm) above grade or less.

BEAM AND JOIST INSTALLATION

The simplest method of beam and joist framing is to have the joists rest on top of the beam (Figure 32), in which case the top of the beam is level with the top of the sill plate (Figure 31). This method is used where the basement has adequate headroom below the beam. When joists are lapped above a beam, the maximum recommended length of lap is 12 in. (300 mm).

Where more clearance under a wood beam is desired, joists may be supported by joist hangers or other structural connectors attached to the beam. In lieu of joist hangers, the National Building Code allows joists to be supported on ledger strips attached to the wood beams (Figure 33). The 2 x 3 in. (38 x 64 mm) ledger strip is nailed to the beam with two 3 1/4 in. (82 mm) nails per joist. The ends of the joists may be spliced as shown in (Figure 33).

Joists framed into the side of a steel beam may be supported on the bottom

Joists supported on top of wood beam

The joists are fastened to the beam by toenailing.

Two 3 1/4 in. (82 mm) nails are used for each joist.

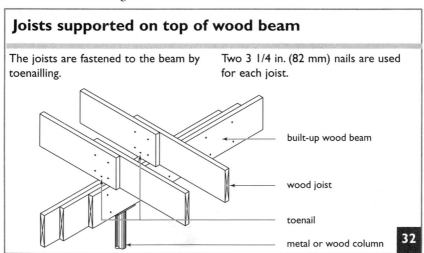

built-up wood beam

wood joist

toenail

metal or wood column

32

flange or on a 2 x 2 in. (38 x 38 mm) ledger strip bolted to the web with 1/4 in. (6.3 mm) bolts spaced 24 in. (600 mm) on centre. The joists should be spliced (Figure 34) and a 1/2 in. (12 mm) space provided on top of the beam to allow for joist shrinkage.

FOUNDATION WALL AND JOIST CONNECTION

The two general types of floor joist construction used over the foundation wall conform either to platform or balloon-frame construction. Platform framing is by far the most common type used.

Joists supported on ledger strips nailed to beam

Two 3 1/4 in. (82 mm) nails per joist.
Splice is nailed to joists with two
3 1/4 in. (82 mm) nails at each end.

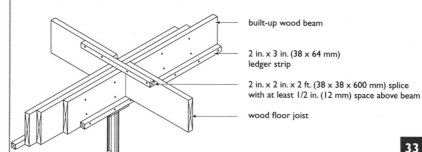

built-up wood beam

2 in. x 3 in. (38 x 64 mm) ledger strip

2 in. x 2 in. x 2 ft. (38 x 38 x 600 mm) splice with at least 1/2 in. (12 mm) space above beam

wood floor joist

33

Joists rest on the bottom flange of the steel beam, or on a wood plate that is bolted to the beam

Joists are joined at the top with
2 x 2 in. (38 x 38 mm) splices.

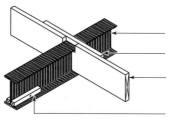

steel beam

2 x 2 in. (38 x 38 mm) splice

joist

alternatively, the joists may be supported on a minimum 2 x 2 in. (38 x 38 mm) wood plate bolted through the web of the beam

34

In platform framing, two methods of wall and joist connection are used and are generally referred to as the sill-plate method and the joist-embedded method.

Sill-plate Method

This method can be used with either concrete or concrete block foundation walls. It consists of a wood sill plate anchored to the foundation wall (Figure 35) for the support and fastening of the joists and header at the ends of the joists. The sill plate is usually supported on the top of the foundation wall. In this case, the bottom of the sill plate should be at least 6 in. (150 mm) above the finished grade.

Where it is desirable to lower the elevation of the main floor, the top of concrete foundation walls may be reduced to 3 1/2 in. (90 mm) in thickness. If siding or stucco is used as an exterior finish, the wall framing is supported on a sill plate anchored to the top of the wall, and the floor joists rest on a separate sill plate located on a ledge formed in the wall (Figure 36). Where a masonry finish is used, such as brick veneer, the masonry is supported on the top of the foundation wall, and the wall framing is supported on the floor framing (Figure 37). If the thickness of the wall is reduced, as noted above, the height of the reduced section should not exceed 14 in. (350 mm).

Joist-embedded Method

This method can be used only with cast-in-place concrete foundation walls. Beams, joists and headers are positioned before the concrete is placed. Floor framing is temporarily supported on the inside concrete form and wedges used to level the framing. Filler pieces placed between the floor joists and along the end walls retain the fluid concrete between the joists. These filler pieces are set flush with the inner face of the foundation wall (Figure 38). Joist headers

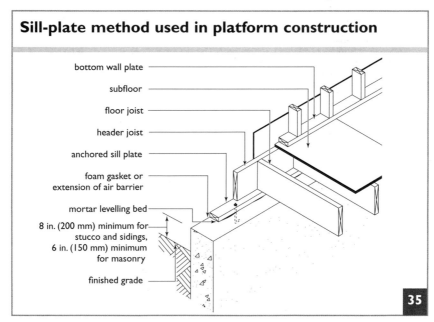

Sill-plate method used in platform construction

- bottom wall plate
- subfloor
- floor joist
- header joist
- anchored sill plate
- foam gasket or extension of air barrier
- mortar levelling bed
- 8 in. (200 mm) minimum for stucco and sidings, 6 in. (150 mm) minimum for masonry
- finished grade

35

and end joists serve as outside forms for the concrete. Beam ends are treated to prevent decay when they are located at or below grade. The concrete is then placed so that at least two-thirds of the depth of each joist is embedded in the concrete, thus providing suitable anchorage for the floor-framing members. The filler pieces are removed, together with the wall forms, when the concrete has set. The same method can be used when the finish of the exterior wall is masonry (Figure 39).

FLOOR JOISTS

Joists are selected to meet strength, deflection and vibration requirements and all of these requirements are reflected in the joist selection tables (Tables 16, p. 374, and 17, p. 375). Strength requirements ensure the floor joist system is strong enough to support the anticipated loads. Deflection requirements ensure that the deformation of the floor under heavy load is within acceptable limits and will not lead to defects, such as cracking of the ceiling below the floor. Vibration

Floor joists supported on a ledge formed in the foundation wall

Joists are toenailed to header and sill plate. Sill plate is anchored to top of foundation wall with anchor bolts. Wall plate supporting the wall framing is fastened to the sill plate with 3 in. (76 mm) nails spaced 16 in. (400 mm) on centre.

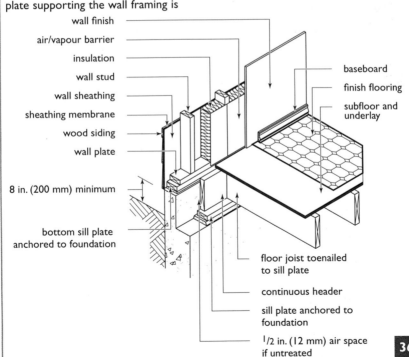

wall finish
air/vapour barrier
insulation
wall stud
wall sheathing
sheathing membrane
wood siding
wall plate

8 in. (200 mm) minimum

bottom sill plate anchored to foundation

baseboard
finish flooring
subfloor and underlay

floor joist toenailed to sill plate

continuous header

sill plate anchored to foundation

1/2 in. (12 mm) air space if untreated

36

Floor joists supported on ledge formed in foundation wall

Joists are toenailed to header and sill plate. Masonry veneer supported on top of foundation wall. Wall framing supported on top of the subfloor.

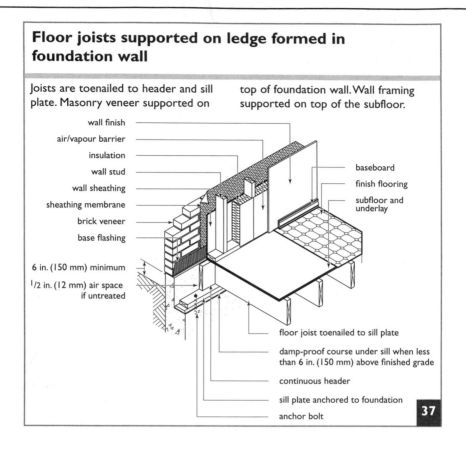

wall finish
air/vapour barrier
insulation
wall stud
wall sheathing
sheathing membrane
brick veneer
base flashing

6 in. (150 mm) minimum

1/2 in. (12 mm) air space if untreated

baseboard
finish flooring
subfloor and underlay

floor joist toenailed to sill plate

damp-proof course under sill when less than 6 in. (150 mm) above finished grade

continuous header

sill plate anchored to foundation

anchor bolt

37

Floor joists embedded in the top of the foundation wall

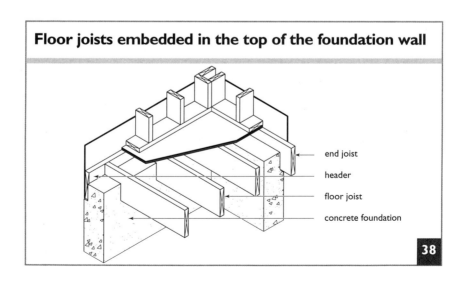

end joist
header
floor joist
concrete foundation

38

Masonry support using joist-embedded method of floor framing

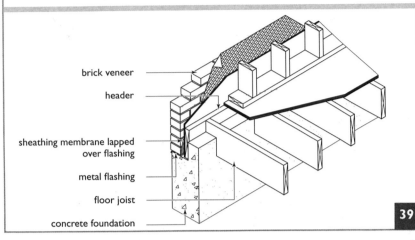

- brick veneer
- header
- sheathing membrane lapped over flashing
- metal flashing
- floor joist
- concrete foundation

39

HEALTHY HOUSING INSIGHT

Alternative Floor Systems

The Healthy Housing principle of resource efficiency may be applied to floor systems by considering alternatives such as engineered wood products (EWPs).

Commonly available alternatives to floor joists are wood I-joists and floor trusses.

On average, wood I-joists and floor trusses use 20 per cent less material than a conventional floor constructed with dimensional lumber, and may permit a wider spacing between members leading to even further reductions in material requirements.

Manufactured in lengths that well exceed those available in conventional lumber, these engineered floor systems may often clear-span the building, avoiding the need for interior bearing walls. This enhances the future adaptability of the house plan while further reducing the amount of material and labour required.

Continued on page 100

Continued from page 99

Whenever using engineered wood products, it is important to strictly adhere to manufacturer's installation instructions.

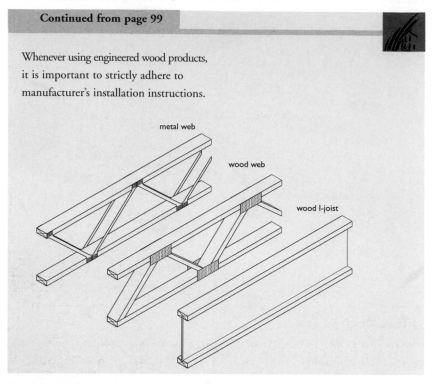

metal web

wood web

wood I-joist

Principles for wood I-joist installation

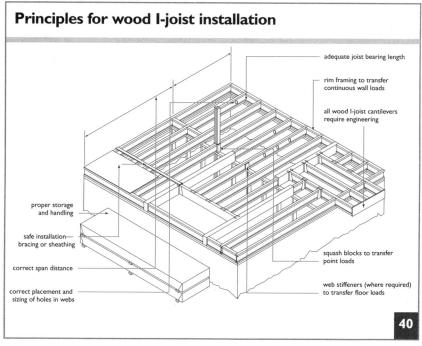

adequate joist bearing length

rim framing to transfer continuous wall loads

all wood I-joist cantilevers require engineering

proper storage and handling

safe installation— bracing or sheathing

correct span distance

correct placement and sizing of holes in webs

squash blocks to transfer point loads

web stiffeners (where required) to transfer floor loads

40

Load transfer requirements for wood I-joists

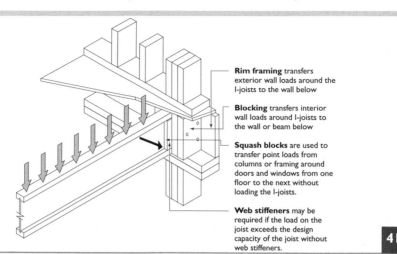

Rim framing transfers exterior wall loads around the I-joists to the wall below

Blocking transfers interior wall loads around I-joists to the wall or beam below

Squash blocks are used to transfer point loads from columns or framing around doors and windows from one floor to the next without loading the I-joists.

Web stiffeners may be required if the load on the joist exceeds the design capacity of the joist without web stiffeners.

41

Floor framing

(1) Subfloor nailed with 2 in. (51 mm) nails to joists.

(2) 1 x 3 in. (19 x 64 mm) continuous wood strapping nailed at bottom with two 2 1/4 in. (57 mm) nails.

(3) 2 x 2 in. (38 x 38 mm) cross-bridging nailed with two 2 1/4 in. (57 mm) nails.

(4) Header joist end-nailed to joists with three 3 1/4 in. (82 mm) nails.

(5) Header toenailed to sill plate with 3 1/4 in. (82 mm) nails 24 in. (600 mm) o.c.

(6) Floor joists toenailed to sill plate with two 3 1/4 in. (82 mm) nails, one on each side.

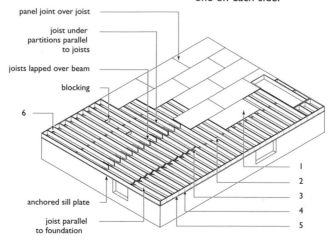

panel joint over joist

joist under partitions parallel to joists

joists lapped over beam

blocking

6

anchored sill plate

joist parallel to foundation

1
2
3
4
5

42

requirements ensure that the floor is adequately stiff so that, for example, foot traffic will not cause china in cabinets to rattle.

Wood floor joists are generally 2 in. nominal (38 mm) thick and either 6, 8, 10 or 12 in. (140, 184, 235 or 286 mm) deep. The size depends upon the loading, length of span, spacing between joists, the species and grade of lumber used, and the deflection that may be allowed. Tables 16, p. 374, and 17, p. 375, show the spans that are allowable for the various grades and species of lumber and for different loading conditions. The allowable spans shown in these

tables are measured between inside edges of the joist supports and have been calculated on the basis of lumber dressed to standard Canadian sizes.

Alternatives to dimension-lumber floor joists include laminated veneer lumber joists, parallel chord trusses and wood I-joists. Allowable spans for these engineered wood products are provided by their manufacturers. Wood I-joists have become common residential floor framing materials because they can span longer distances and, because they are manufactured from dry wood materials, they shrink less. Typical residential wood I-joist sizes are 9-1/2 in.

Framing for floor openings where-double-headers and double-trimmers are used

(1) First trimmer nailed to first header with three 4 in. (101 mm) or five 3 1/4 in. (82 mm) nails.

(2) First header nailed to tail joists with three 4 in. (101 mm) or five 3 1/4 in. (82 mm) nails.

(3) Second header nailed to first header with 3 in. (76 mm) nails spaced 12 in. (300 mm) apart longitudinally.

(4) First trimmer nailed to second header with three 4 in. (101 mm) or five 3 1/4 in. (82 mm) nails.

(5) Second trimmer nailed to first trimmer with 3 in. (76 mm) nails spaced 12 in. (300 mm) apart longitudinally.

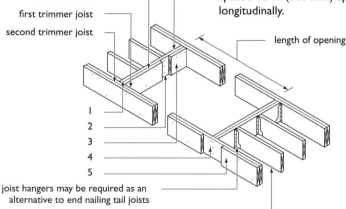

first header
second header
first trimmer joist
second trimmer joist

length of opening

1
2
3
4
5

joist hangers may be required as an alternative to end nailing tail joists

tail joist

43

(241 mm) and 11-7/8 in. (302 mm). Although they are made from wood, wood I-joists have particular installation details that differ from dimension lumber joists. Successful installations depend on several rules (Figure 40) such as proper location of web holes and adequate load transfer mechanisms at the points of support.

Wood I-joists are optimized for spanning and due to their thin webs, less capable of handling vertical loads (for example, from load-bearing walls above). For this reason, special blocking techniques are used to transfer vertical loads around the wood I-joists (Figure 41). The manufacturers of wood I-joists produce comprehensive technical information that describes these requirements in more detail and this information is recommended reading for those considering floors with wood I-joists.

Where a sill plate is used, the joists are installed after the sill plates have been leveled on the mortar bed and anchored to the foundation wall. As already described, where joists are embedded in the top of the foundation wall, they are installed before the foundation wall is placed. The joists are located and spaced according to the design.

Joist spacing of 16 in. (400 mm) on centre is most commonly used, although for heavy loads or when space is limited, 12 in. (300 mm) spacing of shallower joists may be substituted. Conversely, if floor thickness is not a limitation, deeper joists at 24 in. (600 mm) spacing may prove more economical. (**Note:** *Metric joist spacings are nominal, and should not be used since panel products are manufactured in imperial sizes.*)

Any joists having a slight bow edgewise should be placed with the crown on top. A crowned joist will tend to straighten out when the subfloor and floor loads are applied.

A header joist is end-nailed or toenailed to each joist. In platform construction, each joist including the end joist parallel to the exterior walls is toenailed to the sill (Figure 42). The inner ends of the joists are supported on top of the beam (Figure 32) or framed into the side of the beam (Figure 33).

When a load-bearing wall runs parallel to the joists, it should be supported by a beam or load-bearing wall in the basement.

Floor plans often require a load-bearing wall to be located at right angles to the floor joists, but offset from the joist support. Load-bearing interior walls at right angles to floor joists should be located not more than 36 in. (900 mm) from the joist support when the wall does not support a floor, and not more than 24 in. (600 mm) from the joist support when the wall supports one or more floors, unless the joist size is designed to support such concentrated loads.

Non-load-bearing partitions parallel to the joists should bear on joists or on blocking between the joists. This blocking should be 2 x 4 in. (38 x 89 mm) lumber and spaced 4 ft. (1.2 m) or less.

When framing for large openings, such as stairwells or fireplaces, trimmer joists are doubled if they support header joists more than 32 in. (800 mm) long. Header joists longer than the 4 ft. (1.2 m) should also be doubled. Where unusually large openings occur, trimmer joists that support header joists more than 6 ft. 6 in. (2 m) long and header joists that are more than 10 ft. 6 in. (3.2 m) long should be designed according to accepted engineering practice.

Nailing and assembly methods generally used in the framing of floor openings are shown in Figure 43.

Joist hangers are often used to support long joist headers and tail joists.

Joist twisting can be reduced and load sharing between joists can be improved by cross bridging, blocking, strapping or a ceiling finish fastened to the underside of the joists. Where a board-type finish is not used, necessary restraint should be provided at intermediate locations between the supports and at distances not greater than 6 ft. 10 in. (2.1 m).

Intermediate support may be provided by the following methods: 1 x 3 in. (19 x 64) mm or 2 x 2 in. (38 x 38 mm) cross bridging or 2 in. nominal (38 mm) full-depth blocking fastened between joists together with continuous wood strapping of 1 x 3 in. (19 x 64 mm) nailed to the bottoms of the joists. Continuous wood strapping, however, is not required when a ceiling finish is provided.

Floor Performance

The floor joist span tables incorporate vibration criteria. The tables recognize that different floor constructions are more "bouncy" or "springy" than others. Therefore, by adding blocking or increasing subfloor thickness, floor joist spans may be increased. Alternatively, engineered wood products such as laminated veneer lumber joists, wood I-joists and parallel-chord trusses may be used, but vibration criteria must be also be considered for these engineered products.

SUBFLOOR

Subflooring should consist of plywood, oriented strand board, waferboard or square-edge, shiplap, or tongue-and-grooved lumber no wider than 8 in. nominal (184 mm). The minimum thicknesses of plywood, oriented strand board, waferboard and lumber for subflooring are shown in Table 18, p. 376.

Plywood and OSB are often used as subflooring under wood-strip flooring or as a combination subfloor and underlay for resilient flooring or ceramic tile. When used as a combination subfloor and underlay, the side joints should be supported on 2 x 2 in. (38 x 38 mm) blocking fitted between the joists unless the edges of the panels are tongue-and-grooved.

Subfloors should be installed with the major axis at right angles to the floor joists and with the end joints staggered and nailed along the edges at 6 in. (150 mm) on centre and 12 in. (300 mm) at intermediate supports. Ringed underlay nails, which are designed to resist withdrawal and "nail popping," or approved staples should be used where the panels provide a combination subfloor and underlay. (See Table 19, p. 376 for details of fastening sheathing and subflooring.)

Floor stiffness can be substantially increased and floor squeaks minimized by applying elastomeric glue between the floor joists and the subfloor. By using this method, the subfloor, adhesive and joists act together as a strengthened floor frame, thus reducing deflection between adjacent joists.

All subfloor panels that do not have tongue and groove joints should be covered with an underlay where a vinyl floor covering is used.

All plywood, oriented strand board and waferboard panels used for subflooring and underlayment should be the exterior type, manufactured with waterproof adhesives.

An underlay is not required where the edges of the subflooring are supported.

For a lumber subfloor, 1 in. nominal (19 mm) thick boards are generally used, though this thickness may be reduced to 11/16 in. (17 mm) where joists are spaced at 16 in. (400 mm) on centre. The boards should be applied so that the end joints occur over the joists. End joints are usually staggered throughout the floor. Boards may be applied at right angles to the joists or diagonally at an angle of 45˚. When the subflooring is laid at right angles to the joists, strip flooring should be placed at right angles to the subflooring unless an underlay is used. Diagonal subflooring permits strip flooring to be laid either parallel to or across the joists. The boards should be nailed with two, 2 in. (51 mm) nails at each support. Lumber subflooring must be covered with a panel-type underlay when the floor is finished with resilient flooring.

FLOOR FRAMING AT PROJECTIONS

Floor joists sometimes project beyond the foundation wall to provide support for a bay window or additional floor space in the upper rooms. The cantilevered portion of the floor framing should not exceed 16 in. (400 mm) for 2 x 8 in. (38 x 184 mm) joists and 24 in. (600 mm) for larger joists. In either case, this projection should not carry loads from additional floors. If the cantilevered floor joists are to carry additional loads, they must be specifically designed for the appropriate loads according to accepted engineering practice. The subflooring is carried to and sawn flush with the outer framing members. Figure 44 shows a typical second-storey projection.

Insulation should be fitted carefully, and placed on top of the soffit finish under the cantilevered floor and up the inside face of the joist header and end joists. The vapour retarder should be placed on the warm side of the insulation and neatly fitted and fastened in place.

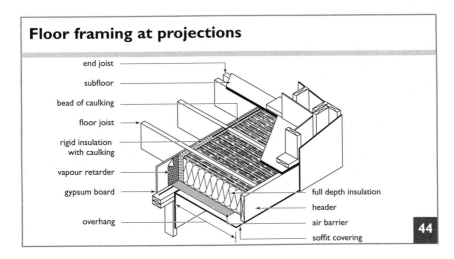

Floor framing at projections

end joist
subfloor
bead of caulking
floor joist
rigid insulation with caulking
vapour retarder
gypsum board
overhang

full depth insulation
header
air barrier
soffit covering

44

SIZING BUILT-UP WOOD BEAMS

Problem

Select two built-up beams that can satisfy the conditions noted below

Conditions

One-storey, brick veneer house
Beam supporting main floor only
Supported joist length is 12 ft. (3.6 m)
Beam span is 13 ft. (4 m)

Species group and grade specified is SPF No. 2 or better.

Selection

Use Table 11, p. 365

Acceptable beams for this application include:
5 - 2 in. x 10 in. (5 - 38 x 235 mm) or
4 - 2 in. x 12 in. (4 - 38 x 286 mm)

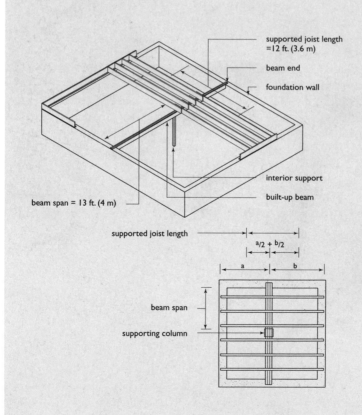

supported joist length =12 ft. (3.6 m)

beam end

foundation wall

interior support

built-up beam

beam span = 13 ft. (4 m)

supported joist length

a/2 + b/2

a

b

beam span

supporting column

SIZING FLOOR JOISTS

Problem

Select a floor joist that is acceptable for the conditions as described below.

Conditions

Joists supporting living room floor.
Joist span is 12 ft.-3 in. (3.75 m).
Bridging will be installed.
Basement ceiling will be not finished.
Species group and grade
specified is SPF No. 2 or better.
Subfloor is 5/8 in. (15.9 mm) plywood
nailed in place.

Also note that drywall or gypsum board ceiling finish can be considered a

strapping. For this example floor joists can be considered braced with bridging and strapping.

Selection

Use Table 16, p. 374

Acceptable floor joist sizes for this application include:
2 in. x 8 in. at 12 in. o.c.(38 x 184 mm at 300 mm o.c.) or
2 in. x 10 in. at 24 in. o.c.(38 x 235 mm at 600 mm o.c.)
Note that any spacing less than 24 in. (600 mm) for the 2 in. x 10 in. (38 x 235 mm) is acceptable.

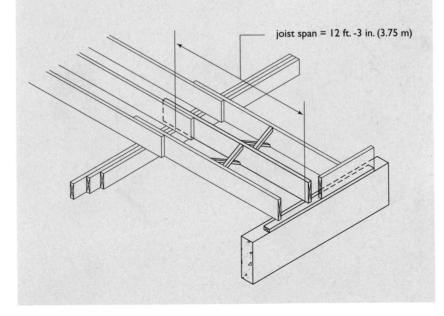

joist span = 12 ft. -3 in. (3.75 m)

If the joist depth is great enough, the space between the insulation and subfloor is usually left open to let the warm air in the ceiling area circulate between the joist spaces. In this way, the floor in the projected area is heated both from below and above, resulting in an even and comfortable floor temperature throughout the room.

To prevent external air infiltration into the cantilevered area, the soffit under the overhang and other parts of the trim should be carefully fitted and caulked where necessary or wrapped with an air barrier.

RELATED PUBLICATIONS

The Canadian Span Book
Canadian Wood Council

Engineering Guide for Wood Frame Construction
Canadian Wood Council

Installation Guide for Residential Wood I-joist Floor Systems
Canada Mortgage and Housing Corporation

Wall Framing

WALL FRAMING

Wall framing includes the vertical and horizontal members of exterior walls and interior partitions. These members, referred to as studs, wall plates and lintels, serve as a nailing base for all covering material and support the upper floors, ceiling and roof. All framing lumber should be grade-stamped, and have a moisture content not exceeding 19 per cent. (See Table 20, p. 377 for nailing practice.)

Exterior wall studs are the vertical members to which the wall sheathing and cladding are attached. They are supported on a bottom plate or foundation sill and in turn support the top plate. Studs usually consist of 2 x 4 in. (38 x 89 mm) or 2 x 6 in. (38 x 140 mm) lumber and are commonly spaced at 16 in. (400 mm) on centre. This spacing may be changed to 12 in. (300 mm) or 24 in. (600 mm) on centre depending on the load and the limitations imposed by the type and thickness of the wall covering used. (See Table 21, p. 379.) Wider 2 x 6 in. (38 x 140 mm) studs may be used to provide space for more insulation. Insulation beyond that which can be accommodated within a 3 ½ in. (89 mm) stud space can also be provided by other means, such as rigid or semi-rigid insulation or batts between 2 x 2 in. (38 x 38 mm) horizontal furring strips, or by attaching rigid or semi-rigid insulation sheathing to the outside of the studs.

The studs are attached to horizontal top and bottom wall plates of 2 in. nominal (38 mm) lumber that are the same width as the studs. The top plate is usually doubled in a load-bearing stud wall.

Lintels are the horizontal members placed over window, door and other openings to carry loads to the adjoining studs. Lintels are usually constructed of at least two pieces of 2 in. nominal (38 mm) lumber, nailed together to form a single unit. The preferable spacer material is rigid insulation. The depth of a lintel is determined by the width of the opening and vertical loads supported. (See Tables 22 and 23, p.380 and p. 382.)

PLATFORM FRAMING

There are two methods of framing a house. Balloon framing was common until the late 1940s, but since that time, platform framing has become the predominant form of house construction.

This method of framing wall sections horizontally on the subfloor prior to erection is widely used. The top and bottom plates are end-nailed to each stud with two nails at least 3 ¼ in. (82 mm) in length. Studs are doubled at openings, the jack stud being cut to support the lintels that are placed on top and end-nailed through the outer studs.

Wall sheathing is usually applied to the framing prior to erection, thus eliminating the need to scaffold for this operation. Some types of sheathing, such as asphalt-impregnated fibreboard, plywood, oriented strandboard and waferboard, will provide adequate bracing to resist lateral loads and keep the wall square. Others, such as rigid glass-fibre, asphalt-coated fibreboard, polystyrene or polyurethane board, will not. In this latter case, the wall should be reinforced

PLANNING AHEAD

Providing the Required Effective Thermal Resistance

Code requirements for minimum levels of effective thermal resistance in wall and other building assemblies depend on climatic conditions and the type of energy source used for space heating.

It is important to understand the difference between the nominal and effective thermal resistance of insulated building assemblies. The nominal thermal resistance refers to the thermal resistance rating of the insulation that is installed. For example, a 2 x 6 in. (38 x 140 mm) wall cavity containing a glass-or mineral-fibre insulation batt has a nominal thermal resistance of about R-20 (RSI-3.52). The effective thermal resistance takes into account interior and exterior sheathings and finishes, and most importantly, the effect of the wood studs that conduct heat at a higher rate than insulation. This effect, known as thermal bridging, reduces the nominal thermal resistance of the building assembly and is reflected in the effective thermal resistance rating. For a wall constructed with wood studs at 16 in. (400 mm) on centres, the effective thermal resistance is R-17.4 (RSI-3.06). In general, the effective thermal resistance is lower than the nominal rating. It is important to select an assembly that will comply with the minimum Code requirement applicable to the house being constructed. The following points should be considered when providing adequate effective thermal resistance values:

➜ Effective thermal resistance values of common building assemblies are provided in the Model National Energy Code for Houses. It is available from the National Research Council.

➜ Wider spacing of framing members reduces thermal bridging and provides higher effective thermal resistance.

➜ Select insulation materials with higher nominal thermal resistance values.

➜ Where structural sheathing is not required, use insulating sheathings in place of structural sheathings to increase the effective thermal resistance of wall assemblies.

➜ Take into account the effect of thicker building assemblies when designing details at the foundation wall/main floor and wall intersection, and at the wall and roof intersection.

Additional consideration should also be given to factors affecting the amount of labour associated with various insulated wall assemblies, particularly in relation to the placement of air barriers and vapour retarders.

with diagonal wood or metal bracing let into the studs.

The complete wall sections are then raised and put in place, temporary braces added and the bottom plates nailed through the subfloor to the floor framing members (Figure 45). The braces should have their larger dimension on the vertical and should permit adjustment of the vertical position of the wall.

Once the assembled sections are plumbed, they are nailed together at the corners and intersections. A strip of polyethylene is often placed between the interior walls and the exterior wall, and above the first top plate of interior walls before the second top plate is applied to attain continuity of the air barrier when polyethylene is serving this function. A second top plate, with joints offset at least one stud space away from the joints in the plate beneath, is then added. This second top

Wall framing used with platform construction

(1) Top plate end-nailed to each stud with two 3 ¼ in. (82 mm) nails.

(2) Top plates nailed together with 3 in. (76 mm) nails 24 in. (600 mm) on centre.

(3) Stud toenailed with four 2 ½ in. (63 mm) nails or end-nailed to bottom plate with two 3 ¼ in. (82 mm) nails.

(4) Top plates at corners and load-bearing partitions are lapped and nailed

together with two 3 ¼ in. (82 mm) nails or the plates are butted together and tied with a metal plate fastened to the top plates with three 2 ½ in. (63 mm) nails on each side of the joint.

(5) Doubled studs at openings and multiple studs at corners and intersections nailed with 3 in. (76 mm) nails 30 in. (750 mm) on centre.

(6) Bottom plate nailed to joist or header joist with 3 ¼ in. (82 mm) nails 16 in. (400 mm) on centre.

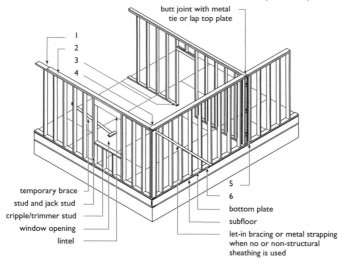

butt joint with metal tie or lap top plate

1
2
3
4

temporary brace
stud and jack stud
cripple/trimmer stud
window opening
lintel

5
6
bottom plate
subfloor
let-in bracing or metal strapping when no or non-structural sheathing is used

Note: Where the lintel exceeds 10 ft. (3 m), the jack stud needs to be doubled on both sides of the opening.

45

PLANNING AHEAD

Installing Special Items Prior to Wall Framing

After the main floor system is completed, and prior to the framing of exterior walls, careful consideration should be given to any special items that need to be installed. One-piece bath or shower units and other large fixtures or equipment that cannot pass through door or window openings must be placed within the building before walls are erected. Similarly, exterior chimneys and chases may also have to be completed before walls are framed. In some cases, such as internal masonry fireplaces supporting roof structural members, it is necessary to have these constructed prior to wall framing in order to avoid interfering with this work.

The following items pertaining to the planning and coordination of trades prior to wall framing should be reviewed before starting any construction.

→ Review plans and specifications carefully to identify any special items that have to be installed prior to wall framing.

→ Order and arrange for delivery of these special items well in advance of wall framing to avoid delays.

→ Coordinate with trades responsible for constructing fireplaces, chimneys and chases to maximize productivity and minimize conflicts.

By carefully planning ahead, proper installation without delays and trade conflicts is possible. Failure to plan ahead may require that some special items are substituted with less suitable items, or altogether omitted from the house.

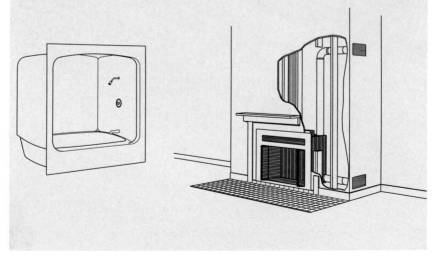

plate usually laps the first plate at the corners and partition intersections and, when nailed in place, provides an additional tie to the framed walls. Where the second top plate does not lap the plate immediately underneath at corner and partition intersections, these may be tied together with 0.036 in. (0.91 mm) galvanized steel plates at least 3 in. (75 mm) wide and 6 in. (150 mm) long, nailed with at least three 2 ½ in. (63 mm) nails to each wall.

Interior partitions supporting floor, ceiling or roof loads are called load-bearing walls; others are called non-load-bearing or simply partitions. Interior load-bearing walls are framed in the same way as exterior walls. Studs are usually 2 x 4 in. (38 x 89 mm) lumber spaced at 16 in. (400 mm) on centre. This spacing may be changed to 12 in. (300 mm) or 24 in. (600 mm) depending on the loads supported and the type and thickness of the wall finish used. (See Table 21, p. 379.)

Partitions can be built with 2 x 3 in. (38 x 64 mm) or 2 x 4 in. (38 x 89 mm) studs spaced at 16 or 24 in. (400 or 600 mm) on centre depending on the type and thickness of the wall finish used. Where a partition does not contain a swinging door, 2 x 4 in. (38 x 89 mm) studs at 16 in. (400 mm) on centre are sometimes used with the wide face of the stud parallel to the wall. This is usually done only for partitions enclosing clothes closets or cupboards to save

Multiple stud arrangements at exterior corner

In the two-stud arrangement, a plasterboard clip is used at the corner for support.

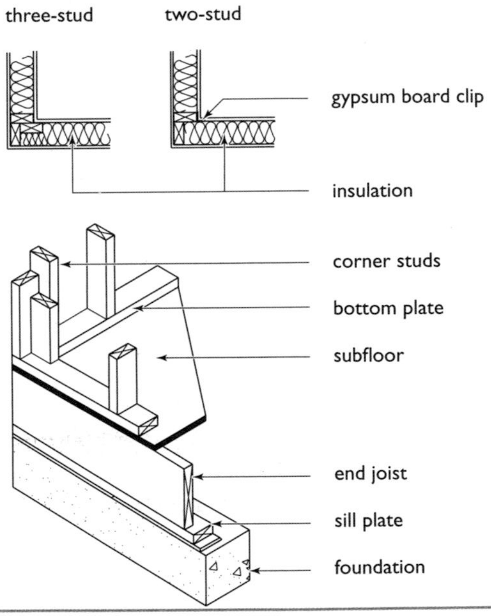

three-stud

two-stud

gypsum board clip

insulation

corner studs

bottom plate

subfloor

end joist

sill plate

foundation

46

Multiple stud arrangements at the intersection of an interior partition with an exterior wall

(A) Two studs are used.

(B) Bracing or blocking is used.

(C) The partition is attached to exterior wall after drywall has been installed.

(D Insulation must be installed before sheathing is applied.

A

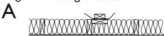

B

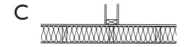

C

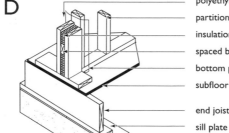

D

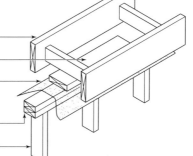

- polyethylene strip
- partition stud
- insulation in spaces between blocking
- spaced blocking
- bottom plate
- subfloor
- end joist
- sill plate
- foundation

47

Horizontal nailing support for interior finish

nailing support provided by 2 in. (38 mm) lumber nailed to top plates with 3 in. (76 mm) nails at 12 in. (300 mm) on centre

ceiling joist

2 x 6 in. (38 x 140 mm) nailing support

polyethylene air/vapour barrier strip (may also be installed between top plates—not required between floors)

plate

stud

48

End-wall framing and nailing support for interior finish using platform construction method

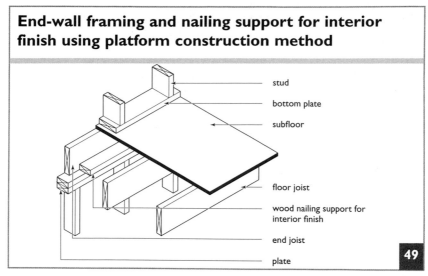

- stud
- bottom plate
- subfloor
- floor joist
- wood nailing support for interior finish
- end joist
- plate

49

space. Since there is no vertical load to be supported by partitions, single studs may be used at door openings. The top of the opening may be bridged with a single piece of 2 in. nominal (38 mm) lumber the same width as the studs. These members provide a nailing support for wall finish, door frames and trim.

A multiple-stud post made up of at least three studs, or the equivalent, is generally used at exterior corners and intersections to secure a good tie between adjoining walls and to provide nailing support for the interior finish and exterior sheathing. Corners and inter-sections, however, must be framed with at least two studs.

Figures 46 and 47 illustrate commonly used exterior corners and partition intersections.

Nailing support for the edges of the ceiling finish is required at the junction of the wall and ceiling where partitions run parallel to the ceiling joists. Figures 48 and 49 illustrate the types of nailing support commonly used.

BALLOON FRAMING

In balloon-framed construction, both the studs and first-floor joists rest on the foundation sill plate (Figure 50) and the centre beam or bearing wall. Studs are toenailed to these supports with four 2 1/2 in. (63 mm) nails; the joists in turn are nailed to the studs with two 3 in. (76 mm) nails. When lumber subfloor is laid diagonally, blocking is required between the joists at the wall lines to support the ends of the boards.

Second-floor joists bear on a 1 x 4 in. (19 x 89 mm) ribbon that has been let into the studs, and the joist are nailed to the studs. The end joists parallel to the exterior walls on both first and second floors are similarly nailed to the studs.

When framing the floor, blocking should be inserted between joists at the wall to support the ends of diagonal subfloor boards. As the spaces between the studs are not interrupted by wall

Wall framing using balloon construction method

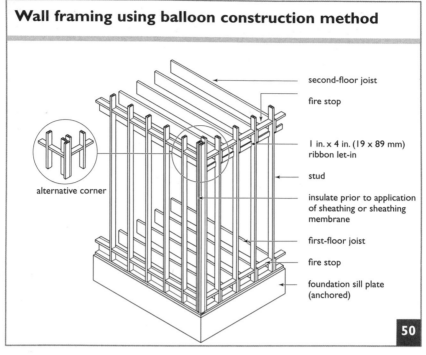

second-floor joist

fire stop

1 in. x 4 in. (19 x 89 mm) ribbon let-in

stud

insulate prior to application of sheathing or sheathing membrane

first-floor joist

fire stop

foundation sill plate (anchored)

alternative corner

50

HEALTHY HOUSING INSIGHT

Minimizing Waste in Wall Framing

The amount of waste generated during wall framing may be significantly reduced through proper planning, and appropriate practices. Consider the following items when planning and building walls:

➜ Use kiln-dried lumber and store it properly to reduce warped and twisted pieces.

➜ Use precision-trimmed studs that are pre-cut to the right length for a standard wall height.

➜ If a standard height wall is not desired, select a height that makes the most use of wall studs.

➜ Space studs at 24 in. (600 mm) on centres wherever possible.

➜ Order lumber for lintels that is a multiple of the lintel length. (A 4 ft. 6 in. (1.5 m) lintel using two members is more economically created with a 10 ft. (3.3 m) length, rather than cutting from two 8 ft. (2.6 m) lengths).

➜ Cut all lumber in one location to make best use of end cuts.

plates (as in platform framing), fire stops are required at floor and ceiling levels to eliminate continuous passages in the wall and thus resist the spread of fire. Lumber blocking 1 ½ in. (38 mm) thick is commonly used for this purpose. Fire stops, however, are not required where the wall space is filled with insulation.

SIZING WALL STUDS

Problem

Select the first-floor wall studs that are able to support the superimposed loads as described below.

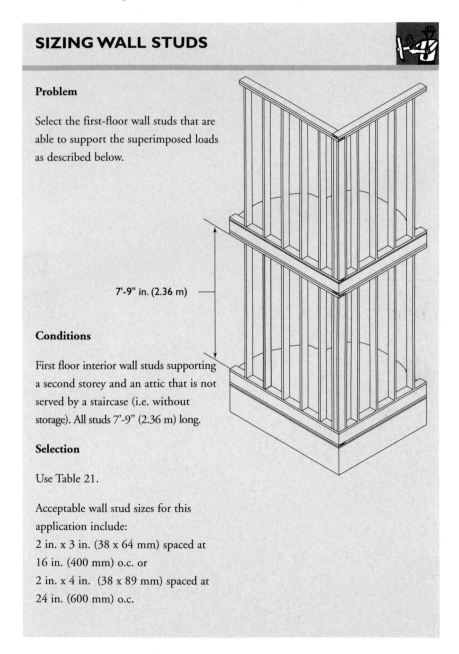

7'-9" in. (2.36 m)

Conditions

First floor interior wall studs supporting a second storey and an attic that is not served by a staircase (i.e. without storage). All studs 7'-9" (2.36 m) long.

Selection

Use Table 21.

Acceptable wall stud sizes for this application include:
2 in. x 3 in. (38 x 64 mm) spaced at 16 in. (400 mm) o.c. or
2 in. x 4 in. (38 x 89 mm) spaced at 24 in. (600 mm) o.c.

Ceiling and
Roof Framing

CEILING AND ROOF FRAMING

There are two basic types of roofs—pitched and low-slope—and each type has many variations.

The slope of a roof is expressed as a ratio of rise-to-run with the vertical component, or rise, always being shown first. There are two conventions for expressing the slope of a roof: imperial and metric.

The imperial convention is based on the use of a framing square, and the run is always expressed as 12, based on 12 inches to a foot. For example, a roof with a slope of 45˚ is expressed as a 12/12 slope. A roof with a 4/12 slope has a rise of 4 inches for every 12 in. of run.

Using the metric convention, for slopes less than 45˚, the first number should always be shown as one. A ratio of 1:5, for instance, indicates a rise

of 1 mm for every 5 mm of horizontal dimension, or 1 m for every 5 m. For slopes steeper than 45˚, the second number (that is, the horizontal component) should always be one to facilitate easy verification. A ratio of 5:1 expresses a rise of 5 mm for a horizontal dimension of 1 mm, or 5 m for each 1 m. The use of mixed units, such as 1 mm in 10 m, should be avoided.

Expressed as a ratio, the standard slope reference of 4 in 12 (or 400 mm in 1200 mm) becomes 1:3; similarly, 3 in 12 becomes 1:4. In special cases, where a high degree of accuracy is required, angular expressions of slope are acceptable.

For purposes of definition, low-slope roofs might be classed as those having less than 1:6 slope. Pitched roofs vary in slope from 1:6 to 1:1 or more (for example, 2:1), depending on the roof covering and the use of attic space.

Roof framing using lightweight roof trusses

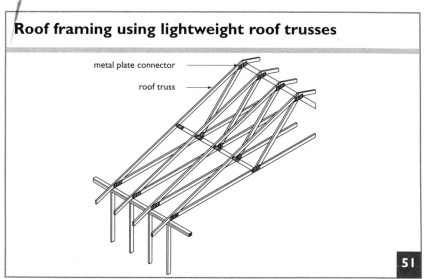

metal plate connector

roof truss

51

L-shape trussed roof

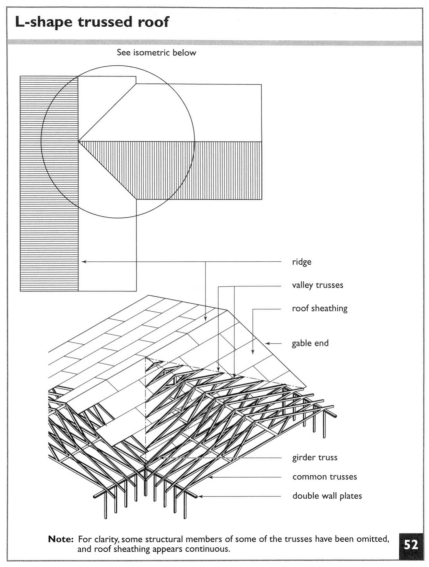

See isometric below

ridge

valley trusses

roof sheathing

gable end

girder truss

common trusses

double wall plates

Note: For clarity, some structural members of some of the trusses have been omitted, and roof sheathing appears continuous.

52

The dimensions of roof joists and rafters for the various grades and species of lumber and for the different live loads encountered are given in (Tables 25 to 28, p. 384-387).

PITCHED ROOFS

Roof trusses are most often pre-assembled, although they can be constructed on site. Pitched roofs can also be stick-built, although this is a time-consuming process. Of the pitched roofs, the gable roof is the simplest to construct, especially

Types of prefabricated roof trusses NEXT TEST

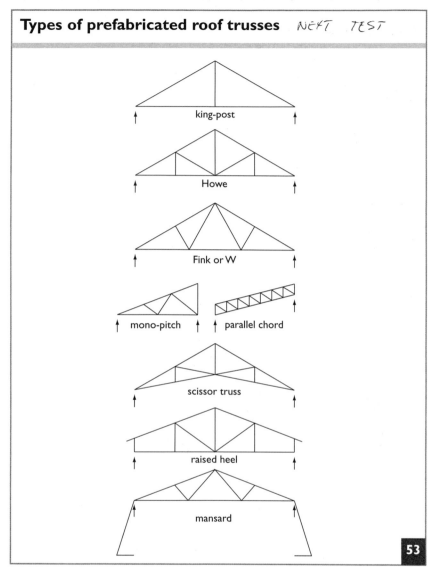

king-post

Howe

Fink or W

mono-pitch   parallel chord

scissor truss

raised heel

mansard

53

with the use of lightweight roof trusses (Figure 51). Other configurations, such as the hip roof and L-shape roof, though more complex, can also be framed with trusses (Figure 52).

Pre-assembled Roof Trusses

Pre-assembled roof trusses offer many advantages in that they save material and speed up the process of enclosing the house. They provide, in one step, a surface for the roof sheathing, a surface for the ceiling finish material and a space for insulation. Ventilation of the attic space is easily accomplished through the eaves or gables or both, and at or along the ridge. In most cases, trusses are designed to span from

Temporary bracing of roof trusses

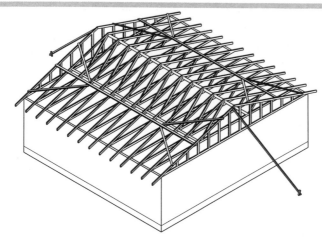

Note: Gable ends are normally sheathed prior to installation of end braces. **54**

exterior wall to exterior wall with no intermediate load-bearing walls to support the roof loads (Figure 53). Thus, the entire house may be used as one large workroom during construction. This increases the flexibility of interior planning, because partitions can be placed without regard to structural requirements. Additional flexibility and speed is gained with pre-assembled components and add-on features such as garage roof trusses, porch roofs and simulated mansards, which can also be supplied by the truss manufacturer.

Metal-plate-connected trusses can be delivered to the construction site and placed on a flat, clean portion of the site. Trusses shorter than a 20 ft. (6 m) span are usually installed by hand. Trusses longer than 20 ft. (6 m) require special lifting techniques to avoid damage.

The trusses must be lifted into position with care to prevent excessive lateral bending. The first to be put in place is the gable truss, which is braced to the ground and wall. Each additional truss is lifted into position, generally 24 in. (600 mm) on centre, toenailed to the top plates and temporarily braced (Figure 54). When all trusses are plumbed and properly positioned, they are braced permanently (Figure 55). The stiffness of the roof is increased after the sheathing has been applied. Trusses must be installed and braced according to the fabricators instructions. Wood trusses must not be cut or altered.

Site Assembly of Pitched Roofs

For on-site construction, the simplest roof is the gable roof (Figure 56A). All rafters are cut to the same length and pattern, and erection is straightforward. A variation of the gable roof may include dormers for additional light, headroom and ventilation (Figure 56B and Figure 56C). However, openable windows and fixed skylights that can be fitted on a slope between rafters will provide ventilation and light without the complexity and cost of framing a dormer.

In the hip roof design, shown in Figure 56D, common rafters are fastened to the ridge board while hip rafters supply the support for the jack rafters.

Important considerations in framing a liveable attic space are insulation and proper air barrier and vapour retarder sealing; these techniques are dealt with in the chapters on "Thermal Insulation" and "Vapour Retarders and Air Barriers Systems." The choice of framing members for structural strength, based on Tables 25 to 28, (p.384-387) may not provide sufficient depth for insulation and necessary ventilation space. Larger size members or a modified framing technique will be needed to meet current standards.

Ceiling joists are used to support the ceiling finish and to act as ties between exterior walls and, in some cases, opposing rafters. They may also provide support for roof loads transferred to them by dwarf

Permanent bracing of roof trusses

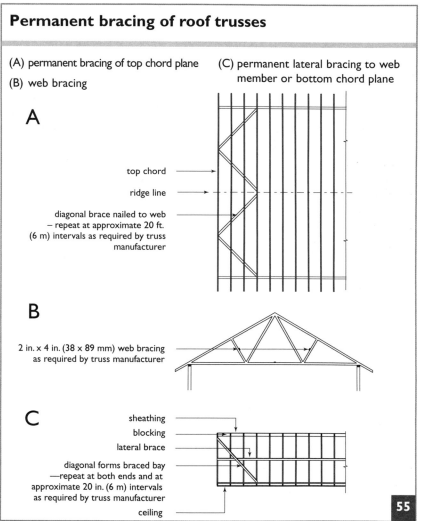

(A) permanent bracing of top chord plane

(B) web bracing

(C) permanent lateral bracing to web member or bottom chord plane

A

top chord

ridge line

diagonal brace nailed to web – repeat at approximate 20 ft. (6 m) intervals as required by truss manufacturer

B

2 in. x 4 in. (38 x 89 mm) web bracing as required by truss manufacturer

C

sheathing

blocking

lateral brace

diagonal forms braced bay —repeat at both ends and at approximate 20 in. (6 m) intervals as required by truss manufacturer

ceiling

55

walls (knee walls) used as intermediate support for rafters, in which case they need to be appropriately increased in size. (See Table 29, p. 388, for ceiling joist spans.) When the joists also support floor loads, their size should be determined by the floor joist tables. (See Tables 15, p. 372 and 16, p. 374.)

In pitched-roof framing, with dimension lumber, the ceiling joists are nailed in place after the interior and exterior wall framing is complete but before the rafters are erected, because the thrust of the rafters will otherwise tend to push out the outside walls. Ceiling joists are generally used to tie the lower ends of the rafters in pitched roofs that slope 1:3 or more. To prevent the rafter ends from moving outward, the ceiling joist is nailed to the side of each pair of rafters (Figure 57). The joists are lapped and nailed together or spliced at the centre load-bearing wall, thus providing a continuous tie across opposing rafters. The number of nails used in the connections depends upon the roof slope, rafter spacing, snow load and width of the house. (See Table 20, p. 377, for nailing practice.)

The additional roof load imposed by dwarf walls that run at right angles to the ceiling joists (Figure 58) should be taken into account when the size of the joists is determined. An increase in the depth of the joists to the next standard depth will usually provide the additional strength required where the roof slope is more than 1:4. When the slope is 1:4 or less, the size of the ceiling joists is determined from span tables for roof joists (Tables 25, p. 384, and 26, p. 385.)

Since hip rafters are about 2 in. (51 mm) deeper than the common or jack rafters, they reduce the space along the end walls to the extent that in low-slope roofs, there may not be enough room to install the outside ceiling joist at normal spacing from the wall. In this case, doubled joists are used and positioned to suit the available space (Figure 59). Tail joists are then added and toenailed to the outside wall plate and end-nailed to the doubled joist. The spacing of these tail joists is usually the same as that of the main ceiling joists.

Rafters are cut to length with the proper angle cut at the ridge and eaves and with notches (known as birdmouths) provided for the wall or rafter plates. The heel or lower part of the rafters should bear directly over the exterior wall. Depending on the plan of the roof and the shape of the outside walls, the rafters are placed:

- directly on the wall plates (Figure 57);

- on a rafter plate nailed to the top of the ceiling joists (Figure 58), or

- on a load-bearing wall supported on the exterior wall plate (Figure 60).

The last method is used where a portion of the outside wall is set back. In this case, the ceiling joists extend beyond the exterior wall and are nailed to the side of the rafters. This provides lateral support for the bearing wall and resists outward and downward movement of the ends of the rafters.

A ridge board (Figure 57) or a ridge beam (Figure 58) is used to ensure a level ridgeline and for ease in erecting and aligning the rafters. Rafters are erected in pairs and nailed to the ridge board or beam. The lower ends are toenailed to the wall plate. Each pair of rafters is usually located directly opposite each other. However, they may be offset

Types of pitched roofs READ OVER

(A) gable

(B) gable dormer   **A**

(C) shed dormer

(D) hip – *cottage*

B

C

D

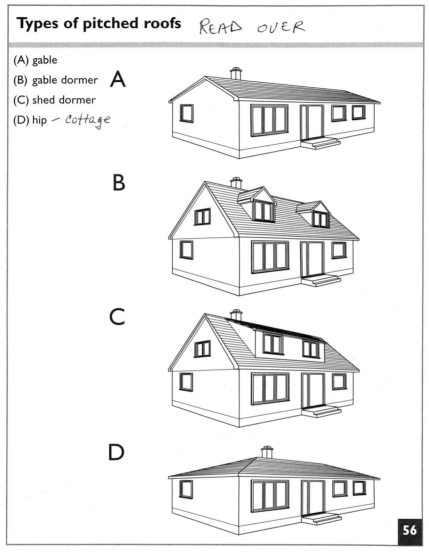

56

at the ridge by their own thickness. This offsetting is required to maintain vertical alignment of the rafters when the lower ends are tied to ceiling joists that have been lapped (rather than butted together) at the centre load-bearing wall (Figure 58).

A roof that slopes less than 1:3 should be vertically supported at the peak.

This can be accomplished by providing a 2 x 6 in. (38 x 140 mm) ridge beam, supported at 4 ft. (1.2 m) intervals by 2 x 4 in. (38 x 89 mm) vertical struts (Figure 58). A load-bearing wall may be used instead of the ridge beam. Since these methods of support reduce the outward thrust of the roof, continuous ties between the lower ends of opposing rafters are not necessary. Ridge beams

Roof framing and attachment ~~Read Test !~~

(A) Ceiling and roof framing with ridge board

  (1) each rafter toenailed to ridge board with four, 2 ¼ in. (57 mm) nails or end-nailed with three, 3 ¼ in. (82 mm) nails

  (2) 1 x 4 in. (19 x 89 mm) strip nailed to top of collar ties at their centre with two, 2 ¼ in. (57 mm) nails when the braces are more than 8 ft. (2.4 m) long

  (3) ceiling joists butted with splice plate over centre bearing

partition. Joists also nailed to each part of rafters (see Table 27, p. 386, for nailing practice)

  (4) collar tie used as intermediate support for rafters nailed to each pair of rafters with three, 3 in. (76 mm) nails at each end

  (5) ceiling joists toenailed to top wall plate with two, 3 ¼ in. (82 mm) nails, one each side

  (6) rafter nailed to plate with three, 3 ¼ in. (82 mm) nails

A

Gable roof

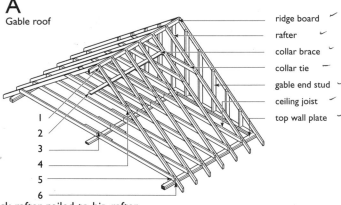

- ridge board
- rafter
- collar brace
- collar tie
- gable end stud
- ceiling joist
- top wall plate

1
2
3
4
5
6

(B) Jack rafter nailed to hip rafter with two 3 1/4 in. (82 mm) nails.

B

Hip roof

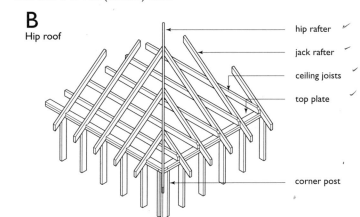

- hip rafter
- jack rafter
- ceiling joists
- top plate
- corner post

57

Rafter heel supported on a rafter plate

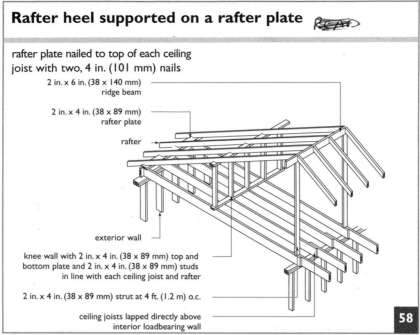

rafter plate nailed to top of each ceiling
joist with two, 4 in. (101 mm) nails

2 in. x 6 in. (38 x 140 mm)
ridge beam

2 in. x 4 in. (38 x 89 mm)
rafter plate

rafter

exterior wall

knee wall with 2 in. x 4 in. (38 x 89 mm) top and
bottom plate and 2 in. x 4 in. (38 x 89 mm) studs
in line with each ceiling joist and rafter

2 in. x 4 in. (38 x 89 mm) strut at 4 ft. (1.2 m) o.c.

ceiling joists lapped directly above
interior loadbearing wall

58

are also required for steeper pitched roofs when the outside ends of the rafters cannot be tied together to resist thrust.

Intermediate support is generally installed between the ridge and exterior walls to reduce the span of the rafters. This reduces the size of the rafters that are required as the span is taken from this intermediate point to the ridge or eave support.

Doubled ceiling joists and stub joists used where hip rafter reduces clear space near the end wall

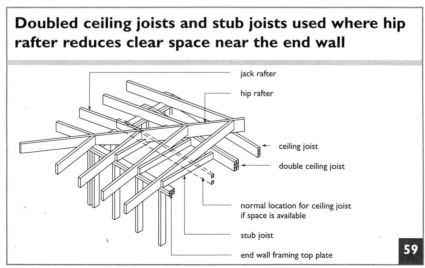

jack rafter

hip rafter

ceiling joist

double ceiling joist

normal location for ceiling joist
if space is available

stub joist

end wall framing top plate

59

For rafters in roofs that slope 1:3 or more, intermediate support is generally provided by a 2 x 4 in. (38 x 89 mm) collar tie nailed to the side of each pair of rafters. Since these ties are in compression and subject to buckling, they should be supported against lateral deflection when more than 8 ft. (2.4 m) long. This can be done by nailing a 1 x 4 in. (19 x 89) mm continuous member at right angles to the collar ties near their centre with three, 3 in. (76) mm nails at each end (Figure 57).

Intermediate support for rafters in roofs that slope less than 1:3 is usually provided by a dwarf-bearing wall (Figure 58) built in the same way as a load-bearing partition, except that a single top plate may be used where the rafters are positioned directly over the studs.

Struts may also be used as intermediate supports for rafters in pitched roofs. A 2 x 4 in. (38 x 89 mm) strut (Figure 60) is nailed to the side of each rafter and supported on a loadbearing partition. The angle of the struts should not be less than 45° to the horizontal.

Rafters that run at right angles to the ceiling joists may be supported at an

Rafter heel supported on loadbearing wall

Ceiling joists project beyond the wall line and are nailed to the rafters (see Table 20, p. 377 for nailing practice). Roof struts 2 x 4 in. (38 x 89 mm) used as intermediate support for rafters.

Struts are nailed to the side of the rafter with three 3 1/4 in. (82 mm) nails and toenailed to bearing wall with two, 3 1/4 in. (82 mm) nails.

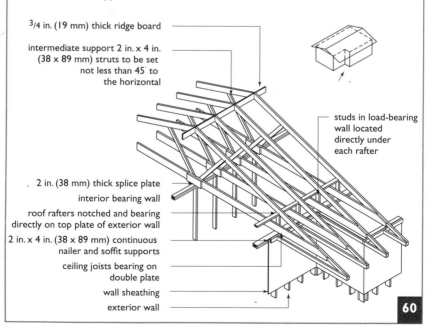

3/4 in. (19 mm) thick ridge board

intermediate support 2 in. x 4 in. (38 x 89 mm) struts to be set not less than 45° to the horizontal

studs in load-bearing wall located directly under each rafter

2 in. (38 mm) thick splice plate
interior bearing wall
roof rafters notched and bearing directly on top plate of exterior wall
2 in. x 4 in. (38 x 89 mm) continuous nailer and soffit supports
ceiling joists bearing on double plate
wall sheathing
exterior wall

60

intermediate point by a dwarf wall sitting on a beam placed between the ceiling joists. The underside of the beam is raised at least 1 in. (25 mm) above the ceiling finish by blocks inserted under the ends of the beam at the exterior walls and centre loadbearing partition. The space thus formed prevents the beam from damaging the ceiling finish when deflected at its centre by the roof loads.

A beam similarly installed may also be used as intermediate support for hip and valley rafters. In this case, a roof strut is used to transfer the load from the hip or valley rafter to the beam.

Where intermediate support is required for a few rafters in the end section on a hip-type roof, a simple form of support can be provided by a beam (sometimes called a "strongback") consisting of two, 2 x 4 in. (38 x 89 mm) members nailed together, set on edge and nailed to the bottom of the rafters. This beam is in turn supported at points along its length by 2 x 4 in. (38 x 89 mm) struts radiating from a common point of support on the centre load-bearing wall. The angle of any strut should not be less than 45° to the horizontal. The ends are cut to fit the selected angle and securely nailed in place.

Hip and valley rafters should be about 2 in. (50 mm) deeper than the common rafters (Figures 57B, 59 and 61).

This additional depth provides full contact with the angle-cut of the jack rafters. In hip roofs, the jack rafters are

---

PLANNING AHEAD

Roof Covering Loads

The tables for sizing roof members assume that a conventional roof covering, such as asphalt shingles, cedar shakes or lightweight metal roofing, is being installed. Some roof coverings, such as terra cotta tile, are much heavier and hence the roof members must be sized accordingly. The following points should be considered when sizing roof framing members supporting heavier than normal roof coverings.

➜ Obtain the unit weight (pounds per square foot or kilograms per square metre) from the manufacturer, and add this to the local snow load. Use

this adjusted snow load to size roof framing members. If the adjusted snow load exceeds that found in the tables, consult a structural designer.

➜ If trusses are being used, notify the truss manufacturer of the additional load due to the heavier roof covering so that these may be sized properly.

➜ Roof trusses cannot be cut or altered. Therefore plan for skylights and other roof installations in advance.

➜ Carefully observe all requirements for bracing and strapping that may be required to properly install and support the roof covering.

---

nailed to the hip rafters and wall plate. Where a valley occurs, the jack rafters are nailed to the valley rafter and ridge.

Dormers, such as small gable dormers, are framed so that the rafters at each side are doubled to support the side studs and valley rafters. The top ends of the valley rafters are supported by a header (Figure 62). The most common method of construction is to install the roof sheathing before the dormer is framed, and then saw the sheathing flush with the framing members around the opening. A bottom plate added on top of the sheathing supports the side studs enclosing the dormer and also serves as a nailing base for the wall sheathing. If future expansion is contemplated or additional rooms are to be built in the attic, consideration should be given when the house is built to framing the roof to accept future dormers. Except for very small attic spaces, attics require an access hatch. The area of the hatch must be at least 3.4 sq. ft. (0.32 m²) with no dimension less than 21 ½ in. (545 mm).

Gable-end Framing and Projections

After the roof-framing members are installed, the gable-end studs are cut to fit and nailed in place. Studs in unfinished attics may be placed with the wide face parallel to the wall. The ends of the studs are then cut to fit the angle of the rafter and are toenailed to the wall plate and to the underside of the rafter with four 2 ½ in. (63 mm) nails at each end (Figure 63).

Construction of the roof projections commonly used at the gable ends is shown in Figures 63 and 64. As with eave projections, the soffit is covered with 1/4 in. (6 mm) sanded plywood or pre-finished aluminum or vinyl sheets, and fascia board is added to the outside framing member.

Roofs that project less than 12 in. (300 mm) over the gable-end wall usually terminate with a framing member sometimes called the rake rafter (Figure 64). A 3/4 in. (19 mm) nailing strip is fastened to the rafter located above the gable-end wall. Blocking spaced at

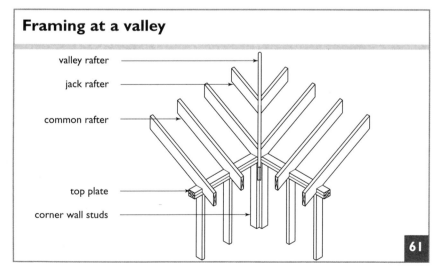

Framing at a valley

valley rafter

jack rafter

common rafter

top plate

corner wall studs

61

Typical dormer framing

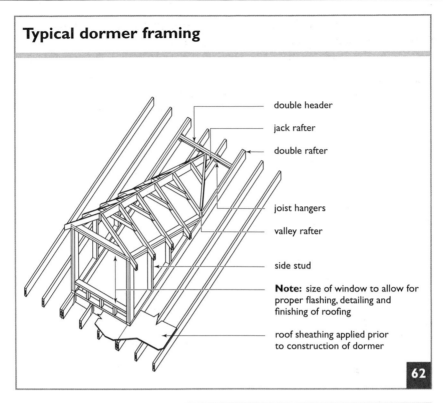

double header

jack rafter

double rafter

joist hangers

valley rafter

side stud

Note: size of window to allow for proper flashing, detailing and finishing of roofing

roof sheathing applied prior to construction of dormer

62

Wide projection at gable end supported by "lookout" rafters   *IMPORTANT*

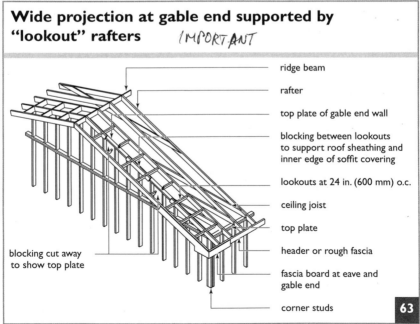

ridge beam

rafter

top plate of gable end wall

blocking between lookouts to support roof sheathing and inner edge of soffit covering

lookouts at 24 in. (600 mm) o.c.

ceiling joist

top plate

header or rough fascia

blocking cut away to show top plate

fascia board at eave and gable end

corner studs

63

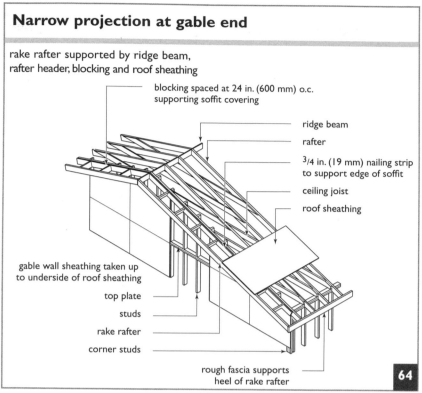

Narrow projection at gable end

rake rafter supported by ridge beam,
rafter header, blocking and roof sheathing

blocking spaced at 24 in. (600 mm) o.c.
supporting soffit covering

ridge beam

rafter

3/4 in. (19 mm) nailing strip
to support edge of soffit

ceiling joist

roof sheathing

gable wall sheathing taken up
to underside of roof sheathing

top plate

studs

rake rafter

corner studs

rough fascia supports
heel of rake rafter

64

24 in. (600 mm) on centre is used to support the soffit covering. This blocking is toenailed to the nailing strip and end-nailed to the rake rafter. The soffit covering is then installed and nailed to these supports. A fascia board is added in the manner previously described.

Gable-end projections extending more than 12 in. (300 mm) beyond the wall should be supported by framing members called "lookouts" (Figure 63). The gable-end studs are placed with the narrow face parallel to the sheathing, and a top wall plate is added. The lookout members, usually the same size as the rafters, are spaced at 24 in.

(600 mm) on centre. The ends are supported by end-nailing to the first rafter and to the header, and toenailing to the wall plate. Blocking is then fitted between the lookouts at the wall line to support the roof sheathing and inner edge of the soffit covering. The soffit covering is nailed to these supports, and a fascia is added as previously described. The length of lookout members should be about twice the width of the roof overhang. A double rafter is used to support the inner ends of the lookout members when they project into the roof more than one and one-half rafter spacings.

HEALTHY HOUSING INSIGHT

Attic Rooms

The Healthy Housing principle of affordability and economic viability may be promoted by considering future conversion of the attic into habitable space. Through proper planning, it may be converted into a high quality living space, deferring initial construction costs until resources are available and needs arise.

Consider these features when planning attic rooms.

➜ Plan stairwells in the house so that they may be extended to the attic space, or determine an appropriate future location for outside stairs.

➜ Size ceiling joists as floor joists, and use insulation that may be transferred to the roof assembly during conversion. Ensure that the roof assembly will accommodate sufficient insulation with an air space above.

➜ A roof slope of 1:1 or steeper is recommended, particularly if a knee wall is not provided. If a knee wall is provided, check local bylaws regarding height restrictions of the building.

➜ Rough in or plan for future services such as electricity, plumbing, heating, ventilation, and telephone.

With the addition of elements such as dormers and skylights, properly planned attics may be converted into high quality living space, easily and economically.

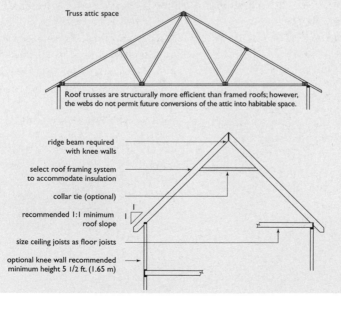

Truss attic space

Roof trusses are structurally more efficient than framed roofs; however, the webs do not permit future conversions of the attic into habitable space.

ridge beam required with knee walls

select roof framing system to accommodate insulation

collar tie (optional)

recommended 1:1 minimum roof slope

size ceiling joists as floor joists

optional knee wall recommended minimum height 5 1/2 ft. (1.65 m)

LOW-SLOPE ROOFS

Low-slope roofs are generally less practical and less durable than pitched roofs, especially in heavy snowfall areas. They are sometimes used to cover extensions of the main house and in combination with upper floor decks. Carports and garages are frequently covered with low-slope roofs.

In low-slope roof construction where rafters also serve as ceiling joists, the term "roof joist" is used. The size of these roof joists is established on the basis of both roof and ceiling loads. (See Tables 25, p. 384 and 26, p. 385.) Rafters chosen for structural adequacy may not, however, provide adequate depth for insulation and ventilation of the roof space. In such cases, wider lumber or engineered wood products should be used.

Roof joists for low-slope roofs are usually laid level, with roof sheathing and a roof covering on top. The underside of the roof joists is used to support the ceiling. A slope of at least 1:50 should be provided for roof drainage by sloping each joist with a ledger strip on the underside of the joist at the bearing wall, or by adding a tapered strip to the top of the joists.

The house design may call for an overhang of the roof beyond the wall or for a parapet wall carried above the roof. Insulation may be added just above the ceiling. In this case, the space above the insulation should be ventilated not only to help prevent condensation in the winter, but also to help remove hot air in the summer. Alternatively, rigid insulation may be installed on top of the roof sheathing and the roof covering placed on the insulation. In this case, the space above the ceiling is not ventilated. Figure 65B shows a simple type of low-slope roof in which the bottoms of the roof joists are level, eliminating the need for separate ceiling joists.

When an overhang is called for on all sides of the house, lookout rafters are ordinarily used (Figure 66). These lookout rafters, which are usually twice as long as the overhang, are toenailed to the wall plate and end-nailed to the first roof joist. If the lookout rafters project into the ceiling area more than one and one-half joist spaces, two roof joists are nailed together to form a header. One outside rafter header is then added and end-nailed to the lookout rafters and roof joists.

This serves as a nailing support for the roof sheathing, fascia board and soffit covering. Such overhangs are generally from 16 to 24 in. (400 to 600 mm) but do not exceed 4 ft. (1.2 m).

Low-sloped roofs, as shown in Figure 65B, may have a ceiling finish attached to the roof joists with the ceiling following the pitch of the roof to form a "cathedral" ceiling. The roof joists are supported on a ridge beam in this case.

Note: Insulation is generally placed between the roof-ceiling joists. A ventilated space of at least 2 ½ in. (63 mm) must be provided between the top of the insulation and the underside of the roof sheathing, unless rigid insulation is used. This can be achieved by placing 2 x 2 in. (38 x 38 mm) cross-purlins over the top of, and at right angles to, the roof-ceiling joists. The 2 x 2 in. (38 x 38 mm) members may be shimmed to provide the required roof slope. Figure 132 shows a cross-section of the completed roof.

Two low-slope roof designs

Rafters may also serve as ceiling joists.

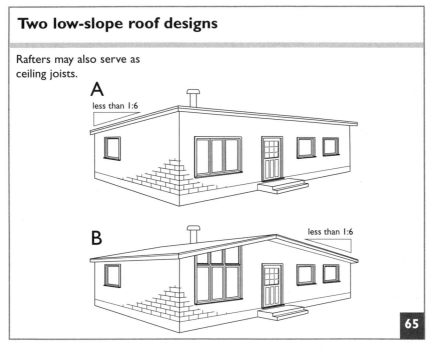

A

less than 1:6

B

less than 1:6

65

Typical construction of low-slope roof with overhang

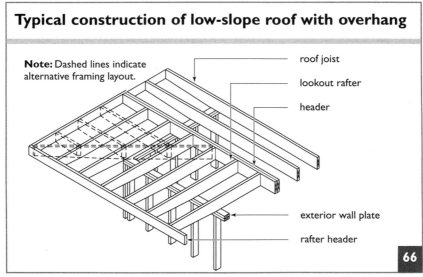

Note: Dashed lines indicate alternative framing layout.

roof joist

lookout rafter

header

exterior wall plate

rafter header

66

ROOF SPACE VENTILATION

For both pitched and low-slope roofs, it is important to provide adequate ventilation of the roof space above the insulation. Even where air barriers and vapour retarders are used, some moisture will leak around pipes and other openings and through the vapour retarder itself. If water vapour is allowed to accumulate in attic spaces and under low-slope roofs, during cold weather it is likely to condense in a cold spot in sufficient quantity to cause damage. Since most types of roof membranes are highly resistant to vapour transmission, vapour in the roof space can't pass through them. The most practical way of removing vapour that enters the roof space is by ventilation.

During cold weather, heat loss through the ceiling insulation combined with exposure to sun may provide enough heat to melt the snow on the roof, but not on the projecting eaves. Water from the melting snow can then freeze and form ice dams at the eavestrough and roof overhang. This may cause water to back up at the eaves, penetrate through the roof and leak into the walls and ceilings. Similar dams may form in roof valleys. A well-insulated ceiling and adequate ventilation will keep attic temperatures low during winter and help prevent snow on the roof from melting. The installation of appropriate eave protection and valley flashings will also prevent potential water damage.

A common method of providing ventilation is to install louvred openings or continuous screened slots in the soffit at the eaves of gable and hip roofs (Figure 67).

Air movement through such openings depends primarily on wind. These are most effective when combined with vents located high on the roof such as roof vents, ridge vents (Figure 68A) or gable end vents (Figure 68B).

Low-slope roofs insulated between the roof joists are difficult to ventilate unless there is clearance above the insulation, and the joist spaces are interconnected to permit free circulation of ventilating air (see Figures 133 and 134, p. 267). These common techniques are not applicable where fine snow can be wind-driven through such vent openings and deposited on the roof insulation. In such situations, local building practices should be followed.

The size of roof vents, expressed as net or free area of the vent openings, depends on the slope and construction of the roof being ventilated.

For roofs with a slope of 1:6, or steeper, the minimum net area of ventilators for attic roof spaces is 1/300 of the insulated ceiling area. For example, a ceiling area of 1,000 sq. ft. (100 m²) requires vents totaling at least 3.33 sq. ft. (0.3 m²) in net area. The area provided should be increased to allow for restrictions, such as louvers, wire cloth or screens.

For roofs with a slope of less than 1:6, and for roofs constructed with roof joists (low-slope roofs and cathedral ceilings), the minimum unobstructed vent area is 1/150 of the insulated ceiling area. Flat, mild sloping and cathedral ceilings require at least twice as much roof vent area as steeper roofs with attics.

HEALTHY HOUSING INSIGHT

Alternative Roof Framing Systems

A number of alternative roof framing systems are available that fulfil the Healthy Housing objective of resource efficiency. These manufactured alternatives use less material, and, due to their advanced engineering, can make use of waste material from less desirable, fast-growing tree species.

Parallel chord trusses provide longer spans than commonly available in dimension lumber and permit the placement of high levels of insulation while providing adequate ventilation of the roof cavity. This advantage is also available through conventional trusses when a raised heel is incorporated. This permits full depth placement of insulation over the exterior wall plates without restricting attic ventilation.

A novel approach to traditional post-and-beam construction involves using beams from timber, glulam or structural composite lumber to support stress skin panels. These structural panels comprise a sandwich of roof sheathing, insulation and an interior panel finish or nailing surface.

A common consideration for all of these alternatives is the need to plan accurately and to adhere to the final plan during construction. Unlike conventional framing approaches, these efficient alternatives are manufactured with precision, and there is much less flexibility for field changes or adjustments.

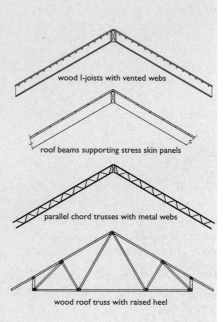

wood I-joists with vented webs

roof beams supporting stress skin panels

parallel chord trusses with metal webs

wood roof truss with raised heel

For all types of roofs, vents should be distributed uniformly on opposite sides of the building, where possible, with at least 25 per cent of the openings located at the top of the space, and at least 25 per cent of the openings located at the bottom of the space.

When planning roof ventilation, it is important to ensure that at least 2 ½ in. (63 mm) of space is provided between the insulation and the underside of roof sheathing. If air ventilation baffles are used, the clearance can be reduced to 1 in. (25 mm) (Figure 131, p. 264). Vents and ceiling insulation should be installed so that airflow through vents and roof spaces is not restricted.

Vents must not allow the entry of rain, snow or insects. Vent type, orientation or proximity to roof obstructions that alter airflow could increase the likelihood of snow or rain entry and care is required to ensure vents are not a source of moisture entry into the building envelope. This may be done by installing blocking adjacent to the wall so that there is a baffle at the wall-soffit junction.

Corrosion-resistant metal or plastic materials should be used for vents and to screen ventilator openings.

Where an access hatch to the attic or roof space is required, ensure that it is fitted with a tightly sealed and insulated door or cover, especially where the access hatch is located within the heated part of the dwelling.

RELATED PUBLICATION

Building Solutions: A Problem Solving Guide for Builders and Renovators
Canada Mortgage and Housing Corporation

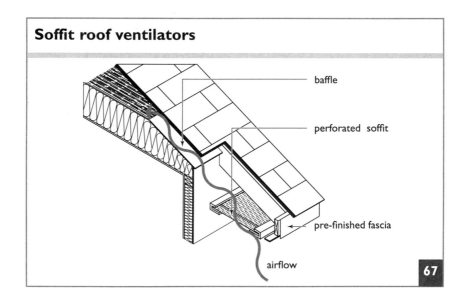

Soffit roof ventilators

baffle

perforated soffit

pre-finished fascia

airflow

67

High-level roof ventilators

(A) ridge vent

(B) gable vent

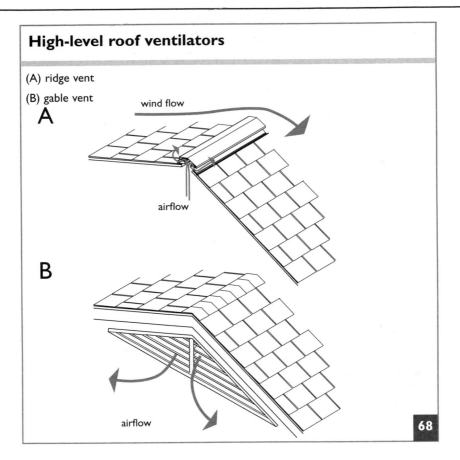

SIZING CEILING JOISTS *TRy*

Problem

Select the minimum ceiling joist that is acceptable for the conditions described below.

Conditions

Attic is inaccessible, without storage.
Ceiling supports insulation and drywall interior finish.
Span is 14' 2" (4.3 m).
Ceiling joist spacing is 16 in. (400 mm).
Species group and grade specified is SPF No. 2 or better.

Selection

Use Table 29, p. 388.

For this application select
2 in. x 6 in. (38 x 140 mm) ceiling joist.

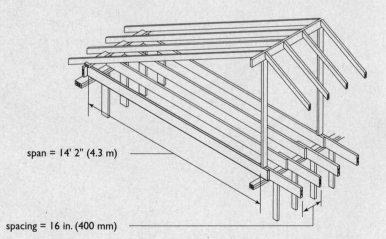

span = 14' 2" (4.3 m)

spacing = 16 in. (400 mm)

SIZING ROOF RAFTERS

Problem

Select the smallest dimension rafter that is able to span the roof as described below.

Conditions

Building location is: Ottawa.
Specified roof snow load is 36 lbs/sq. ft. (1.72 kPa).
Roof slope is 1:3.
Rafter span is 15 ½ ft. (4.7 m).
Species group and grade specified is SPF No. 2 or better.
Shingle roofing to be used.
Lower ends of the rafter are restrained.

Selection

Use Table 27, p. 386.

Acceptable rafters include:
2 in. x 8 in. (38 x 184 mm) at 12 in. o.c. (300 mm o.c.)
2 in. x 10 in. (38 x 235 mm) at 24 in. o.c. (600 mm o.c.)

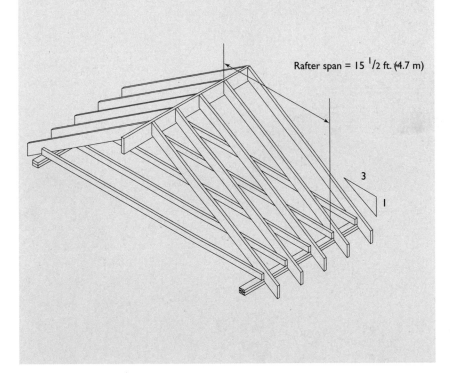

Rafter span = 15 ¹/2 ft. (4.7 m)

3

1

SIZING ROOF JOISTS

Problem

Select the roof joists that are able to span the roof as described below.

Conditions

Building location is: Ottawa.
Specified roof snow load is 36 lbs/ft² (1.72 kPa).
Roof slope is 1 in 3.
Roof joist span is 13' 9" (4.19 m).
Species group and grade specified is SPF No. 2 or better.
Shingle roofing to be used.
Lower ends of the roof joists are restrained.

Selection

Use Table 25, p. 384.

Acceptable roof joists include:
2 in. x 10 in. (38 x 235 mm) at 16 in. o.c. (400 mm o.c.)
2 in. x 12 in. (38 x 286 mm) at 24 in. o.c. (600 mm o.c.)

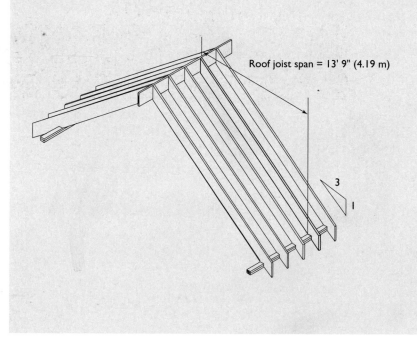

Roof joist span = 13' 9" (4.19 m)

3

1

Flashing

FLASHING

Flashing is provided, where necessary, to prevent the entry of water through joints between materials. Proper installation of flashing is important, as is the selection of the most suitable materials for each specific location.

The minimum recommended weights and types of materials for flashing are shown in Table 31, p. 390.

Aluminum flashing should be isolated from masonry or concrete or coated with an impervious membrane to reduce the possibility of corrosion.

Flashing should be used at the junction of roofs and walls, roofs and chimneys, over window and door openings, in roof valleys and in other critical areas. Flashing should remove water away from the building envelope and to do so, should be sloped at least 6 per cent, as well as accommodate possible shrinkage of the wood framing. The flashing should extend at least 2 in. (50 mm) above the joint and at least 13/32 in. (10 mm) below the joint and extend beyond the face of the lower surface at least 3/16 in. (5 mm).

A typical example of construction requiring flashing is at the intersection of two types of materials, as shown in Figure 69. The stucco is separated from the wood siding below by a wood drip cap. To prevent the water from entering the wall, pre-formed flashing is installed over the drip cap to form a drip at the outside edge. The flashing should extend at least 2 in. (50 mm) above this drip cap and under the sheathing membrane. This type of flashing is also used over the heads of windows and doors unless they are well protected by a roof overhang. Where the vertical distance between the top of the trim and the underside of the overhang is more than one-quarter of the overhang's horizontal projection, flashing should always be used. For curved openings, the trim is considered to be the lowest height before the trim becomes vertical.

The heads and sills of openings in masonry-veneer, wood-frame walls should be flashed. Head flashing should extend from the front edge of the lintel, up and over the lintel and on up under the sheathing paper. Where a jointed masonry sill is used, the flashing should extend from the outer edge under the masonry sill up to the underside of the window or door sill.

Flashing should also be used at the junction of roof surfaces and walls. If built-up roofing is used, a cant strip should be provided to avoid a right-angle bend in the membrane and consequent puncturing. The built-up roofing is carried at least 6 in. (150 mm) up the wall of the house over the cant strip and sheathing. The sheathing paper is then lapped 4 in. (100 mm) over the edge of the roofing. When the siding is placed on the wall, a clearance of at least 2 in. (50 mm) should be allowed between the siding and the roof to keep the siding well clear of water draining down the roof surface (Figure 70).

Where stack vents penetrate the roof, they should be flashed to prevent moisture entry.

Typical flashing between two different materials

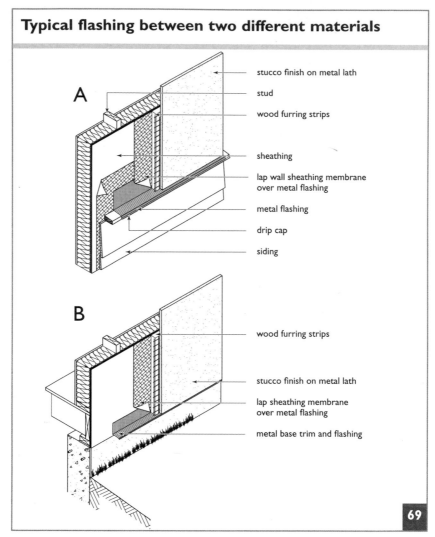

A
- stucco finish on metal lath
- stud
- wood furring strips
- sheathing
- lap wall sheathing membrane over metal flashing
- metal flashing
- drip cap
- siding

B
- wood furring strips
- stucco finish on metal lath
- lap sheathing membrane over metal flashing
- metal base trim and flashing

69

Flashing should be used where two roof lines intersect to form a valley. Depending on the shingling method used, valleys are referred to as open or closed. Open valleys are commonly flashed with one layer of sheet metal at least 24 in. (600 mm) wide or with two layers of roll roofing installed over continuous sheathing. When roll roofing is used, the bottom layer may be Type S or Type M mineral surface material (mineral surface down), at least 18 in. (450 mm) wide. This layer is centred on the valley and fastened along the edges with nails spaced 16 to 18 in. (400 to 450 mm) apart. A 4 in. (100 mm) band of cement is then applied along the edges of the bottom layer, and a strip of Type M mineral surface roll roofing approximately 36 in. (914 mm) wide is placed over the first layer (mineral surface up). The top layer is fastened along the edges with only enough nails to hold it in place until the shingles are applied. The roof shingles are stopped on a line 4 to 6 in. (100 to

Open valley and shingle flashing

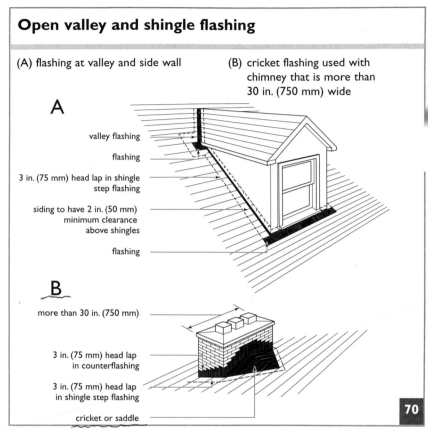

(A) flashing at valley and side wall

(B) cricket flashing used with chimney that is more than 30 in. (750 mm) wide

A

valley flashing

flashing

3 in. (75 mm) head lap in shingle step flashing

siding to have 2 in. (50 mm) minimum clearance above shingles

flashing

B

more than 30 in. (750 mm)

3 in. (75 mm) head lap in counterflashing

3 in. (75 mm) head lap in shingle step flashing

cricket or saddle

70

150 mm) from the centre of the valley, this distance being greater at the eaves than at the ridge (Figure 70A).

Closed valleys are generally flashed with one layer of sheet metal, 0.006 in. thick. Each course of shingles is continued across the valley, ensuring that shingle nails are not placed within 3 in. (75 mm) of the valley centre line at the ridge or 5 in. (125 mm) at the eaves. Where rigid shingles are used, they are cut to fit the centre line of the valley, but these should not be used with the closed valley method or roofs that slope less than 1:1.2.

Flashing squares (sometimes called "step-flashing" or "shingle flashing") should be used at the intersections of shingled roofs with walls or chimneys. This type of flashing is installed at the time the shingles are applied. One square is used at each course and is bent up along the wall under the sheathing membrane (Figure 70A). The siding will cover the flashing along the wall, except for the clearance allowed. These squares should be large enough to give a good lap at the roof and wall line, and the head lap should be no less than 3 in. (75 mm). On the roof slopes behind a chimney, the flashing should extend both up the roof and up the chimney to a point equal in height to the counterflashing of the chimney, but in any case not less than 1½ times the shingle exposure.

Flashing is used at the intersection of a roof with a masonry wall or chimney. The base flashing should extend at least 6 in. (150 mm) up the side of the chimney or masonry veneer. The base flashing is fitted tightly against the masonry and lapped under the shingles at least 4 in. (100 mm). A through-wall counter flashing should extend over the base flashing, through the full depth of the brick veneer and air space behind, and extend at least 6 in. (150 mm) up the wall sheathing. The building paper should lap at least 3 in. (75 mm) over the top of the through wall flashing (Figure 71).

A common alternative is to extend the base flashing at least 6 in. (150 mm) up the face of the brick and imbed it at least 1 in. (25 mm) into the horizontal and vertical mortar joints. Unlike the previous method, this flashing installation does not direct any water that is inside the brick veneer to the exterior and this water may leak into the wall. Counterflashing is applied to all sides of the chimney where it penetrates the roof.

If the upper side of a chimney is more than 30 in. (750 mm) wide, a cricket or saddle should be installed (Figure 70B). These are often made of sheet metal and should be placed over a wood-framed support constructed during roof-framing operations. The saddle should be suitably flashed at the roof and counterflashed at the chimney. Open joints and laps should be soldered or sealed, or a locked joint used. A saddle is not required, however, if the metal flashing is carried up both the roof and the chimney to a height at least equal to one-sixth the chimney width. This shingle flashing should never be less than 1½ times the shingle exposure and the chimney counterflashing never less than 6 in. (150 mm).

RELATED PUBLICATION

Best Practice Guide: Flashings
Canada Mortgage and Housing Corporation

Flashing at sloped roof-wall intersection with brick veneer

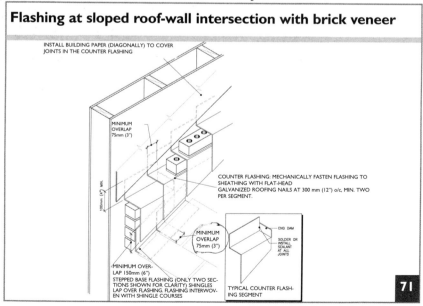

INSTALL BUILDING PAPER (DIAGONALLY) TO COVER JOINTS IN THE COUNTER FLASHING

MINIMUM OVERLAP 75mm (3")

100mm (4") MIN.

COUNTER FLASHING: MECHANICALLY FASTEN FLASHING TO SHEATHING WITH FLAT-HEAD GALVANIZED ROOFING NAILS AT 300 mm (12") o/c, MIN. TWO PER SEGMENT.

MINIMUM OVERLAP 75mm (3")

END DAM

SOLDER OR INSTALL SEALANT AT ALL JOINTS

MINIMUM OVER-LAP 150mm (6")
STEPPED BASE FLASHING (ONLY TWO SEC-TIONS SHOWN FOR CLARITY) SHINGLES LAP OVER FLASHING. FLASHING INTERWOV-EN WITH SHINGLE COURSES

TYPICAL COUNTER FLASH-ING SEGMENT

71

Roof Sheathing
and Coverings

ROOF SHEATHING AND COVERINGS

ROOF SHEATHING

Roof sheathing is applied over roof trusses or rafters and usually consists of plywood, oriented strandboard (OSB), structural wood panels or lumber. Sheathing provides a nailing base for the roof covering and laterally braces the roof framing.

Installing Roof Sheathing

When plywood or OSB is used for roof sheathing, it is laid with the face grain at right angles to the framing (Figure 72). Sheathing-grade structural wood panels are used for this purpose. To obtain a good tie across the roof framing, the end joints of the panels should be staggered on the framing members. The edges of the panels should be separated by at least ⅛ in. (2 to 3 mm) to prevent buckling when minor expansion occurs during wet weather.

The thickness of the plywood, OSB or structural wood panel used for roof sheathing depends to some extent on the spacing of the rafters, roof joists or trusses and whether the edges of the sheets are supported. To prevent damage to the roof covering when thinner panels are used, the joints running across the framing should be supported by 2 x 2 in. (38 x 38 mm) blocking, nailed securely between the

Application of structural wood-panel roof sheathing

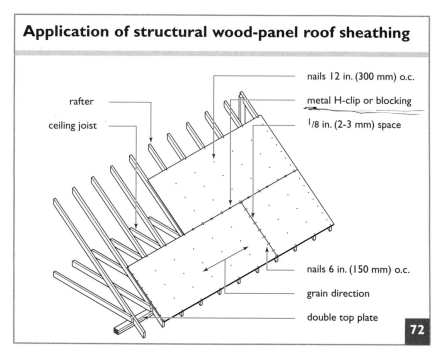

rafter

ceiling joist

nails 12 in. (300 mm) o.c.

metal H-clip or blocking

¹/8 in. (2-3 mm) space

nails 6 in. (150 mm) o.c.

grain direction

double top plate

72

roof framing members, or by metal H-clips inserted between sheets. The latter method is widely used because the installation is simple and economical. Minimum thicknesses for plywood and other roof sheathing are shown in Table 32, p. 390. Table 20, p. 377, identifies the nail and staple requirements for roof sheathing. It is good practice to stagger the location of fasteners at the edges of adjoining panels. Staple fastening for ⅜ in. (9.5 mm) roof sheathing must be 1⁄16 in. thick, 1 ½ in. long with a ⅜ in. crown (1.6 mm thick, 38.1 mm long with a 9.5 mm crown), and be driven with the crown parallel to the framing. (See Table 35, p. 392.) Thicker roof sheathing, no less than 5/8 in. (15.5 mm), is required for built-up roofing on a low-slope roof to be used as a walking deck. In these cases, Table 18, p. 376, should be used to determine the minimum thickness for the sheathing.

Under materials requiring solid and continuous support, such as asphalt shingles and built-up roofing, lumber sheathing must be laid closed, or edge to edge (Figure 73B). The boards are usually ¾ in. nominal (19 mm) thick, but this thickness may be reduced to 11/16 in. (17 mm) where supports are spaced at 16 in. (400 mm) on centre. Boards 8 in. nominal (184 mm) or less wide are nailed to the framing members with two, 2 in. (51 mm) nails per bearing. Those wider than 8 in. nominal (184 mm) should be nailed with three, 2 in. (51 mm) nails per bearing. Boards wider than 12 in. nominal (286 mm) should not be used for roof sheathing. For a wood shingle roof, the roof boards may be spaced the same distance apart on centre as the shingle exposure. This method (Figure 73A), commonly used in damp climates, permits freer movement of air around the boards and under shingles, thus reducing the possibility of decay.

Installation of wood-board roof sheathing

(A) spaced method

(B) closed method

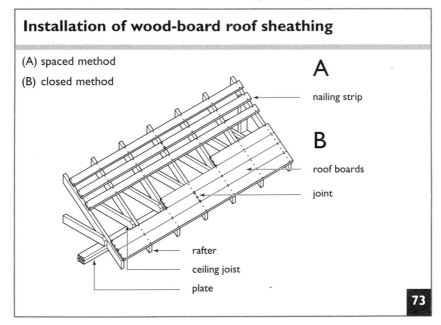

A — nailing strip

B — roof boards

joint

rafter

ceiling joist

plate

73

Roof Sheathing Details

Where openings occur in the roof structure for interior chimneys, the roof sheathing and framing members should have a clearance of 2 in. (50 mm) from the finished masonry, or metal chimney, on all sides for fire protection (Figure 74). This clearance may be reduced to ½ in. (12 mm) for exterior masonry chimneys. Roof sheathing should be securely nailed to the rafters and headers around the opening.

HEALTHY HOUSING INSIGHT

Roof Sheathing Options

There are a large number of roof sheathing options available for wood-frame construction. Some of these products are more resource-efficient than others, depending on the roof application as well as the geographic location of the building. Consider the following points for the appropriate selection of roof sheathing materials.

Avoid Overdesign

When it comes to roof sheathings, thicker is not necessarily better. The requirements in local building codes represent adequate strength and durability, with a factor of safety added on to ensure good performance, provided the material is properly installed. Avoiding the use of thicker sheathings saves money and forest resources.

Wood Product Selection

Use wood products that come from forests where sustainable forestry practices are employed.

Consider Local Materials

In many areas, using local materials is more appropriate than importing materials. For example, using rough-sawn boards as roof sheathing is preferred in many parts of Canada over engineered wood products. The selection of local materials encourages employment and reduces the use of energy associated with the transport of imported materials.

Select an Appropriate Roof Covering

The type of roof covering selected often determines the number of roof sheathing options available. When metal-or wood-shake roof coverings are used, spaced boards may serve as the roof sheathing, utilizing a fraction of the wood compared to sheet-type roof sheathings.

Keep in mind that no matter what type of roof sheathing option is selected, the quality of workmanship is a key consideration.

Roof sheathing detail at a valley and at a chimney opening

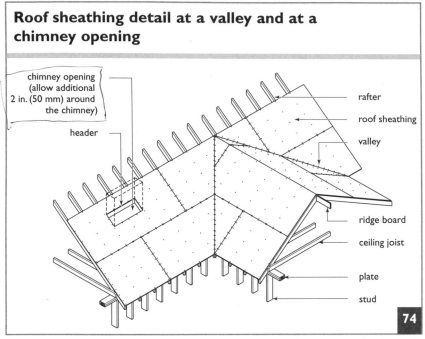

chimney opening (allow additional 2 in. (50 mm) around the chimney)

header

rafter

roof sheathing

valley

ridge board

ceiling joist

plate

stud

74

Roof sheathing at valleys and hips should be fitted to give a tight joint and should be securely nailed to the valley or hip rafter (Figure 74). This will provide a solid and smooth base for flashing.

Flashing is discussed in detail in the previous chapter. Refer to this discussion for more information.

ROOF COVERINGS

The roof covering is usually installed as soon as the roof framing and the sheathing have been completed and before any other interior or exterior finishing work starts. This sequence produces a weatherproof working space within the building early in the construction process other trades enabling to begin their work. It also protects the lumber and interior panel products from excessive moisture.

Roof coverings should provide a long-life, water-resistant finish that will protect the building and its contents from rain and snow. Many materials have withstood the test of time and have proven satisfactory under various conditions.

Asphalt shingles are by far the most commonly used roof covering for pitched roofs. Galvanized steel or aluminum roofing is also common in some regions. At normal roof pitches, metal roofs will generally shed snow, a desirable characteristic in heavy snowfall areas. Roll roofing, wood shingles, hand-split shakes, sheet metal and concrete or clay tile among others are also used. For low-slope or low-pitched roofs, built-up roofing with a gravel topping or cap sheet is frequently used. The choice of materials may be influenced by cost, local code requirements or local preferences based upon past experience.

The minimum and maximum slopes for the different types of roof coverings are presented in Table 33, p. 391.

The minimum slope of roofs is 1:6 for asphalt shingles (using a low-slope application), 1:4 for wood shingles, and 1:3 for hand-split shakes and asphalt

HEALTHY HOUSING INSIGHT

Roof Covering Materials Selection

The quality and performance of roof covering materials is an extremely important aspect of wood-frame house construction, due to the costly water damage that may result from a leaky roof and the considerable expense associated with roof replacement. There are several key considerations involved in selecting an appropriate roof covering material.

→ The source of the material may be renewable or non-renewable. Asphalt-based, metal, clay and concrete roof coverings use non-renewable materials. Wood products are generally renewable when harvested from a properly managed forest.

→ The material may be produced from recycled material, or it may be recyclable or non-recyclable. Generally, the use of recycled materials should be encouraged to conserve natural resources, whereas non-recyclable materials should be avoided.

→ The material may have a relatively short or long service life. This factor, balanced against initial cost, may significantly influence the final selection of a roof covering material.

The brief comparison of roof covering options that follows is presented in an ascending order of cost and useful service life.

The predominant roof covering used in wood-frame house construction is asphalt shingles. While these products are being recycled in some areas, for most areas they may be considered non-recyclable. Their useful service life ranges between 15 and 25 years. Some manufacturers of asphalt shingles require that 15 lb. building paper be installed under asphalt shingles.

Wood shingles obtained from properly managed forests are renewable and provide a useful service life comparable to asphalt shingles.

Metal roofing is non-renewable but recyclable, and depending on the type of metal used, may have a significantly longer service life in comparison with asphalt or wood shingles.

Clay and concrete tiles are non-renewable, but often completely reusable due to their stability and long service life. These types of roof coverings require greater structural support. Installation procedures are more difficult than conventional roofing.

shingles (using normal application). Built-up roof coverings are rarely used on roofs where the slope exceeds 1:4.

Ice damming occurs when inadequate insulation or major air leaks allow heat from inside the building envelope to escape through the roof and cause melting of snow on the roof. It can also occur in localized areas where sun melts snow even in freezing temperatures. As temperatures fluctuate, the melted snow turns to ice that progressively grows larger (Figure 75). When

Eave protection

IMPORTANT

(A) Heat from the building melts snow where the ceiling insulation is inadequate.

Trapped water moves behind the shingles and leaks into the building envelope.

(B) Eave protection directs leaked water to the eave where it can escape.

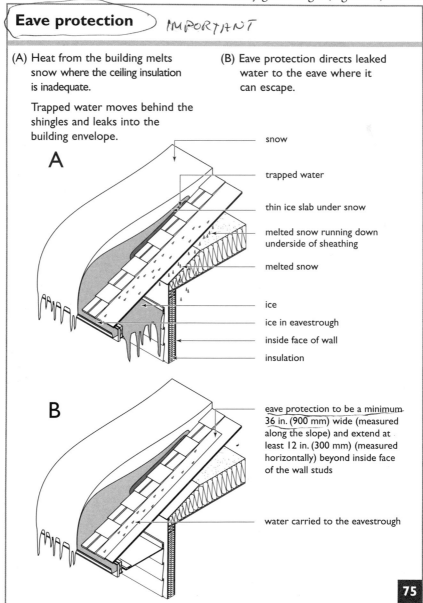

A

- snow
- trapped water
- thin ice slab under snow
- melted snow running down underside of sheathing
- melted snow
- ice
- ice in eavestrough
- inside face of wall
- insulation

B

eave protection to be a minimum 36 in. (900 mm) wide (measured along the slope) and extend at least 12 in. (300 mm) (measured horizontally) beyond inside face of the wall studs

water carried to the eavestrough

75

a thaw occurs, this ridge of ice causes a dam that prevents melt water from escaping down the roof. The trapped water backs up under shingles and there is a likelihood that leakage into the attic, ceiling and wall will result. There are two corrective measures to take. To prevent ice damming from occurring, attention needs to be paid during construction to the location and adequacy of the ceiling insulation. Skylights should be situated away from the areas where ice damming is likely. In addition, eave protection should be provided. This protection usually consists of either Type S (smooth surface) or Type M roll roofing laid with the joints lapped at least 4 in. (100 mm) and cemented together, or a peel-and-stick bituminous membrane. Placed over the roof sheathing, this protection sheet extends from the edge of the roof to a line at least 12 in. (300 mm) beyond the inside of the inner face of the exterior walls, thus preventing water penetration through joints in the roof sheathing. The eave protection must extend at least 36 in. (900 mm) up the roof slope from the outer edge of the soffit and at least 12 in. (300 mm) inside the interior face of the wall.

Methods of flashing shingled roofs at valleys, chimneys and intersecting walls are described in the chapter on "Flashing."

Asphalt Shingles on Slopes 1:3 or Greater

Asphalt strip shingles should be a minimum No. 210 grade. Square-butt strip shingles are usually 12 x 36 in. (310 x 915 mm) or 13 1/4 x 39 3/8 in. (335 x 1000 mm) in size, have three tabs and should be laid with 5 in. (130 mm) or 5 3/4 in. (145 mm) of their width exposed to the weather. Since there are approximately 21 to 26

strips in a bundle, a bundle will cover about 32 sq. ft. (3 m²).

Bundles should be piled flat for storage so that strips will not curl when the bundles are opened. Care should be taken in piling shingles on the roof; if too many are piled together, the load capacity of the framing may be exceeded.

The method of laying an asphalt-shingle roof is shown in (Figure 76). Eave protection is first provided by one of the methods already described. A starter strip comprised of shingles with their tabs removed is then placed along the eaves before the first course of shingles, so that it extends at least ½ in. (12 mm) beyond the eaves, rakes and fascia board to form a drip edge. Starter strips with metal drip edges can also be used. This projection prevents water from backing up under the shingles by capillary action. A shingle strip laid with the tabs facing up the roof slope is often used for this purpose. Type M (mineral-surfaced) roll roofing may be used as a starter strip and when continued up the roof slope will also serve as eave protection. The starter strip is nailed along the bottom edge at 12 in. (300 mm) intervals. The first course of shingles is then laid with the butt edge in line with the bottom of the starter strip.

In shingle application, the exposure distance is important and the exposure depends on the roof slope and the type and length of shingle used.

Several chalk lines will help align the shingle courses so that tabs and tab notches will be in a straight line. This gives a good appearance. Each shingle strip should be stapled or nailed. Four large-head roofing nails should be used on each strip and should be long enough to penetrate at least 1/2 in. (12 mm) into the roof sheathing. Good nailing is important. When a nail penetrates a crack or knothole, another nail should be driven alongside into sound wood. Most asphalt shingles are self-sealing; a strip of adhesive on the underside of the tab seals the shingle to the one beneath. If the shingles used are not self-sealing, cementing the tabs is recommended.

Plastic cement can be used for this purpose with a spot approximately 1 in. (25 mm) in diameter being placed under the centre of each tab. Interlocking and other special shingles should be laid according to the manufacturer's directions.

Asphalt Shingles on Low Slopes of 1:6 to 1:3

Additional precautions must be taken on low slopes to ensure a waterproof roof covering. Except for the first two courses, three thicknesses of shingles are used on the entire roof including hips and ridges. This is achieved by using an exposure of not more than one-third the full height of the shingle. A starter strip is first installed as described for higher-sloped roofs, but laid on a continuous band of cement not less than 8 in. (200 mm) wide. The first course of shingles is then cemented to the strip with a continuous band of cement that is 4 in. (100 mm) wider than the shingle exposure. For example, a 10 in. (250 mm) band of cement should be used when the shingle exposure is 6 in. (150 mm). The succeeding courses of shingles are laid on a band of cement 2 in. (50 mm) wider than the shingle exposure, so that an 8 in. (200 mm) band is used when the exposure is 6 in. (150 mm).

To avoid defacing the exposed surface of the shingles with cement, the band should be located between 1 and 2 in. (25 and 50 mm) above the butt edge of each succeeding course of shingles. Each shingle strip should be stapled or nailed in place with four nails.

Application of asphalt shingles

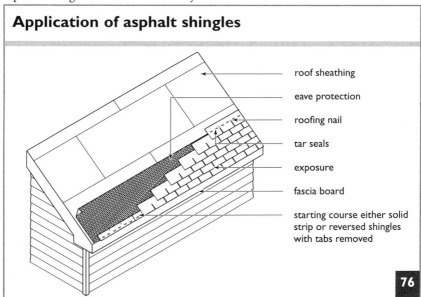

- roof sheathing
- eave protection
- roofing nail
- tar seals
- exposure
- fascia board
- starting course either solid strip or reversed shingles with tabs removed

76

If cold application cement is used, it should be applied at a rate of approximately 1 gal./100 sq. ft. (0.5 L/m²) of cemented area. Hot application cement is applied at a rate of approximately 0.2 lb./sq. ft. (1 kg/m²) of cemented area. The above technique is necessary only for slopes lower than 1:4 since there are special low-slope shingles of sufficient length to maintain the three thicknesses necessary at this roof pitch.

Wood Shingles

Wood shingles commonly used for houses are No. 1 and No. 2 grade. Red or white cedar are the principal species of wood used for shingles, because their heartwoods have high decay resistance and low shrinkage. Other species are also used for shingles but should be preservative-treated. The width of wood shingles varies, but the maximum width is 14 in. (350 mm) and the minimum width is 3 in. (75 mm).

Figure 77 illustrates the proper method of laying a wood-shingle roof. As is the case for asphalt shingles, underlay and roofing felt is not usually required for wood shingles, but eave protection, as described previously, should be installed.

The first shingle course should be laid double with the upper shingles overlapping the joints in the course beneath and both rows extending about 1 in. (25 mm) beyond the fascia boards at the eaves. This precaution will prevent water from backing up underneath the shingles. Shingles should be laid 1/4 in. (6 mm) apart to allow for swelling when wet. The joints between shingles in one course should be offset at least 1⁹⁄₁₆ in.

Installation of wood shingles

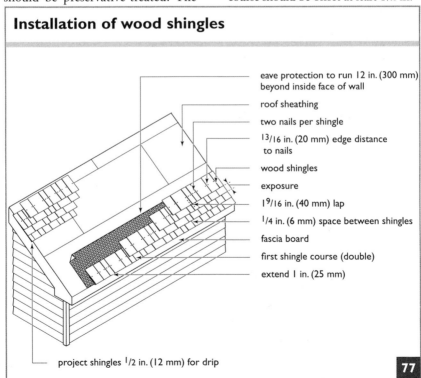

- eave protection to run 12 in. (300 mm) beyond inside face of wall
- roof sheathing
- two nails per shingle
- 13/16 in. (20 mm) edge distance to nails
- wood shingles
- exposure
- 19/16 in. (40 mm) lap
- 1/4 in. (6 mm) space between shingles
- fascia board
- first shingle course (double)
- extend 1 in. (25 mm)
- project shingles 1/2 in. (12 mm) for drip

77

(40 mm) from the joint between shingles in the course below. The joints in succeeding courses should be spaced so that the joint in one course is not in line with the joints in the two previous courses laid.

Only two nails should be used for each shingle. The distance of the nails from the butt edge of the shingle being nailed should be the shingle exposure plus 1 %₆ in. (40 mm), with an edge distance of about ¹³⁄₁₆ in. (20 mm). For example, if the shingle exposure is to be 5 in. (125 mm), add 1 %₆ in. (40 mm), and thus the nail should be 6 %₆ in. (165 mm) from the butt edge of the shingle being nailed. Shingles are fastened with hot-dip galvanized or other corrosion-resistant shingle nails. Flat grain shingles wider than 8 in. (200 mm) are sometimes split and nailed as two shingles to avoid problems with cupping and warping.

Hand-split Shakes

Cedar hand-split shakes must not be less than 18 in. (450 mm) long and 4 in. (100 mm) wide. They must also be no wider than 13 3/4 in. (350 mm). The butt thickness should be between 3/8 and 1 1/4 in. (9 and 32 mm) (Figure 78).

Shakes may be applied over spaced or closed roof sheathing. When spaced sheathing is used (Figure 73A), 1 x 4 in. (19 x 89 mm) or wider strips are placed on centres equal to the weather exposure at which the shakes are to be laid, but never more than 10 in. (250 mm). In areas where wind-driven snow conditions prevail, closed roof sheathing is recommended.

Proper weather exposure is important. As a general rule, 7 ½ in. (190 mm) exposure is recommended for 18 in. (450 mm) shakes, and a 10 in. (250 mm)

Installation of hand-split shakes

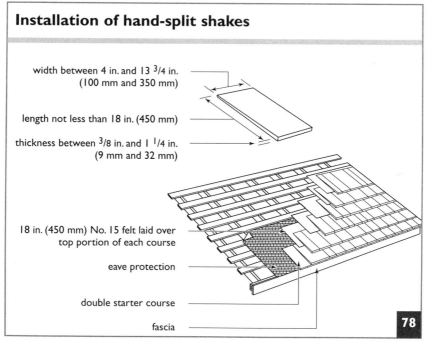

width between 4 in. and 13 3/4 in. (100 mm and 350 mm)

length not less than 18 in. (450 mm)

thickness between 3/8 in. and 1 1/4 in. (9 mm and 32 mm)

18 in. (450 mm) No. 15 felt laid over top portion of each course

eave protection

double starter course

fascia

78

exposure for 24 in. (600 mm) shakes. The minimum recommended roof pitch for hand-split shakes is 1:3.

A 36 in. (900 mm) strip of No. 15 roofing felt should be laid over the sheathing boards at the eave line. The beginning or starter course of shakes should be doubled; for extra texture, it can be tripled. The bottom course or courses can be 15 in. (380 mm) or 18 in. (450 mm) shakes, the former being made expressly for this purpose.

After each course of shakes is applied, an 18 in. (450 mm) wide strip of No. 15 roofing felt should be laid over the top portion of the shakes, extending onto the sheathing. The bottom edge of the felt should be positioned above

the butt at a distance equal to twice the weather exposure. For example, 24 in. (600 mm) shakes laid with 10 in. (250 mm) exposure would have felt applied 20 in. (500 mm) above the shake butts. Thus, the felt will cover the top 4 in. (100 mm) of the shakes and extend out about 15 in. (350 mm) onto the sheathing (Figure 78).

Shakes should be spaced between 1/4 to 3/8 in. (6 to 9 mm) apart. Side joints should be offset no less than 1-9/16 in. (40 mm) over the adjacent courses. When straight split shakes are used, the "froe-end" (the end from which the shakes have been split and which is smoother) should be laid uppermost (towards the ridge).

Finish at ridge and hips

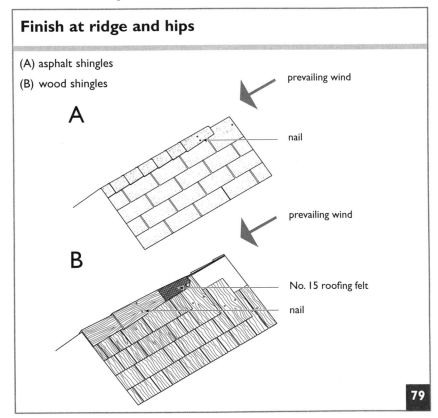

(A) asphalt shingles

(B) wood shingles

A — prevailing wind — nail

B — prevailing wind — No. 15 roofing felt — nail

79

Finish at Ridge and Hips

The most common type of finish is shown in Figure 79A. Asphalt shingle squares (one-third of a strip) are used over the ridge or hip and blind-nailed. Each shingle is lapped to provide the same coverage as the roofing shingles. It is good practice to lay the ridge cap so as to provide the maximum protection from the prevailing wind.

In the case of wood shingles, 6 in. (150 mm) wide shingles are alternatively lapped and blind-nailed (Figure 79B). Flashing is sometimes used under a wood-shingle ridge.

Built-up Roofs

Built-up roof coverings should be installed by roofing firms that specialize in this work. Roofs of this type may have three or more layers of roofing felt. Each layer is mopped down with tar or asphalt, the final surface being coated with the same material. The surface is then covered with gravel (embedded in the asphalt or tar) or with a cap sheet. This covering provides ballast and protection from the sun's ultraviolet radiation. It is important to note that coal tar products and asphalt products are not compatible and must not be used together.

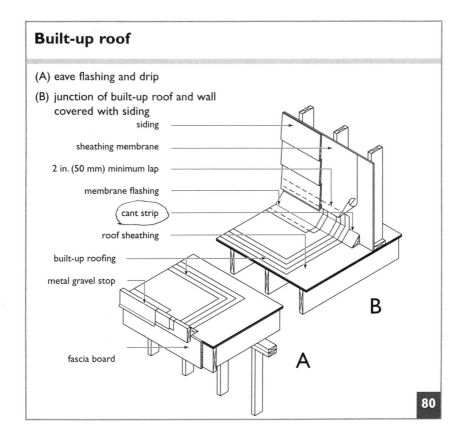

Built-up roof

(A) eave flashing and drip

(B) junction of built-up roof and wall covered with siding

- siding
- sheathing membrane
- 2 in. (50 mm) minimum lap
- membrane flashing
- cant strip
- roof sheathing
- built-up roofing
- metal gravel stop
- fascia board

B

A

80

The eave line of projecting roofs is usually finished with metal edging or flashing. A gravel stop or cant strip is used in conjunction with the flashing at the eaves when the roof is covered with gravel (Figure 80A). Where built-up roofing is finished against another wall (except a masonry-clad wall), the roofing is mopped to the cant strip and turned up the wall at least 6 in. (150 mm). The wall sheathing paper and siding is then applied over the roof membrane (Figure 80B).

Details of sheet metal roofing

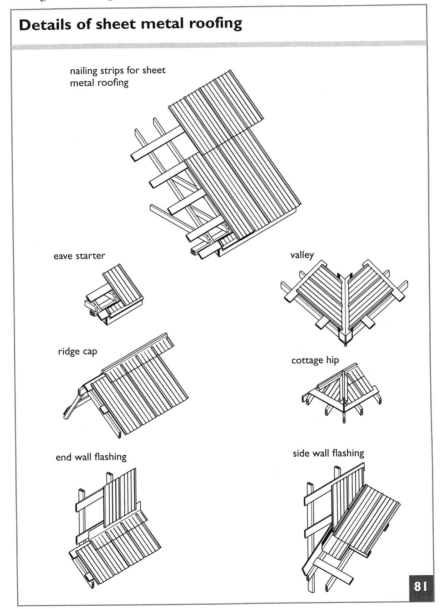

nailing strips for sheet metal roofing

eave starter

valley

ridge cap

cottage hip

end wall flashing

side wall flashing

81

Where a built-up roof intersects a masonry-clad wall, the roof membrane is similarly returned up the face of the masonry. Counterflashing is then added. This counterflashing should be embedded into the mortar joints at least 1 in. (25 mm), extending down the wall about 6 in. (150 mm) and lapping over the flashing at least 4 in. (100 mm).

Single-ply membranes can also be used for low-slope roofs. They consist of various synthetic materials that are resistant to freeze-thaw cycling, ozone attack and ultraviolet degradation. They are relatively simple to lay, but are not often used on the small roofs that are typically part of wood-frame construction.

Sheet Metal Roofing

Sheet metal roofing is manufactured in 30 to 36 in. (762 mm to 914 mm) widths, depending on the profile of the corrugation, and in any lengths specified by the builder. It comes with the necessary accessories for treating the various details of the roof, such as hips, valleys, eave starters and edges (Figure 81). The usual method of fastening the metal roof sheets is to lay 1 x 4 in. (19 x 89 mm) wood nailing strips across the rafters at no more than 16 in. (400 mm) on centre.

For more positive attachment and better nailing, 2 x 4 in. (38 x 89 mm) purlins can be used. There must be a nailing strip underneath each end joint (Figure 81). The choice of metal thickness, whether steel or aluminum, will depend on the local snow load, but should not be less than 0.013 in. (0.33 mm) for galvanized steel, 0.018 in. (0.46 mm) for copper or zinc and 0.019 in. (0.48 mm) for aluminum. Where sheet metal roofing spans between spaced supports, it must be capable of supporting the specified live loads. The required thicknesses for specific snow loads are given in tables provided by the manufacturer. The minimum slope for sheet metal roofing is 1:4, unless the manufacturer provides written confirmation that a lower slope has been tested and proven.

Concrete and Clay Tile Roofing

When considering the use of concrete or clay tile, it must be remembered that these materials are considerably heavier than other roofing systems, and thus the roof supporting structure of rafters or trusses must be designed to withstand the additional load. A professional engineer should be consulted to obtain a proper design. Simulated versions of tile roofing do not normally require a special structural design. Be sure to follow manufacturer's recommendations.

CHECKING BACK

Adequate Sizing of Roof Framing Members

Depending on the type of roof covering materials being installed, it may be necessary to check the sizing of roof framing members. The typical sizes of roof framing members correspond to conventional roof covering materials such as asphalt shingles, cedar shakes or lightweight metal roofing. If clay or concrete roof coverings are being used, it will likely be necessary to resize roof-framing members accordingly.

➜ Check back to the chapter on "Ceiling and Roof Framing" to ensure that the roof-framing members are adequately sized.

➜ Check with the roof-covering manufacturer for the higher loads imposed by heavyweight roof coverings, and use this data when sizing roof-framing members.

HEALTHY HOUSING INSIGHT

Minimizing Waste in Roof Construction

Roof waste may be significantly reduced through proper planning and construction practices. Consider the following points when planning and building roofs.

➜ Avoid ordering much more material than is required, unless arrangements for returning unused goods to suppliers have been made.

➜ Where possible, make the lengths of roofs a multiple of 16 in. (400 mm) or 24 in. (600 mm) so that wasted roof sheathing is minimized.

➜ Collect and store waste materials to promote complete recycling—avoid mixing waste construction materials.

Separate materials individually for better recycling opportunities.

➜ Use the short pieces of lumber from floor and wall framing as blocking or lookouts.

When using materials that are not recyclable, consider alternative uses. For example, waste clay roofing tile may be used as splash blocks for rainwater leaders or as creative landscape elements. Waste concrete roof coverings may be broken up and used along with granular materials as backfill. For more insights into managing construction waste, refer to "Applying the 4 Rs of Wood-Frame Construction" in the "Framing the House" chapter.

Wall Sheathing and Exterior Finishes

WALL SHEATHING AND EXTERIOR FINISHES

Wall sheathing is the outside covering used over the wall framework and is nailed directly to the wall framing members. Sheathing provides a nailing base for some types of siding and backing for others. It can also be used to brace the structure, although in most cases sufficient bracing is provided by the interior wall finish. Insulating sheathing materials will not normally provide the required temporary or permanent bracing. When such sheathing is used, let-in braces of wood or metal can be used as bracing if required. Sheathing must be applied to the gable ends and walls when the exterior cladding is a type that requires solid backing.

Several types of sheathing are used in present-day construction: fibreboard, gypsum board, plywood, oriented strand board, rigid insulation and lumber. Table 24, p. 383, lists the various types of sheathing and the minimum thickness necessary to provide sufficient backing for exterior finishing materials.

TYPES AND INSTALLATION OF SHEATHING

Oriented Strand Board (OSB) and waferboard are structural panels made from thin, short wood wafers that are bonded together with a waterproof, phenolic adhesive. While waferboard contains wafers that are randomly arranged; oriented strand board contains wafers that are narrower and are oriented in the long direction of the panel. This gives the panel added strength and rigidity in the long direction. The panels are cut into sheets 4 ft. (1.2 m) wide and usually 8 ft. (2.4 m) long. The designation O-1 or O-2 indicates an oriented panel, while an R-1 designation indicates a panel containing randomly arranged wafers.

The minimum thickness that should be used is 5/16 in. (7.9 mm) for studs up to 2 ft. (600 mm) on centre and 1/4 in. (6.35 mm) for studs up to 16 in. (400 mm) on centre. OSB is more readily available than waferboard and is often identified with a panel mark rating rather than a thickness. When using rated OSB, the panel mark rating must correspond to the stud spacing (Table 24).

Panel-type sheathing, such as fibreboard, plywood, oriented strand board or waferboard, is often applied vertically. The panels are nailed to the wall framework before the wall is raised to position. This sequence helps the wall maintain its squareness, avoids the need for scaffolding, and closes the house in as soon as the framing is completed. Often the window openings are covered by the sheathing panels and are not cut until after the windows are delivered.

The sheathing panels can also be applied horizontally, in which case the vertical joints should be staggered wherever possible.

A space at least 1/8 in. (2 to 3 mm) wide should be left between the sheets to permit expansion without buckling.

The panels are nailed to the framing at 6 in. (150 mm) on centre along the edges, and 12 in. (300 mm) along the intermediate supports (Figure 82).

Plywood is usually sheathing grade, unsanded, laminated with a waterproof adhesive, and may contain knots. The minimum thickness for exterior type plywood wall sheathing should be 5/16 in. (7.5 mm) for studs 24 in. (600 mm) on centre, and 1/4 in. (6 mm) for studs up to 16 in. (400 mm) on centre. Sheets are 4 ft. (1.2 m) wide and usually 8 ft. (2.4 m) long.

Fibreboard sheathing should be at least 7/16 in. (11.1 mm) thick for studs 24 in. (600 mm) on centre and 3/8 in. (9.5 mm) for studs 16 in. (400 mm) on centre. It is supplied in sheets 4 ft. (1.2 m) wide and generally 8 ft. (2.4 m) long, and is usually impregnated with an asphalt material to increase water resistance.

Gypsum board sheathing consists of a gypsum filler faced on both sides with treated paper. It should be at least 1/2 in. (12.7 mm) thick for studs 24 in. (600 mm) on centre and 3/8 in. (9.5 mm) thick for studs 16 in. (400 mm) on centre. It is supplied in sheets 4 ft. (1.2 m) wide and 8 ft. (2.4 m) long. The sheets are applied horizontally across the studs and nailed to the framing members.

Insulating sheathing is available in a number of types. One type is a semi-rigid, glass-fibre panel with an exterior vapour-permeable, waterproof membrane. The others are rigid panels of either expanded polystyrene, extruded polystyrene, polyurethane, isocyanurate or phenolic material. They come in different thicknesses, and the insulating value per unit thickness varies.

Insulating sheathing is installed on the wall like any other panel sheathing but

Vertical and horizontal application of panel-type sheathing

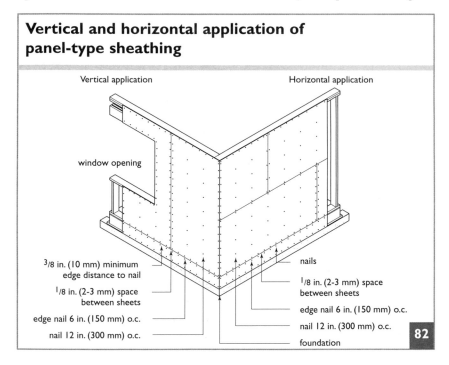

Vertical application

Horizontal application

window opening

3/8 in. (10 mm) minimum edge distance to nail

1/8 in. (2-3 mm) space between sheets

edge nail 6 in. (150 mm) o.c.

nail 12 in. (300 mm) o.c.

nails

1/8 in. (2-3 mm) space between sheets

edge nail 6 in. (150 mm) o.c.

nail 12 in. (300 mm) o.c.

foundation

82

Lumber sheathing application

(A) horizontal and diagonal application

(B) sheathing started at foundation wall

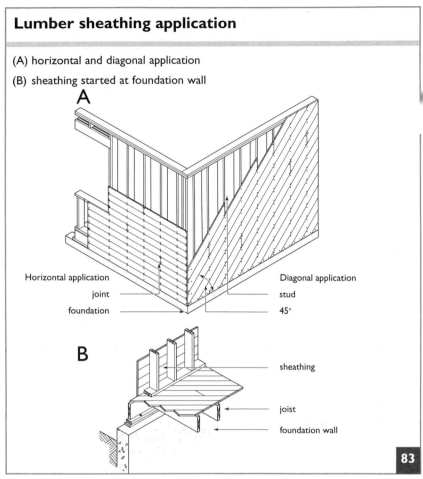

A

Horizontal application

joint

foundation

Diagonal application

stud

45°

B

sheathing

joist

foundation wall

83

with special, large-headed nails. A good reason for fastening this insulating sheathing before the wall is raised is its lightness and, for some types, its brittleness. Even a mild wind can make it difficult to install insulating sheathing on the vertical. Rigid glass fibre sheathing with a vapour-permeable membrane can serve as an air barrier when the joints are sealed with contractor sheathing tape.

There are two methods of installing sheathing down to the foundation sill. Either the panel extends beyond the bottom wall plate by the required length and the missing part at the top plate is filled in, or longer panels of 9 ft. (2.74 m) length are used, where available, to cover the wall down to the sill area. It is advantageous to cover the header and sill with the same wall sheet because this reduces air infiltration.

Lumber sheathing, which should not be less than 11/16 in. (17 mm) thick, is used in boards 6 to 12 in. (140 to 286 mm) wide. It is milled in a shiplap, tongue-and-groove or square-edge pattern. The boards are nailed at each stud with two nails for the 6 to 8 in.

(140 and 184 mm) widths and three for the 10 to 12 in. (235 and 286 mm) widths. End joints in the board must be placed over the centre of the studs with the joints staggered on different studs. Lumber sheathing may be put on either horizontally or diagonally (Figure 83A) and is extended beyond the subfloor to cover the header joist and the sill plate (Figure 83B). The angle cuts in the diagonal approach require more time and materials.

WALL SHEATHING MEMBRANE

Sheathing membrane (traditionally referred to as sheathing paper) should be water-resistant but vapour-permeable. New non-paper products, such as spunbonded polyolefins and poly-propylenes, are being used today. The sheathing membrane's function is to provide a second barrier to the entry of any wind and rain that might penetrate the cladding. It is also intended to direct water that penetrates the cladding over the flashing at the base of the wall. It must be permeable enough, however, to permit any water vapour to escape from the interior that may penetrate imperfections in the air barrier system and vapour retarder. One layer of sheathing membrane is generally used over wall sheathing and may be applied horizontally or vertically with 4 in. (100 mm) laps at the joints. At horizontal flashings, the upper sheet should be lapped over the lower sheet to direct moisture outward.

Where wall sheathing is not used, two layers of sheathing membrane are needed unless a large panel siding such as plywood is used. Both layers are applied vertically, with the joints lapped 4 in. (100 mm) at the studs. Both layers are stapled to the framing members, the top layer with staples spaced every 6 in. (150 mm) along the edges of the sheet to hold it securely in place.

RAINSCREEN

A key function of exterior walls is the control of rain penetration. Without proper detailing and construction, the exterior surfaces of walls can admit water into the building cavity, leading to premature deterioration of walls and mold. Although exterior sheathing may appear watertight, rain may enter at penetrations such as windows, doors, vent hoods, electrical outlets and balcony attachments. In parts of Canada where rain and wind-driven rain occur regularly, a rainscreen can be used to provide reliable wall performance. A rainscreen is a construction method that adds a second line of defence to water penetration and includes an airspace between the two barriers so that a) water entering the first line of defence can escape back to the outside and b) the space between the walls can dry between wettings. A rainscreen is comprised of an inner and an outer barrier to rain penetration. The two barriers are separated by an air space that is vented to provide a capillary break. A brick veneer-faced wall with a 1 in. (25 mm) space between the brick and the sheathing constitutes a rainscreen, provided there is an escape route for moisture at the bottom of the wall. A vinyl or wood cladding rainscreen uses strapping to separate the cladding from sheathing and sheathing membrane. Screen is used at the bottom to deter insects.

PLANNING AHEAD

Sheathing Membranes and Air Barrier Systems

Sheathing membranes are required beneath siding, stucco or masonry veneer. Membranes that are permitted for this application are intended to be of the breather type, permitting any humidity in the walls to vent to the outside. At the same time, these membranes are designed to prevent bulk water, generally caused by wind-driven rain, from penetrating the exterior walls.

Air barrier systems are required in all building envelopes to prevent air leakage that can cause internal moisture damage and waste energy. In some cases, the requirements for the air barrier system and the vapour retarder are met by using polyethylene located on the interior that is carefully sealed at joints and penetrations. In other cases, the air barrier system may include a separate membrane applied to the exterior face of the wall.

When combining the requirements for sheathing membranes and air barriers systems, the following points should be considered:

➜ Ensure that the air barrier membrane conforms to the requirements for sheathing membrane materials. It must allow water vapour (humidity) to escape from inside to outside.

➜ Install the air-barrier membrane so that it is continuous and airtight. Typically, taping joints and sealing penetrations is required to provide an effective barrier to air leakage.

➜ When exterior insulating sheathing is used, products that incorporate an air-barrier membrane may also be considered.

➜ In most cases, when a sheathing membrane is required, it makes sense to use a material that also serves as an air-barrier membrane.

➜ When in doubt, consult your local building department prior to construction for acceptable materials and methods.

It is important to resolve the type of air-barrier system and how it will be installed prior to the installation of wall sheathings and exterior finishes. Plan ahead by referring to the requirements for air barrier systems in the "Vapour Retarders and Air Barrier Systems" chapter.

HEALTHY HOUSING INSIGHT

Exterior Cladding Selection

Exterior cladding options are numerous because many new materials and systems are being continuously introduced. Appropriate choices for exterior cladding materials should take into consideration the following issues.

Durability and Maintenance

Exterior claddings should last the life of the building and be easy to maintain. Avoid exterior claddings that local experience shows have poor performance. Also consider the time and cost associated with exterior claddings that require frequent maintenance.

Resource Efficiency

Materials may be renewable or non-renewable, new or recycled, recyclable or non-recyclable and reusable or non-reusable. The use of non-recyclable and non-reusable materials is less desirable.

Compatibility and Adaptability

Exterior claddings should be compatible with the building system being constructed.

For example, in wet regions of the country where wind-driven rain commonly occurs, exterior claddings that do not serve as rainscreens should be avoided. Exterior claddings should also be adaptable if numerous changes to the building are foreseeable over its useful life. Typically, siding, panel and stucco type claddings are more adaptable than masonry veneer types.

In addition to these fundamental issues, the following points regarding the performance of entire wall systems may be considered.

→ Walls represent among the most expensive elements to retrofit in a building, especially when window replacement is included. When using exterior claddings such as masonry veneer, ensure that better practices in terms of thermal insulation levels and window quality are followed, otherwise future retrofit costs will often prove prohibitive.

→ Exterior claddings seldom significantly improve the energy efficiency of a building.

EXTERIOR CLADDING

Because the type of exterior cladding used on the walls will greatly affect the appearance of the house and the

amount of maintenance, it should be selected with care. Common types of cladding are: metal, vinyl, hardboard or lumber siding; panel siding made of plywood, oriented strand board, waferboard or hardboard; wood shingles or shakes; stucco, and masonry cladding such as clay and concrete brick, concrete block and stone.

There are indications that some sheathing membranes, such as spunbonded polyolefins, can be affected by surfactants (soapy residues). Surfactants can reduce the water repelling capability of a membrane by changing the viscosity of water and can be produced by a) certain types of wood species or b) additives mixed with the stucco to improve workability during installation. As the primary function of the sheathing membrane is moisture control, any breakdown of the moisture-penetration control barrier offers the possibility of water entry into the building envelope. Wood claddings with high tannin content should be installed over strapping so that the cladding is not in direct contact with the sheathing membrane. For stucco, a building system that separates the stucco from the sheathing membrane should always be used.

Most siding can be affected by moisture and should be kept 8 in. (200 mm) off the ground and 2 in. (50 mm) from an adjoining roof surface. Methods of flashing over window and door openings and between different types of wall covering are described in the chapter on "Flashing."

Metal and Vinyl Sidings

Metal and vinyl sidings are used extensively and are virtually maintenance free since they come with factory-finished surfaces. They are produced in different shapes and patterns, some of which simulate the appearance of wood bevel

Types of siding

(A) aluminum or vinyl

(B) bevel or feather-edge

(C) drop siding

(D) tongue-and-groove with V-joint

(E) board-on-board

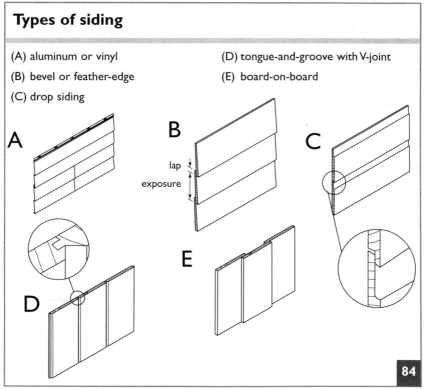

84

siding and vertical board and batten. They are made in configurations designed for continuous interlocking between boards so that only the upper side of the board is nailed, while the bottom edge is locked to the upper part of the board below (Figure 84A, p. 179). Interior and exterior corners, termination points of the soffit and gable ends as well as windows and doors, are built with specially designed trim pieces. The installation follows the same simple steps that are generally applicable to any kind of siding with a small 6 to 8 in. (150 to 200 mm) width.

Horizontal Application. The wall is prepared by applying the sheathing membrane as described. In wet and humid coastal climates, furring on the wall is recommended to provide a rainscreen and a vented space to facilitate drying. A level line is established around the house for the starter strip, which is normally placed a minimum of 6 to 8 in. (150 to 200 mm) above finished grade. All trim pieces for corners, windows, doors and openings and starter strips are fastened. The siding

is then applied in successive courses to the underside of the soffit.

Laps of adjacent boards should be staggered more than 24 in. (600 mm) apart and should all face in the same direction away from the general viewing angle.

An important point that must be remembered in each step of the installation is the need to let the siding, especially vinyl siding, expand and contract with temperature changes. Always follow the manufacturer's installation instructions when installing siding.

In the case of vinyl siding, the change in dimension could be from 1/4 to 1/2 in. (6 to 12 mm). If movement is restricted, buckling will occur. For this reason, the nails should be placed in the centre of the nail slots and not be hammered tight to the wall.

Vertical Application. The same general rules apply to vertical application as to horizontal. Using the vertical method, the starting point is a corner of the building with the appropriate corner trim. All other trim pieces also precede the installation of the siding.

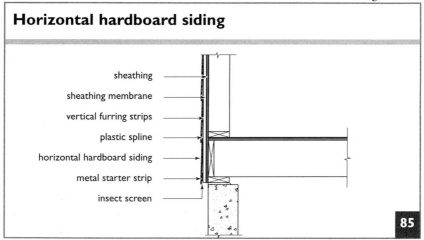

Horizontal hardboard siding

sheathing
sheathing membrane
vertical furring strips
plastic spline
horizontal hardboard siding
metal starter strip
insect screen

85

Hardboard Siding

Hardboard horizontal siding comes with a primed or prefinished surface in a variety of colours. It often has plastic splines (Figure 85, p. 180) that function as locking devices between panels. It is installed in a similar manner to metal and vinyl siding. In some cases, manufacturers suggest installing the siding over furring. Follow the installation instructions from the manufacturer.

Lumber Siding

Lumber siding should be sound and free of knotholes, loose knots, checks or splits. Easy working qualities and freedom from warp are desirable features. The species most commonly used are cedar, pine and redwood. It has also become more common to use pressure-treated lumber for siding. Pressure-treated siding may be manufactured from pine or other species. The moisture content of the siding at the time of application should be the same as it will experience in service, that is, about 12 to 18 per cent, depending on the region's humidity and climate.

In wet, humid climates, such as the coastal regions of Canada, an air space is often formed behind the siding to prevent water penetration and to vent moisture away from the wall. This is done by mounting the siding on furring strips nailed on top of the sheathing paper to the studs behind. In these cases, a screen should be installed at the base of the rainscreen at foundations, windows and doors to prevent insects and the top should be blocked to compartmentalize the wall.

Horizontal Application. Bevel or feather-edge siding (Figure 84B, p. 179) generally starts with the bottom course of boards furred out as shown in (Figure 86B, p. 179). A ¼ in. (6 mm) thick furring strip is used for this purpose. Each succeeding course overlaps the upper edge of the lower course, the minimum lap being usually 1 in. (25 mm). Spacing for the siding should be carefully laid out before the board is applied. To determine the maximum board spacing (or exposure), the minimum lap should be deducted from the overall width of the siding. The number of board spaces between the soffit and the bottom of the first course at the foundation wall should be such that the maximum exposure will not be exceeded. This may mean that the boards will have less than the maximum exposure. Where possible, the bottom of the board that is placed over the top of the windows should coincide with the top of the window cap (Figure 86A, p. 182).

Bevel siding should have a butt thickness of at least ½ in. (12 mm) for widths of 8 in. (184 mm) or less and ⁹⁄₁₆ in. (14.3 mm) for widths greater than 8 in. (184 mm). The top edge should not be less than ³⁄₁₆ in. (5 mm) thick.

Drop (or matched) siding should be at least ⁹⁄₁₆ in. (14.3 mm) thick and 8 in. nominal (184 mm) or less in width. It comes in a variety of patterns with matched or shiplap edges. Figure 84D, p. 179, shows a common pattern for drop siding.

Where bevel or drop siding is used, the butt joints between boards in adjacent courses should be staggered as much as possible. Butt joints should be made over a stud. The siding should be carefully fitted and be in close contact with other members and adjacent pieces. Ends should be sealed. Loose-fitting joints allow water to get behind the siding which can cause paint deterioration around the joints and lead to decay at the ends of the boards. One method sometimes used to obtain a tight joint is to place a small bead of caulking compound or putty along the end of each board after it is nailed and then press the next board into the compound. The excess compound is struck off, leaving a smooth waterproof joint. Joints occurring elsewhere, such as at window or door trim, can be similarly treated.

Installation of siding

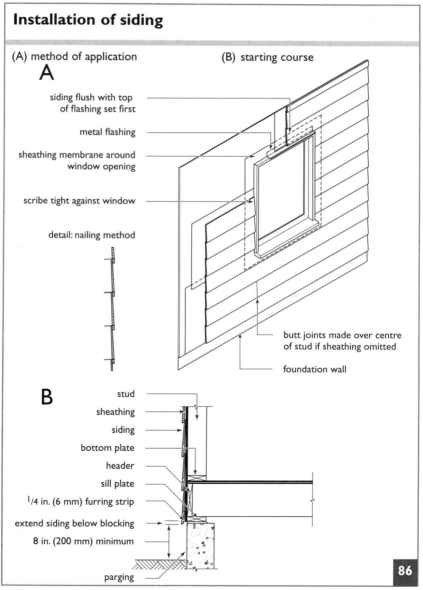

(A) method of application

A

siding flush with top of flashing set first

metal flashing

sheathing membrane around window opening

scribe tight against window

detail: nailing method

(B) starting course

butt joints made over centre of stud if sheathing omitted

foundation wall

B

stud

sheathing

siding

bottom plate

header

sill plate

1/4 in. (6 mm) furring strip

extend siding below blocking

8 in. (200 mm) minimum

parging

86

Bevel and drop siding should be face-nailed to lumber sheathing or studs. The size of the nail depends on the thickness of the siding and the type of sheathing used. One method of nailing often used is to drive the nail through the siding just above the lap so that the nail misses the top edge of the piece of siding beneath. (See the nailing method detail in Figure 86.) This method permits each siding board to expand and contract as the moisture content changes. Thus, there is less tendency for the boards to split as may occur when both edges of the board are nailed. Since the amount of swelling or shrinking is proportional to the width of the wood siding, nailing above the lap is more important with wide boards than with narrow boards.

Vertical Application. Lumber siding that can be applied vertically includes: plain matched boards; patterned matched boards; square-edge boards covered at the joints with a batten strip, or square-edge boards spaced apart and covered with another board. Vertical siding is usually 9/16 in. (14.3 mm) thick. Boards should not be wider than 12 in. nominal (286 mm). Vertical boards may be fastened to 9/16 in. (14.3 mm) lumber sheathing, 1/2 in. (12.5 mm) plywood or 1/2 in. (12.5 mm) oriented strand board or waferboard, 2 x 2 in. (38 x 38 mm) blocking fitted between the studs at 24 in. (600 mm) on centre or to horizontal furring strips. The furring may be 1 x 3 in. (19 x 64 mm) lumber where the framing is spaced not more than 16 in. (400 mm) on centre or 2 x 4 in. (19 x 89 mm) lumber where the framing is spaced not more than 24 in. (600 mm) on centre. Butt joints should be mitred to

prevent the entry of water into the joint. When the spaced method (sometimes called "board-on-board") is used (Figure 84E), the boards next to the wall are normally wider than the top boards and are fastened with one row of nails near the centre of each board. The top board is then applied so that it laps the edges of the first board at least 1 in. (25 mm). These top boards are fastened with two rows of nails driven slightly outside the edges of the boards underneath. This method of nailing permits the wider board to expand and contract without splitting.

The board-and-batten method uses square-edge boards that are ordinarily 8 in. nominal (184 mm) or less in width. The boards are applied with the edges at least 1/4 in. (6 mm) apart and fastened with one row of nails near the centre of each board. To cover the joint, a narrow batten is used that laps the edges at least 1/2 in. (12 mm). This batten is fastened with one row of nails driven in the joint between the two boards, so that the boards may swell or shrink without splitting either the boards or the batten strip. Since the batten also serves to prevent the board edges from curling outward, the nailing should be secure and closely spaced.

Tongue-and-groove matched siding (Figure 84C) is commonly 8 in. nominal (184 mm) or less in width. The first board is face-nailed near the grooved edge and angle-nailed through the tongue. Each successive board is fitted tightly to the preceding board and angle-nailed through the tongue. A nail set is used to finish off the nailing.

Nails cost little compared with the cost of the siding and labour, but the use of good nails is important. It is poor economy to buy siding that will last for years and then fasten it with nails that will rust badly within a short period. Corrosion-resistant nails, such as hot-dipped galvanized nails, will hold the siding permanently and will not disfigure the paint surface. Casing or siding nails are normally used for this purpose. Heads are driven flush with the face of the siding and later covered with paint. If finishing nails are used, the heads should be set below the surface and the hole filled with putty after the prime coat of paint is applied. The length of the nails depends on the thickness of the siding and the type of sheathing used. Nails should be long enough to penetrate at least 1 in. (25 mm) into the nailing support.

Plywood Panels

Exterior-type plywood is also used as a wall covering. The plywood sheets are made with a plain or grooved surface and are usually applied vertically. The joints may be V-grooved or flush or may be covered with battens. Plywood is available with a resin-impregnated kraft paper laminated to the face. This provides a smooth, moisture-resistant surface that resists checking or splitting after painting.

The minimum thickness of plywood applied as sheathing is 1/4 in. (6 mm). It may be applied directly to unsheathed wall framing. The minimum thickness used is 1/4 in. (6 mm) for stud spacings of 16 in. (400 mm) on centre and 5/16 in. (8 mm) for spacing of supports up to 24 in. (600 mm) on centre. This assumes the face grain is installed at right angles to supports. Where the face grain is installed parallel to supports, the minimum thickness is 5/16 in. (8 mm) and 7/16 in. (11 mm) for studs spaced at 16 in. (400 mm) and 24 in. (600 mm), respectively.

After the plywood panels are cut and fitted, all edges should be protected with a suitable paint or sealer before installation. A 1/8 in. (2 to 3 mm) space between the sides and ends of the panels and butted ends of the battens will permit expansion without bulging. Vertical joints are filled with caulking or covered with a batten. Horizontal joints are flashed or lapped at least 1 in. (25 mm).

The edges of plywood panels should be supported and fastened with corrosion-resistant nails, usually 2 in. (51 mm) long. The nails are spaced 6 in. (150 mm) along the edges and 12 in. (300 mm) at intermediate supports.

Hardboard Panels

Hardboard is also produced in sheets with a variety of finishes and may be applied over sheathing or to unsheathed walls. The minimum thickness of sheets should be at least 1/4 in. (6 mm) on supports that are not more than 16 in. (400 mm) on centre. It is fastened to the framing member or to sheathing with corrosion-resistant nails at least 2 in. (51 mm) long. Nails are spaced 6 in. (150 mm) along the edges and 12 in. (300 mm) along intermediate supports. A gap of at least 1/8 in. (2 to 3 mm) should be provided between sheets.

Corner Treatment for Siding

The method of finishing siding at the corners may be influenced by the house design. Corner boards may be appropriate to some designs and mitred joints to others.

For lumber siding applied horizontally (Figure 87), mitred corners are most common, but metal corners or corner boards may also be used.

Mitred corners (Figure 87B) must fit tightly and smoothly for the full depth of the mitre. To maintain a tight fit at the mitre, it is important that the siding is properly seasoned before delivery and protected from rain when stored at the site. The ends are often set in caulking compound or putty when the siding is applied.

At interior corners, the siding is usually butted against a corner strip of 1 or 1 1/2 in. (25 or 38 mm) material, depending upon the thickness of the siding.

Metal corners (Figure 87C), used as a substitute for mitred corners, are made of light-gauge metals such as aluminum or galvanized steel. The application of metal corners requires less skill than making good mitred corners or fitting siding to a corner board.

Corner treatment of siding

(A) corner boards

(B) mitred corner

(C) metal corner

(D) siding return on main roof, showing corner boards

Mitred or metal corners can also be used on the return, depending on the design.

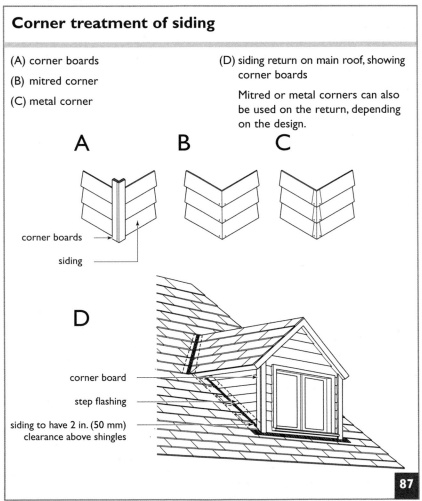

A

B

C

corner boards

siding

D

corner board

step flashing

siding to have 2 in. (50 mm) clearance above shingles

87

Corner boards (Figures 87A and D) are generally used with drop siding, but may be used with other types of siding as well. The boards are made of 1 or 1 1/2 in. (25 or 38 mm) material, depending on the thickness of the siding. The corner boards are applied against the sheathing with the siding fitted tightly against the narrow edge of the corner boards. Joints between the siding and corner boards should be filled with caulking compound or putty when the siding is applied.

Plywood and hardboard are usually lapped at the corners or fitted to a corner board. Lumber siding applied vertically is lapped at the corners.

Wood Shingles and Machine-grooved Shakes

Wood shingles or machine-grooved shakes are sometimes used for wall covering. A large selection is available, including special wall shingles in lengths of 16, 18 and 24 in. (400, 450 and 600 mm), that are factory-painted or stained.

Shingles are usually separated into three grades. The first grade is composed of clear shingles, all heartwood, and all edge grain. The second grade consists of shingles with clear butts and permits defects in the part of the shingle that is normally covered in use. The third grade includes shingles that have defects other than those permitted in the second grade. These shingles may be used for under-coursing.

Shingles are made in random widths varying in the first grade from 2 1/2 to 14 in. (65 to 350 mm); only a small proportion of the narrow width is permitted in the first grade. Shingles of a uniform width, known as dimension

shingles, are also available. Widths of 4, 5 or 6 in. (100, 125 or 150 mm) may be specified. Table 34, p. 392, shows the commonly used exposure and thickness of wood shingles and machine-grooved shakes. Lumber, oriented strand board, waferboard or plywood sheathing should be used under shingles or shakes.

When the single-course application is used, the joints in succeeding courses should be offset at least 1 9/16 in. (40 mm), and care must be taken to ensure that the joints in any two or three courses do not line up.

To obtain deep shadow lines, shingles can be laid in what is called double-coursing. This may be done by using a lower grade shingle under the shingle exposed to the weather. The exposed shingle butt extends about 1/2 in. (12 mm) below the butt of the undercourse. Where double-coursing is used, wider exposure to the weather is possible. Joints in the outer course should be offset from joints in the undercourse by at least 1 9/16 in. (40 mm).

Shingles should be fastened with corrosion-resistant nails. Shingles up to 8 in. (200 mm) wide require only two nails. Those more than 8 in. (200 mm) wide require three. Nails should be driven about 13/16 in. (20 mm) from the edges and 1 in. (25 mm) above the exposure line for single-course application, and 2 in. (50 mm) for double coursing.

Stucco Finishes

Stucco is a mixture of Portland cement and well-graded sand, with hydrated lime added to make the mixture more plastic. An alternative stucco mixture calls for replacing the lime with masonry cement. Table 36, p. 393, lists the proportions for the preparation of these two stucco mixes. Other proprietary stucco mixes are available. Their formulations will vary depending on the manufacturer of the mix.

Usually applied in three coats (two base coats and one finish coat), the stucco is held in place by stucco mesh or wire lath. A variety of finish coats are available, from standard coloured cement finishes to finely textured acrylic finishes. The "pebble dash" finish is seldom used except in retrofit applications.

Stucco reinforcing of self-furring welded mesh, or fully primed or galvanized woven mesh, is stretched horizontally over sheathing paper, with the joints in the mesh lapped at least 2 in. (50 mm). External corners are reinforced either by extending the mesh from one side 6 in. (150 mm) around the adjacent corner, or by vertical strips of reinforcing that extend 6 in. (150 mm) on either side of the corner. Stucco must be at least 8 in. (200 mm) above finished grade except where it is applied over concrete or masonry. In high exposure areas (frequent high rainfall and/or strong wind-driven rains), stucco finishes should include a furred and drained airspace of no less than 19 mm (3/4 in.) between the stucco and the sheathing membrane to create a rainscreen. The top of the cavity should be vented and baffled to keep rain from blowing into the cavity. The bottom of the drainage cavity must be vented to the exterior and flashed.

A layer of heavyweight building paper, lapped 4 in. (100 mm) at the edges, must be applied over the sheathing. It is very important to apply flashings around penetrations in the walls. The building paper must be carefully applied around window openings and lapped correctly to ensure that water does not enter at the window flanges. Tar-saturated felts or papers should not be used beneath the stucco. The tar can bleed through the stucco causing unsightly discolouration.

Galvanized steel fasteners should be used to hold the mesh in place. Suitable fasteners are 1/8 in. (3.2 mm) diameter nails with heads that are about 7/16 in. (11.1 mm) or 0.078 in. (1.98 mm) thick staples. Fasteners are spaced 6 in. (150 mm) vertically and 16 in. (400 mm) horizontally, or 4 in. (100 mm) vertically and 24 in. (600 mm) horizontally. Other fastening patterns may be used, provided there are at least two fasteners per square foot (20 fasteners per square metre) of the wall surface. Where the sheathing is other than lumber, waferboard or plywood, the fasteners should penetrate the sheathing and go into the framing member (stud or plate) at least 1 in. (25 mm).

The base coat consists of two layers of stucco. The first layer or "scratch coat" is applied to a thickness of 1/4 in. (6 mm) that completely embeds the wire lath or mesh. The scratch coat surface must be scored or raked to provide a bonding key for the second coat. Curing time will depend on outdoor temperature and weather conditions. It is not uncommon to allow 48 hours of cure time before the second coat is applied.

Just before putting on the second coat, the base is dampened to ensure a good bond between the coats. The second coat is applied at least 1/4 in. (6 mm) thick and firmly trowelled into the scored surface of the base.

A variety of finishes is available today, from standard white or coloured cement to modified and acrylic finishes. Acrylic finish coats are often applied over conventional Portland cement, with good results. It is important that the chosen product has good weatherability and is vapour-permeable. In cases where a wall requires a fire rating, the base coat thickness will need to be sufficiently thick.

For finish coats, the second coat should be moist-cured for at least 48 hours and then left to dry for five days, preferably longer, before the finish coat is applied. The base should be dampened to ensure a good bond and the finish applied to a depth of at least 1/8 in. (3 mm).

In dry, warm weather, fresh stucco should be kept damp to ensure proper curing. In cold weather, each coat of stucco should be kept at a temperature of at least 50⁰F (10⁰C) for 48 hours after application.

Masonry Veneer

If masonry veneer is used for the exterior cladding of above-grade walls, the foundation must include a supporting ledge or offset wide enough to allow a space of about 1 in. (25 mm) between the masonry and the sheathing paper (Figure 88). Insulated concrete form (ICF) foundations use a reinforced flare at the top of the foundation to support the weight of brick veneer (Figure 89).

A base flashing should extend from the outside face of the wall over the top of the ledge and at least 6 in. (150 mm) up the wall behind the sheathing paper. Corrosion-resistant metal ties, nailed to the studs and embedded in the mortar joints between the masonry, should be used to tie the veneer to the framework. When fastened to every other stud, they are usually spaced 32 in. (800 mm) apart horizontally and 16 in. (400 mm) vertically. Alternatively, when fastened to every stud, they may be spaced 24 in.

Masonry veneer support on foundation wall

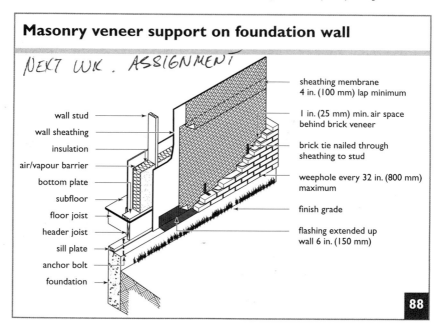

NEXT WK. ASSIGNMENT

- wall stud
- wall sheathing
- insulation
- air/vapour barrier
- bottom plate
- subfloor
- floor joist
- header joist
- sill plate
- anchor bolt
- foundation

- sheathing membrane 4 in. (100 mm) lap minimum
- 1 in. (25 mm) min. air space behind brick veneer
- brick tie nailed through sheathing to stud
- weephole every 32 in. (800 mm) maximum
- finish grade
- flashing extended up wall 6 in. (150 mm)

88

(600 mm) horizontally and 20 in. (500 mm) vertically, or 16 in. (400 mm) horizontally and 24 in. (600 mm) vertically, depending on the stud spacing.

Weepholes serve both a venting and a drainage function. They should be placed about 32 in. (800 mm) apart in the bottom course of the masonry

veneer and above-grade windows and doors. This can be done by omitting part of the mortar from the vertical joints, or by inserting plastic tubes in the joints.

Masonry veneer should be at least 3 1/2 in. (90 mm) thick where there are raked joints and 2 3/4 in. (75 mm) thick where the joints are unraked.

Support of masonry veneer on an ICF foundation

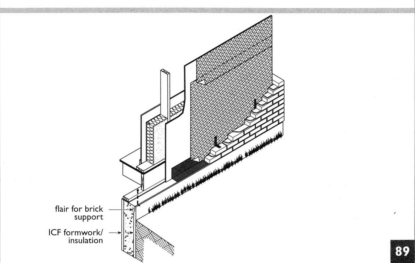

flair for brick support

ICF formwork/ insulation

89

PLANNING AHEAD

Painting and Staining

If an exterior finish requiring painting or staining is being installed, plan ahead to minimize work and potential problems.

➜ Prepare for painting and staining as the exterior finish is being installed. If nails have to be countersunk and the holes filled prior to painting or staining, do this as the materials are being installed.

➜ For difficult-to-access areas and decorative wood trims or mouldings, sealing and priming these before installation will ensure complete coverage and simplify the application of finish coats.

For more information on exterior finishes, refer to the chapter entitled "Painting."

HEALTHY HOUSING INSIGHT

Minimizing Waste in Wall Sheathings and Claddings

The reduction of waste from wall sheathings and exterior claddings requires careful planning and proper construction practices. The following points should be considered when dealing with wall sheathings and exterior claddings.

➡ Only order the amount of material that is required plus a small amount for wastage and rejection. Before ordering materials, make suitable arrangements for returning unused goods to suppliers.

➡ Always store and handle materials carefully. Waste often results from damage that can be avoided. Keep materials covered with a tarp on site.

➡ Have one person cut all materials in one location to make better use of offcuts.

➡ Use standard wall heights so that sheathing and panel materials do not have to be cut in length. Where possible, make the lengths of walls a multiple of 16 in. (400 mm) or 24 in. (600 mm) to better utilize offcuts.

➡ A small amount of exterior cladding waste is practically unavoidable. Where services are available, collect and store waste materials for recycling.

For general insights into managing construction waste, refer to Applying the 4 Rs of Wood-Frame Construction in the "Framing the House" chapter.

If a brick veneer is used, the bricks selected should be hard, absorb little water and be manufactured for exposure to the weather. Stone veneers should be selected from the materials known locally to be durable.

Brick or stone should be laid in a full bed of mortar. Care should be taken to avoid dropping mortar into the space between the veneer and sheathing paper, because this will block the cavity behind the veneer. Outside joints must be tooled to a smooth finish to provide maximum resistance to water penetration. Mortar mix proportions should conform to those shown in Table 6, p. 358.

Masonry laid during cold weather should be protected from freezing until after the mortar has set. The temperature of the masonry and mortar should be maintained above 41°F (5°C) for at least 24 hours after installation.

Windows and Doors

WINDOWS AND DOORS

The proper selection and installation of windows and doors is a very important aspect of wood-frame house construction. Windows and doors are often able to play a role in a number of systems within the building. Daylight, view, natural ventilation and means of egress are all affected by the windows and doors that are selected. Poor installation affects energy efficiency and can also provide an entry point path for water into the building envelope.

Poor quality windows and doors can lead to high energy bills and maintenance costs. Irrespective of their quality, window and door problems may also be caused by poor installation. Unlike paint and wallpaper, the cost of replacing poorly performing windows and doors is extremely high, and often disruptive. It is usually more cost-effective to invest in good quality windows and doors, and to ensure that these are properly installed, rather than having to upgrade these components later.

There are several important factors to consider when selecting windows and doors. The energy efficiency of doors, and particularly windows, is a critical consideration. These components can account for a large portion of a dwelling's heat loss. It is important to consider the size and swing of exterior doors, not only to comply with building code requirements, but also to accommodate the easy movement of people and furnishings into and out of the dwelling. The size and style of windows should be carefully considered since this will influence the appearance of the house as well as the natural ventilation and lighting. Durability and maintenance are two additional factors that apply to any exterior component of the dwelling, and especially to windows and doors. Finally, some thought should also be given to providing adequate resistance to forced entry through the type and location of windows and doors.

Light, View and Ventilation

Windows and doors with glazing can provide light and view for the occupants provided they are appropriately sized and located. Except for bedrooms, which require windows of at least 10 per cent of the bedroom floor area, the NBC no longer requires other rooms to have windows. However, it is recommemded that specific rooms have unobstructed windows large enough to allow natural light. Normally, living rooms, dining rooms and bedrooms should have glazing equal to no less than 10 per cent of the area of the room. Other rooms, such as dens and family rooms, should have window areas equal to at least 5 per cent of the floor area of the room. Windows promote healthful indoor spaces that provide for the psychological well-being of the occupants.

Windows can also provide natural ventilation by allowing outside air to flow inside and inside air to escape. Openable windows can eliminate the need for mechanical ventilation during the non-heating seasons. For most rooms where the window is used to provide natural ventilation, this means an unobstructed, openable window area of at least 3 sq. ft. (0.28 m²) should be provided. Bathrooms should have a window at least 1 sq. ft. (0.09 m²). Unfinished basements should have openable windows that represent at least 0.2 per cent of the basement floor area if non-heating season mechanical ventilation is to be eliminated.

While windows can provide benefits of light, view and ventilation they can also pose a fire hazard to adjacent properties. Because fire can spread from windows to adjacent houses, building codes place strict limits on the amount of glazing in walls that are close to property lines. Unprotected, glazed openings are not permitted in walls that are within 4 ft. (1.2 m) of a property line. Walls more than 4 ft. (1.2 m) may contain limited glazed openings depending on the distance from the property line and the area of the wall facing the property line. Consult your local building department for specific requirements.

Means of Egress

Windows can play a part in the building's means of egress, allowing occupants to escape to the outdoors if fire blocks the usual exit paths from the room. Each basement bedroom needs to have at least one outside window (or exterior door) openable from the inside without the use of tools or special knowledge and without the need to remove sashes or hardware. These windows should have an unobstructed open portion with no dimension less than 15 in. (380 mm) and with an open area of at least 3.8 sq. ft. (0.35 m²) as shown in Figure 90. For example, a window with an opening that measures 18 x 30 in. (450 x 750 mm) would conform to this requirement.

It is recommended that the sill for the escape window be no higher than 5 ft. (1.5 m) above the floor. Where a security grill is installed over a basement window, it must be possible to remove the grill from the interior without special tools or knowledge. The window must be capable of staying open during an emergency without the need for props or supports. Where a window opens into a window well, a clearance of 22 in. (550 mm) must be provided in front of the window. Access can be improved to windows high on walls and intended to serve as egress windows by using built-in furniture.

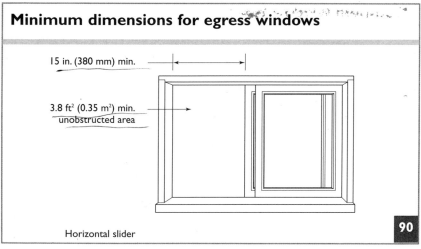

Minimum dimensions for egress windows

15 in. (380 mm) min.

3.8 ft² (0.35 m²) min. unobstructed area

Horizontal slider

90

The furniture can act as a step, allowing easy escape in fire situations.

Window Types

There is a wide variety of windows available in several common types (Figure 91). Each type has its own advantages and disadvantages that should be carefully considered when selecting windows.

Fixed windows are generally the least expensive, and usually offer the best level of energy efficiency and resistance to forced entry. They do not offer any natural ventilation and cannot serve as a means of egress from the dwelling in case of fire.

Single-or double-hung windows are a traditional design. Only one sash (usually the bottom unit) operates in single-hung windows, while both sashes operate in double-hung units. Prior to advances in window technology, these windows did not perform well in terms of ease of operation and air leakage. However, modern types have been developed that satisfy these requirements and that also offer good resistance to forced entry.

Horizontal and vertical slider windows are easy to operate, and, because they do not project out from or into the dwelling, they do not become obstacles to movement. Sliders tend to be less airtight than casement, awning and tilt-and-turn windows because their weatherstripping is exposed to wear due to friction.

Casement and awning windows are among the more expensive types. Due to their operation, these windows are very airtight and offer good resistance to forced entry. Casement windows are well suited to deflecting prevailing winds into the dwelling for natural ventilation and passive cooling. Awning windows have the advantage of shedding rain effectively when open.

Tilt-and-turn windows are the most flexible of all window types. Some can act like casement and awning windows. These windows can be very airtight when fitted with compression-type closing devices.

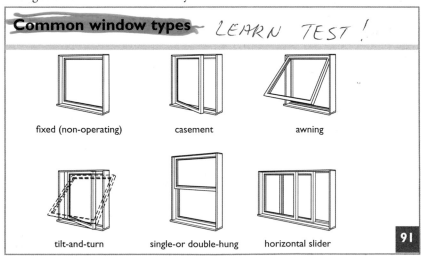

Common window types *LEARN TEST!*

fixed (non-operating)   casement   awning

tilt-and-turn   single-or double-hung   horizontal slider

91

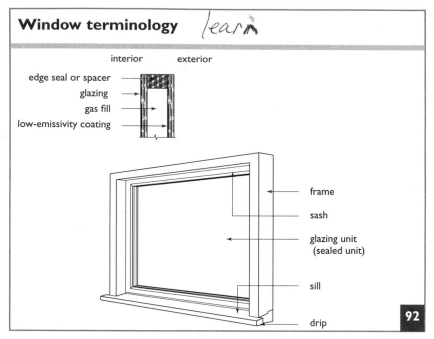

Window terminology *learn*

interior   exterior

edge seal or spacer

glazing

gas fill

low-emissivity coating

frame

sash

glazing unit
(sealed unit)

sill

drip

92

Before proceeding with a discussion of window performance and selection criteria, it is important to become familiar with some common window terms. These terms have been summarized in Figure 92.

Window Performance

Significant advances in window technology have been achieved through ongoing research and development by government and industry. These improvements are available as options in most manufacturer's products. It is important to appreciate how these contribute to improved performance when making a selection.

Multiple Glass Layers

In order to reduce the potential for condensation, windows that separate heated space from unheated space or the exterior must be at least double-glazed. Each additional layer of glazing helps to increase the inside surface temperature of the innermost layer of glass, thereby reducing the potential for condensation.

Condensation, a common homeowner complaint, can be reduced by installing good, energy-efficient windows. Some condensation on windows is normal and should be expected, particularly around the edges of the glazing during cold weather. Nonetheless, double-and triple-glazed windows with thermally broken frames and good quality spacers can go a long way towards reducing the likelihood of condensation in today's houses.

Low-emissivity Coatings

A large proportion of the heat loss and gain through a window is due to radiation—a process where warmer objects radiate heat to cooler objects, as in the case of the sun warming the earth with its radiant energy. A low-emissivity (low-E) coating is a thin metallic film deposited on glass that acts as a mirror to radiant heat, reflecting it back into the dwelling during cold weather, and back to the outdoors during hot weather. Low-emissivity coatings work to reduce heating and cooling bills. They provide a double-glazed window with about the same performance as a clear, triple-glazed window, but at less additional cost. An increasing number of window manufacturers are offering low-E glazings as a standard feature due to their improved resistance to condensation on the inside glazing during cold weather.

Gas Fills

Another innovation in window technology is the replacement of air with inert gas fills between layers of glass in a sealed unit. Inert gases have a higher insulating value than air because they are heavier, resulting in lower convective and conductive heat losses between the panes of glass. Argon is the most commonly used gas due to its availability and low cost. Gas fills are a cost-effective upgrade over conventional air-filled glazings.

Edge Seals

The thermal efficiency of a sealed glazing unit can be significantly improved by using a low-conductivity edge seal or spacer between panes of glass. Traditionally, edge seals have been made of aluminum which conducts heat rapidly, resulting in cold areas around the edges of glazing units. Plastic, silicone and glass fibre spacers are now used to reduce thermal conductivity at the perimeter of sealed glazing units.

Frames with Thermal Breaks

Window frames made from metal, plastic or fibreglass can conduct a large amount of heat unless a thermal break made from an insulating material is provided. Without thermal breaks, window frames can become so cold that frost forms on the inside during extremely cold weather. This is not a problem in wood windows, due to the relatively higher insulating value of wood, or in windows that have extruded frames filled with insulating materials. It is important to check the construction of windows to ensure that the frames are either well insulated or have a thermal break.

Energy Rating

The Energy Rating (ER) is a useful measure of the overall heating season performance of a window based on three factors: 1) solar heat gain; 2) heat loss through frames; and 3) air leakage heat loss. The ER rating is for a standard test-size window and not a particular window. The ER rating also depends on the type of window. For example, fixed windows typically have a better (higher) ER rating than operable windows. Because all windows are evaluated the same way, a comparison can be made between window types made by different manufacturers. The ER may be positive or negative. A positive ER indicates that on average, the window gains more heat from incoming solar energy than it loses over the heating season. Most ER ratings for windows are negative, as can be seen in Figure 93. Typical effective thermal resistance values for a casement window are provided in Figure 93 in both imperial (R) and metric (RSI) units. Numerous studies on cost-effective, energy-efficiency improvements to new housing indicate that as a minimum, windows should have an ER of approximately -11 or higher for operable windows and about -3 or better for fixed windows. This translates into a double-glazed window with low-E coating and argon gas fill. Higher efficiency windows are recommended in the colder regions of Canada.

Airtightness, Water Resistance and Wind Load Resistance

Windows in Canada are expected to conform to the CSA standard, *CAN/CSA-A440-M, Windows.* The standard includes a window classification system that rates windows according to their airtightness, water resistance and wind load resistance characteristics. Normally, the ratings achieved by each window are marked on the window. Windows installed in houses should be identified as meeting the A1 (airtightness), B1 (water resistance), and C1 (wind load resistance) ratings of the CSA standard.

Window Selection

Windows are seldom selected solely on the basis of minimum building code requirements for light and natural ventilation. The contribution of windows to the external appearance of the dwelling, a pleasing view, privacy, natural light and passive solar heating are often more important considerations. The style and operating characteristics of windows should be carefully considered. The provision of effective natural ventilation does not require every window to be operable. The selective

Comparison of typical window thermal efficiencies

Thermal performance of a typical casement window with low-conductivity edge seal			
R (RSI) energy rating	Aluminum frame with thermal break	Wood or vinyl frame	Fibreglass frame
Double-glazed clear with air fill	1.59 (.28)/-40.6	2.04 (.36)/-24.9	2.38 (.42)/-19.0
Double-glazed low-E with air fill	1.99 (.35)/-32.7	2.67 (.47)/-17.1	3.12 (.55)/-11.5
Double-glazed low-E with argon	2.10 (.37)/-29.0	2.90 (.51)/-13.3	3.46 (.61)/-8.0
Triple-glazed clear with air fill	1.99 (.35)/-32.7	2.84 (.50)/-11.8	3.18 (.56)/-10.8
Triple-glazed low-E with air fill	2.21 (.39)/-27.9	3.41 (.60)/-9.5	3.86 (.68)/-6.2
Triple-glazed low-E with argon	2.33 (.41)/-25.2	3.69 (.65)/-6.8	4.25 (.75)/-5.4

93

use of operating windows can reduce window costs, thereby permitting an investment in higher quality windows.

Durability and maintenance should be considered both for exterior and interior applications. Maintenance-free finishes are highly recommended to reduce the need to paint windows. These are also advisable for two- and three-storey houses where access for maintenance is difficult. In areas such as bathrooms, water-resistant interior finishes are recommended. This avoids potential water damage to sashes and frames, reducing the need for frequent maintenance.

Security is another consideration in the location and type of windows. This aspect of window selection is further discussed in the Healthy Housing Insight later in this chapter.

Window Installation

Windows are normally installed after the house framing and roof covering are complete. Proper scheduling should ensure delivery of the windows at this stage. However, it may be necessary to accept earlier delivery and arrange for storage of the windows on site. It is recommended to store windows upright on a dry, level surface, in their original packaging, and to leave the temporary bracing in place. When stored outside, a vented platform covered with a large tarpaulin is the preferred means of storage. Remember to label and store screens separately. If left on windows during construction, screens may be damaged or clogged with dust.

Prior to installation, it is important to review the manufacturer's installation instructions, and ensure that all of the proper tools, fasteners and materials are available. Windows must be installed plumb and level within the rough opening, using shims to make the window true and keep the spaces around it even. Improper window installation can result in moisture leakage problems. Good practice for window installation involves the use of and lapping of water-impermeable sheathing membranes to form a good drainage plain (Figure 94). Depending on the technique used to insulate and air-seal the window breaching (the gap between the window and the rough opening), air-sealing may be performed prior to, or after, installing the window. The most common technique now being employed involves applying polyurethane foam to insulate and air-seal the breaching in one step. Some modern windows rely on sealant as the only protection against water ingress at the sill-to-cladding joint. Older windows relied on self-flashing sills with drip notches to direct water away from the base of the window. Windows with the sill configuration shown in Figure 95 provide additional protection. Windows must be attached securely to framing members (Figure 96).

Sequence for window installation

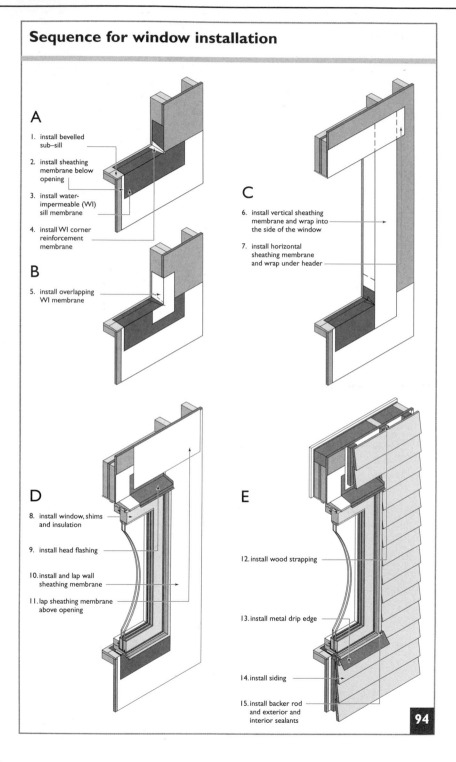

A

1. install bevelled sub–sill
2. install sheathing membrane below opening
3. install water-impermeable (WI) sill membrane
4. install WI corner reinforcement membrane

B

5. install overlapping WI membrane

C

6. install vertical sheathing membrane and wrap into the side of the window
7. install horizontal sheathing membrane and wrap under header

D

8. install window, shims and insulation
9. install head flashing
10. install and lap wall sheathing membrane
11. lap sheathing membrane above opening

E

12. install wood strapping
13. install metal drip edge
14. install siding
15. install backer rod and exterior and interior sealants

94

Exterior Doors

Exterior doors, like windows, contribute to the external appearance of a dwelling and are most often selected on the basis of style and finish. With the exception of custom doors, most exterior doors come as pre-hung manufactured units ready for installation within a rough opening. Exterior doors are typically manufactured in wood, steel, plastic and fibreglass. Wood doors are normally solid, while other types consist of inner and outer structural panels filled with insulation. These modern door types are generally more

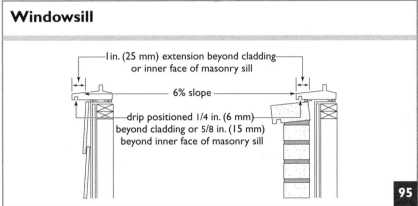

Windowsill

1 in. (25 mm) extension beyond cladding or inner face of masonry sill

6% slope

drip positioned 1/4 in. (6 mm) beyond cladding or 5/8 in. (15 mm) beyond inner face of masonry sill

95

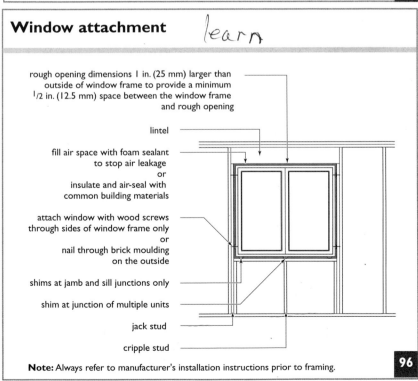

Window attachment   *learn*

rough opening dimensions 1 in. (25 mm) larger than outside of window frame to provide a minimum 1/2 in. (12.5 mm) space between the window frame and rough opening

lintel

fill air space with foam sealant to stop air leakage
or
insulate and air-seal with common building materials

attach window with wood screws through sides of window frame only
or
nail through brick moulding on the outside

shims at jamb and sill junctions only

shim at junction of multiple units

jack stud

cripple stud

Note: Always refer to manufacturer's installation instructions prior to framing.

96

Door hardware requirements

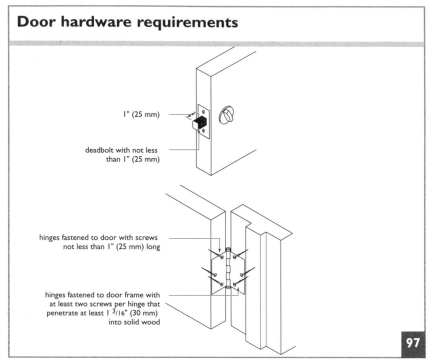

1" (25 mm)

deadbolt with not less than 1" (25 mm)

hinges fastened to door with screws not less than 1" (25 mm) long

hinges fastened to door frame with at least two screws per hinge that penetrate at least 1 3/16" (30 mm) into solid wood

97

energy efficient. However, wood doors have proven performance and a traditional appearance that has maintained their popularity in the marketplace. Irrespective of the style and appearance of the door, a number of common considerations are worth noting.

Hardware, in particular locksets and hinges, are important items both in terms of functionality and durability. The main entry door to a dwelling will be locked and unlocked, opened and closed countless number of times over its useful life. Low-cost hardware may not be the least costly in the long run.

The National Building Code contains requirements for resistance to forced entry for door hardware. Deadbolt locks in exterior doors to houses should have a cylinder with no fewer than five pins and a bolt throw of at least 1 in. (25 mm). Double doors should have

heavy duty bolts top and bottom with an engagement of at least 5/8 in. (15 mm). Hinges need to be fastened to wood doors with wood screws not less than 1 in. (25 mm) long, and to wood frames penetrating at least 1 3/16 in. (30 mm) into solid wood. Refer to Figure 97.

Resistance to forced entry extends beyond door hardware to the framing for the door as well. Solid blocking should be provided on both sides of the doorway at lock height between the jamb for the door and the structural framing so that the jambs resist spreading by force. Additional screws in the drywall around the doorframe will also strengthen resistance to forced entry.

Weatherstripping is the primary line of defence against air leakage around doors, and should be carefully examined when selecting an exterior door. It

Pre-hung manufactured door

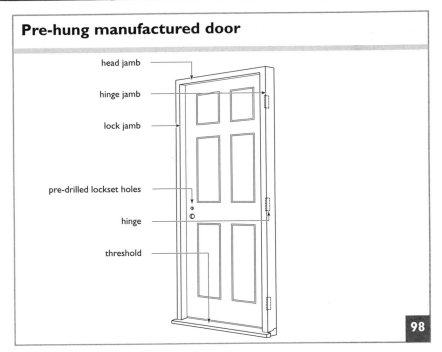

head jamb

hinge jamb

lock jamb

pre-drilled lockset holes

hinge

threshold

98

should be effective, durable and easy to replace. Air leakage of items such as mail slots should also be considered.

Glazing in exterior doors should be thermally efficient, and depending on its size and location, may also have to be tempered for added safety. Generally, glass sidelights greater than 20 in. (500 mm) wide that could be mistaken for a door and glass in storm or sliding doors is required to be safety glass. Double-glazed sidelights are recommended. When no glazing is provided, a door viewer should be considered for security purposes. Similar to windows, glazing in side doors near property lines may be restricted depending on the distance to the property line.

The installation of pre-hung doors should always be carried out according to the manufacturer's installation instructions, otherwise warranties may be voided.

At present, practically all windows and doors are purchased and installed as complete manufactured systems (Figure 98). There may be cases, however, where a custom door or window may be desired, or an existing window in an older house may require replacement. In these cases, certain components may have to be milled prior to assembly and installation. Refer to the next chapter, "Exterior Trim and Millwork" for further information on site-assembled windows and doors.

RELATED PUBLICATION

How to Lock Out Crime: Protecting Your Home Against Burglary
Canada Mortgage and Housing Corporation

HEALTHY HOUSING INSIGHT

Resistance to Forced Entry

A significant aspect of occupant health and well-being involves security within the dwelling through appropriate resistance to forced entry measures. The National Building Code provides minimum measures for doors and windows, however, a number of other issues relating to home security should also be considered. Forced entry remains a reality regardless of neighbourhood. The following issues should be considered when designing and building the home.

Discouraging Forced Entry

➜ Window and door locations can either encourage or discourage attempts at forced entry. Basement windows located out of sight from the street and neighbouring homes are common forced entry points. As well, any windows that are accessible from the ground should be provided with secure locking hardware. Side and rear doors should not be located within recesses or behind any types of screens, such as lattices or planters.

➜ Landscaping should not shield or conceal doors and windows. Shrubs and hedges, planted in front of basement windows, provide convenient hiding places, unless they are very low to the ground.

➜ Outdoor lighting may be an unintentional aid to forced entry if high-intensity lights are focused away from the dwelling towards the street or neighbouring homes. The glare from these lights makes the areas adjacent to the home less visible. Instead, the light should be directed to the building or immediate surroundings. The installation of outdoor lighting with motion detectors at key locations is recommended.

➜ Indoor lighting controls allow for the automatic operation of lights to simulate an occupied home. These are recommended for households that experience frequent or lengthy absences.

➜ Home security systems are a more expensive and effective means of discouraging forced entry. Home security systems range from simple types installed by the homeowner, to sophisticated systems monitored by security companies.

A well-planned system of resistance to forced entry measures cannot guarantee complete home security; however, it will discourage some of the most common types of attempts at forced entry.

Exterior Trim
and Millwork

EXTERIOR TRIM AND MILLWORK

Exterior trim (that part of the exterior finish other than the wall covering) includes such items as window and door trim, soffits, rake or gable trim and fascia. Much of this material is cut, fitted and nailed into place on the job. Other materials or assemblies, such as louvres and shutters, are usually shop-manufactured.

The properties desired in materials used for trim are good painting and weathering characteristics, easy working qualities and maximum freedom from warpage. Sealing the end joints or mitres of members exposed to moisture is recommended.

Nails or screws used for fastening trim should be corrosion-resistant, aluminum, galvanized or stainless steel. When finishing nails are used, they must be countersunk and then puttied after the prime coat is applied. This method of fastening will generally prevent rust stains at nailheads. Fasteners must be compatible with the metal trim to avoid galvanic reaction between dissimilar metals, such as aluminum and steel.

EAVE PROJECTION

The eave overhang gives some protection to the wall and connects the roof and wall. Soffits are usually closed in with pre-finished metal or vinyl panels or 1/4 in. (6 mm) sanded plywood nailed at 6 in. (150 mm) on centre along the edges and 12 in. (300 mm) at intermediate supports. The exterior finish is then butted up to the underside of the soffit. A fascia board added as a finished covering for the rafter header usually extends about 1/2 in. (12 mm) below the soffit covering to form a drip edge. The three general types of eave construction are shown in Figure 99.

A narrow eave projection (Figure 99A) is sometimes used on roofs with a steep slope. Here, the rafters are projected a short distance over the wall plate and the ends are cut to suit the angle required for the rafter header and soffit covering. The soffit covering is nailed to the angled surface of the rafter. Where the soffit covering is less than 5 1/2 in. (140 mm) wide, a 1 in. (19 mm) board is generally used for this purpose, because the board does not require support along its edges.

When wider eave projections are used with a horizontal soffit, blocking is installed to support the soffit covering (Figure 99B). A 1 in. thick (19 mm) nailing strip is placed on top of the sheathing along the wall and nailed to the framing. This strip supports the inner ends of the blocking and edges of the soffit covering. The blocking, which may consist of 2 x 2 in. (38 x 38 mm) material, is usually spaced at 24 in. (600 mm) on centre. It is toenailed to the nailing strip and end-nailed to the rafter header. The soffit covering and fascia board are then nailed in place.

Roof projection at eaves

(A) narrow eave projection

(B) wide eave projection with horizontal soffit

(C) wide eave projection with sloped soffit

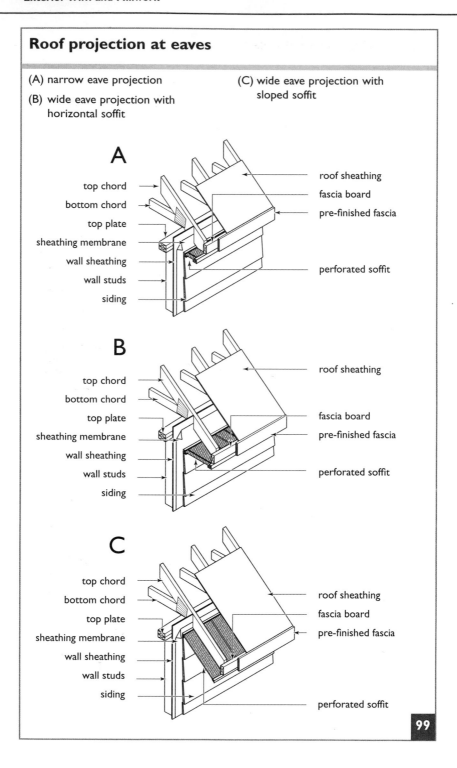

99

Eave and gable-end intersections

(A) Eave soffit is terminated at the wall line and gable-end soffit is continued to the fascia board at the eave.

(B) Eave soffit is sloped on same plane as gable-end soffit.

(C) Eave soffit carried out to the rake rafter and gable-end soffit is returned down to meet the eave soffit.

(D) Soffit and fascia detail using vinyl or aluminum.

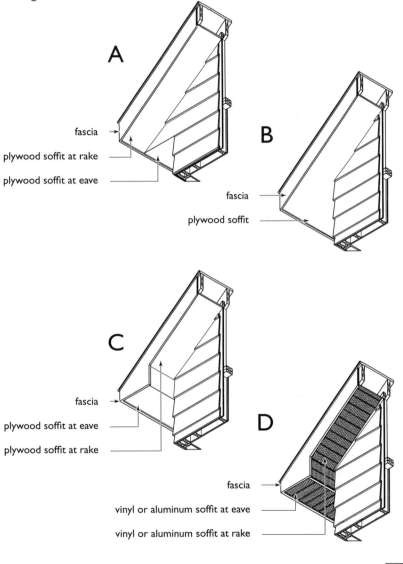

A

fascia

plywood soffit at rake

plywood soffit at eave

B

fascia

plywood soffit

C

fascia

plywood soffit at eave

plywood soffit at rake

D

fascia

vinyl or aluminum soffit at eave

vinyl or aluminum soffit at rake

100

Where the blocking provides partial support for the roof overhang (Figure 60), 2 x 4 in. (38 x 89 mm) material is used. The members are securely nailed to the side of each rafter and butted against a 2 x 4 in. (38 x 89 mm) nailing strip placed along the wall over the sheathing. This type of support is usually confined to overhangs of not more than 4 ft. (1.2 m).

Sloped soffits that follow the line of the projected rafter (Figure 99C) are sometimes used instead of horizontal soffits. In this case, the soffit covering is nailed to the underside of the rafter. The outer edge of the soffit covering is nailed to the rafter header and the inner edge to 2 x 2 in. (38 x 38 mm) blocking placed between the rafters.

EAVE AND GABLE-END INTERSECTIONS

Eave and gable-end intersections can be trimmed in various ways depending on how the eave projection is finished. Figure 100 A through D shows three types of commonly used intersections.

Where a sloped soffit is used at the eave projection, the soffit of the gable-end projection is carried through on the same plane as the eave soffit (Figure 100B).

Where a horizontal soffit is used at the eave projection, the eave soffit may be carried through to the rake rafter (Figure 100C). In this case, the soffit of the gable-end projection is terminated at the side wall and returned down to intersect the eave soffit. The fascia board at the gable end is increased in width at the eave to close in the end of the eave soffit.

Another type of intersection sometimes used with a horizontal eave soffit has the eave soffit terminating at the side wall (Figure 100A). The gable-end sheathing and siding is continued out to the edge of the eaves and serves as a covering for the end of the soffit. The gable-end soffit is carried down beyond the side wall and terminates at the eave.

WINDOW FRAMES AND SASHES

Windows are used in a house principally to provide light and air, but they are also an important part of architectural design. Windows are available in many types, each having its own advantages. The principal opening types are vertical sliding, horizontal sliding, casement and awning. Window frames and sashes may be made of wood, metal, fibreglass or plastic or a combination of these materials.

All windows should shed water and snow and be easy to reglaze if damaged. Construction of sash and frame must normally meet recognized window standards. Normally, windows need to meet standards for air infiltration, watertightness and wind load resistance. In living areas of the house, the glass area should be about 10 per cent of the floor area. In bedroom areas, this can be reduced to about 5 per cent, but each bedroom should have at least one window that is openable from the inside without the use of tools or special knowledge, and adequately sized for emergency exit. In kitchens, bathrooms and unfinished basements, no windows are required if electric lighting and mechanical ventilation are provided.

Excessive areas of glazing should be avoided, as much more heat is lost through windows than through an equivalent area of insulated wall. Generally, a total glass area of about 12 per cent of the floor area of the house is adequate. On the other hand, energy-efficient windows with unshaded southern exposure can contribute positively to the heating of the house, especially when combined with heavy drapes or insulated shutters that can be closed on cloudy days and at night. For thermal insulation, new high-performance windows are available in most locations in Canada.

Insulating glass units made of spaced sheets of glass are placed in window sashes or frames. These windows with multiple glazings, selective coating and charged with argon or krypton can significantly reduce energy costs.

Double-glazing consisting of two sheets of glass sealed to a perimeter spacer is normally used in Canadian houses. Window units consisting of an inner and outer sash also give similar insulating values. Both types of double-glazing insulate better than single glazing and are less subject to condensation problems.

Where the total house air leakage has been reduced by good, airtight construction, interior humidity levels may be higher. Double-glazing or storm windows in winter are a minimum requirement if excessive condensation on the window panes is to be avoided.

Good windows will be less effective if their installation does not produce a near-perfect air seal around the perimeter. Since it is not practical to obtain an airtight fit where the sash contacts the frame, weatherstripping is often used at these points to reduce air infiltration. Most manufacturers make complete window units with the sash fitted and glazed, with weatherstripping, operating balances and hardware installed. Units combining screens and storm sash are also available.

Wood window sashes and frames should be treated to resist decay or be made of a wood species that is decay-resistant, ensuring a longer life.

The exterior, brick, stop trim may be attached to the window frame when the window is fabricated, or the window may be ordered without a brick stop. To provide space for adjustment, the framework around the opening is usually slightly larger than the window. Wedges and shims are used to adjust the frame in the opening, and when in position, the window frame is nailed through the wedges to the wall framing. The exterior trim is also nailed to the studs and lintel. The space around the window frame is later filled with insulation (Figure 94).

EXTERIOR DOORFRAMES AND DOORS

Exterior doorframes generally consist of 1 3/8 in. (35 mm) thick side and head jambs and a 1 3/4 in. (44 mm) sill. While a hardwood sill is more durable, a sill made of softwood with metal threshold may also be used. Frames are rabbetted to form stops for the main door. Stops for a screen or combination door are provided by the edge of the jamb and the exterior trim.

The doorsill should bear solidly on the floor framing (Figure 101), and the frame should be well nailed to the opening framework. This is usually done by adjusting the frame with wedges and then nailing through the trim and wedges into the studs. Exterior doors should be weatherstripped at the top, bottom and sides. For improved resistance to forced entry, the jamb of the door frame at the lock height should be shimmed on both sides immediately above and below the lock location. In addition, blocking should join the studs of the door opening with the adjacent studs.

Main doors should not be less than 1 3/4 in. (44 mm) thick. They should be at least 32 in. (810 mm) wide and 6 ft. 6 in. (1.98 m) high. Wood storm doors should be 1 3/8 in. (35 mm) thick and metal doors at least 1 in. (25 mm) thick. Additional screws in the drywall around the doorframe will also provide greater strength to resist forced entry.

Exterior doors are generally either the flush or panel type. For methods of hanging doors and installing hardware, see the chapter on "Interior Doors, Frames and Trim."

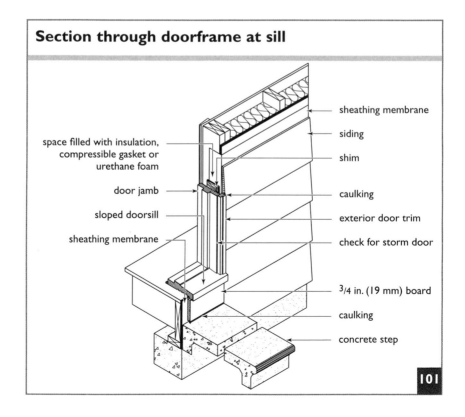

Section through doorframe at sill

- sheathing membrane
- siding
- space filled with insulation, compressible gasket or urethane foam
- shim
- door jamb
- caulking
- sloped doorsill
- exterior door trim
- sheathing membrane
- check for storm door
- 3/4 in. (19 mm) board
- caulking
- concrete step

101

Flush doors are made with structural wood panels or other suitable facings applied over a light framework and core. A core built of solid pieces of wood is called a solid core; a core built as a grillage is called a hollow core. Solid-core construction is generally preferred for exterior doors, particularly in cold climates, because this method of construction minimizes warping from differences in humidity or temperature on opposite sides of the door. Glazed panels may be inserted into solid-core doors.

Panel doors consist of stiles (solid vertical members), rails (solid cross members), and panels (thinner parts filling the spaces between stiles sand rails). Many types containing various wood or glass panels are available. Metal or wood-faced doors whose cores are filled with rigid insulation are becoming more common. They should be used whenever a separate storm door is not provided.

Sliding doors, either fully or partially glazed, are sometimes used for access to patios or garden areas. All glazed areas in doors should be double-glazed safety glass. Transparent glass in doors and sidelights, which could be mistaken for unobstructed passageways, should be safety glass, such as tempered or wired glass.

Doors that lead from the house to the garage must provide a gas-tight barrier to prevent automobile exhaust fumes from entering the house. These doors should be tight-fitting, weatherstripped, and provided with a self-closing device.

HEALTHY HOUSING INSIGHT

Maintenance and Durability Considerations

The maintenance and durability of exterior trim and millwork are important considerations when planning and constructing the dwelling. The following factors should be carefully examined prior to construction.

➜ The maintenance costs of exterior trim and millwork can often exceed the cost of the originally installed materials over the useful life of the building. In general, any type of painted finish, and especially those applied on site, will demand frequent refinishing.

➜ When maintenance is labour-intensive and required frequently, it is often not performed properly. This situation is commonly encountered in the entry level and fixed-income, elderly housing markets. The durability of these building elements may suffer severely as a consequence.

As a general rule, maintenance-free and durable finishes on exterior trim and millwork are recommended. Many appropriate materials meeting these criteria are available. The slightly higher premiums associated with these alternatives have been proven to be cost-effective investments.

Stairs

STAIRS

Stairways should be designed, arranged and installed to afford safety, adequate headroom and space for the passage of furniture. In general, there are two types of stairs in a house: those between finished areas, usually referred to as main stairs, and those which lead to areas used only for storage, laundry and heating equipment, such as unfinished basements or attics. The main stairs, built to provide ease and comfort, are often a feature of design, while stairs to unfinished basements and attics are usually somewhat steeper and narrower and are built of less-expensive materials. If the basement or attic is to be used as a living space, however, the stair dimensions should be similar to those of the main stairs. Stairs may be built in place or built as units in a shop and set in place.

Ramps built for wheelchair (barrier-free) access require consideration of width, steepness, guards and approaches to doors. This is a very specific design issue, and readers should refer to Parts 3 and 9 of the NBCC and to other related publications.

Stair Design Terminology

The following are terms often used in stair design (Figure 102 to 106):

Baluster: Vertical member in a guard placed between the handrail and the tread in the open portion of a stairway, landing or balcony (Figure 105D).

Effective Depth: The portion remaining after the stringer has been cut out or ploughed (rabetted) to fit the treads and risers (Figure 104).

Guard: Protective barrier, with or without openings, placed alongside the open portion of a stairway, landing or balcony.

Handrail: A rail running parallel to and on at least one side of the stairs, to be grasped when ascending or descending.

Headroom: The vertical distance from the outer edge of the leading edge (nosing) line to the underside of the ceiling above (Figure 104).

Landing: A flat platform incorporated in a stairway, at least as wide and as long as the width of the stairs. Normally used to change direction of the stairs at right angles and to avoid the use of winders.

Leading edge (nosing): The projection of the tread beyond the face of the riser (Figure 104).

Newel: The main post for the handrail at the start and finish of the stairs, and the stiffening post at changes of direction and landings.

Rise: The vertical height of a step (Figure 102).

Riser: Closed riser: The vertical board under a tread.

Open riser: The vertical board under the tread is omitted and the tread is supported on the stringers only.

Run: The horizontal distance measured from riser to riser (Figure 102).

Stringer: The member supporting the treads and risers.

Cut-out (Open): A stringer cut out to fit the treads and risers ((Figure 106B and C).

Ploughed (housed): A stringer grooved to receive the exact profile of the treads and risers (Figure 105C).

Total Rise: The distance measured vertically from finish floor to finish floor.

Stair detail

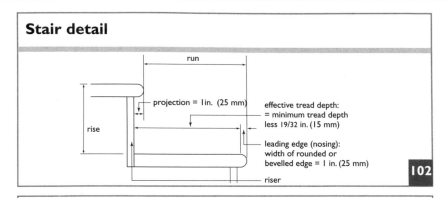

run

rise

projection = 1 in. (25 mm)

effective tread depth:
= minimum tread depth
less 19/32 in. (15 mm)

leading edge (nosing):
width of rounded or
bevelled edge = 1 in. (25 mm)

riser

102

Types of stair designs

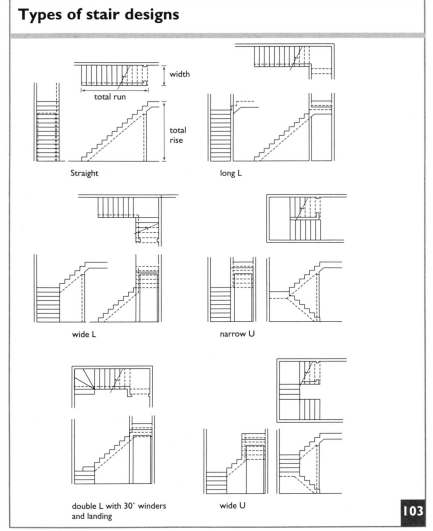

width

total run

total rise

Straight

long L

wide L

narrow U

double L with 30° winders
and landing

wide U

103

Stairway design

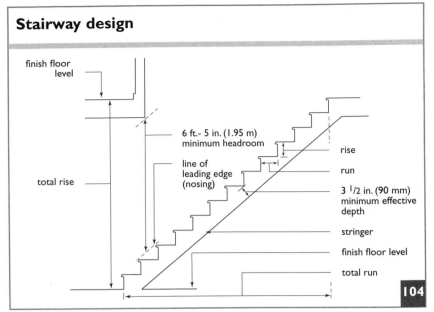

finish floor level

6 ft.- 5 in. (1.95 m) minimum headroom

total rise

line of leading edge (nosing)

rise

run

3 1/2 in. (90 mm) minimum effective depth

stringer

finish floor level

total run

104

Total Run: The distance measured horizontally from finish floor on one level to finish floor on another.

Tread: The horizontal plane of a step.

Winder: A radiating or wedge-shaped tread converging on a centre point at an angle of 30˚ or 45˚.

Ratio of Rise-to-run

The relation between the rise and the run should conform to well-established rules. Experience has shown that a rise of 7 to 7 ½ in. (180 to 190 mm) with a run of about 9 3/4 to 10 ¼ in. (250 to 265 mm) combines both comfort and safety. These dimensions are commonly used for main stairs.

Although the dimensions presented above may be considered desirable, space does not always permit their use. If such is the case, the following limitations should be observed: all stairs should have a maximum rise of 7 7/8 in. (200 mm), a minimum run

of 8 1/4 in. (210 mm), and a minimum tread width of 9 1/4 in. (235 mm) (Figure 102). As well, stairs should have a rise no less than 5 in. (125 mm), a run or tread width no more than 14 in. (355 mm). These dimensions apply to stairs serving only one dwelling unit.

Stairway Design

Stairways may have a straight, continuous run without an intermediate landing, they may consist of two or more runs with changes in direction, or they may be curved, in which case special design criteria are applicable. In the best and safest practice, a landing is introduced at any change in direction. However, the turn may also be made with radiating treads called winders. The length or width of any landing must not be less than the width of the stairs. Stairs must be at least 34 in. (860 mm) wide measured between wall faces. The vertical height of any flight of stairs cannot exceed 12 ft. (3.7 m). Each step should have the same height.

Parts of stairs

(A) risers and treads tongued and grooved together

(B) risers and treads connected with angle blocks

(C) housed stringers

(D) cut-out stringer (open) showing balusters and mitre-nosing return

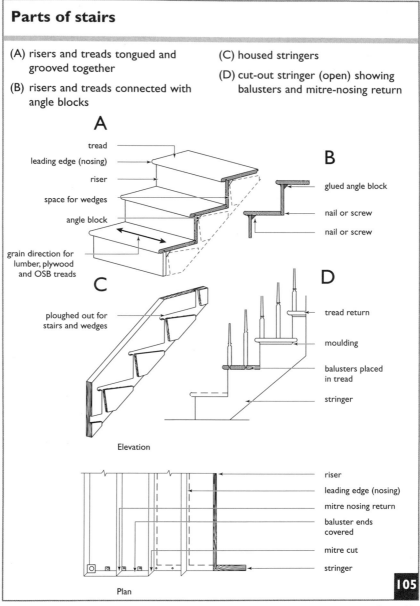

A

- tread
- leading edge (nosing)
- riser
- space for wedges
- angle block
- grain direction for lumber, plywood and OSB treads

B
- glued angle block
- nail or screw
- nail or screw

C
- ploughed out for stairs and wedges

D
- tread return
- moulding
- balusters placed in tread
- stringer

Elevation

- riser
- leading edge (nosing)
- mitre nosing return
- baluster ends covered
- mitre cut
- stringer

Plan

105

The diagrams in Figure 103 show some different types of stairway designs. If winders are necessary because of cramped space, they must form an angle of either 30˚, (three treads for a maximum allowable 90˚ turn), or 45˚ (two treads for a maximum allowable 90˚ turn). Experience has shown that 30˚ winders are easier to negotiate. Only one set of such winders is permitted between floor levels.

Basement stairs

(A) ploughed stringers

(B) cut-out stringers

(C) cut-out stringers with finish member nailed to the outside of the stringer

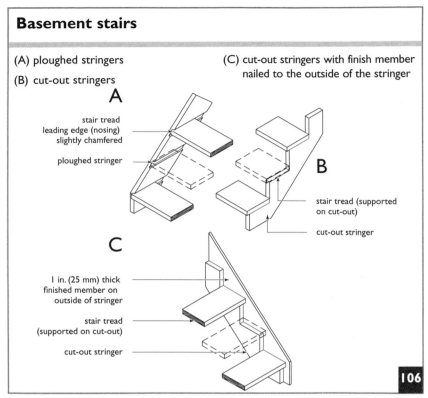

A

stair tread leading edge (nosing) slightly chamfered

ploughed stringer

B

stair tread (supported on cut-out)

cut-out stringer

C

1 in. (25 mm) thick finished member on outside of stringer

stair tread (supported on cut-out)

cut-out stringer

106

Once the location and width of the stairway and any landings, if required, have been determined, the next step is to fix the rise and the run. To fix the rise, the exact distance between the finish floors of the two storeys under consideration is divided by 7 1/4 in. (184 mm), a comfortable riser height. This calculation gives the number of risers needed over the total rise. Round up the number that results from this calculation to the next whole number. The run is determined by dividing the required number of treads into the total run of the stairs.

For example, if the total rise is 8 ft. 11 in. or 107 in. (2718 mm) and if each riser is 7 1/4 in. (184 mm), then 14.8 risers are needed (i.e., 107/7.25 = 14.8). Rounding up, 15 risers will be required each at 7.13 in. (181 mm) (i.e., 107/15 = 7.13). Alternatively 14 risers at 7.64 in. (192 mm) would be appropriate when space is limited.

It is important to remember that the minimum headroom for a stairway and landings must be 6 ft. 5 in. (1.95 m) (Figure 104). A sloped or bevelled edge on leading edges (nosings) makes the tread more visible. The size and shape of the slope or bevel must be limited to safeguard against tripping or slipping (Figure 102).

Stringers

The treads and risers are supported on stringers that must always be solidly supported, firmly fixed, and properly positioned. The stringers may be either cut out (Figures 105D and 106B and C) or ploughed (Figure 105C) to fit the outline of the treads and risers.

Stringers should not be less than 1 in. (25 mm) thick when they are supported along their length or 1 ½ in. (38 mm) when supported only at the top and bottom. The overall depth should be at least 9¼ in. (235 mm), and when the stringer is cut out to fit the treads and risers, the portion remaining should not be less than 3½ in. (90 mm) deep. A third stringer should be used when the width of the stairs is more than 35 in. (900 mm). This may be increased to 48 in. (1200 mm) where risers support the front of the treads. Treads should be at least 1 ½ in. (38 mm) thick when used with open risers. This thickness can be reduced to 1 in. (25 mm) where the stringers are not more than 29 in. (750 mm) apart or where the tread is supported by a closed riser attached to the treads.

The wall stringer may be ploughed out to the exact profile of the tread and riser with sufficient space at the back to take wedges (Figure 105C). The top of the riser may be connected to the bottom of the tread by angle-blocks glued to both surfaces, with screws added to reinforce the joint. The bottom of the riser is attached to the back of the tread with screws (Figure 105B). Another method is to tongue the top of the riser into the front of the tread and the back of the tread into the bottom of the next riser (Figure 105A). The wall stringer is nailed to the wall, the nails being located behind the treads and risers. The treads and risers are fitted together and forced into the space ploughed into the wall stringer, where they are set tight by driving and gluing wood wedges behind them.

The wall stringer thus shows above the profiles of the treads and risers as a finish against the wall and is often made continuous with the baseboard of the upper and lower floors.

If the outside stringer is an open stringer, it may be cut out to fit the risers and treads. The edges of the risers are mitred with the corresponding edges of the stringer, and the leading edge of the tread may be returned on its outside edge along the face of the stringer (Figure 105D).

Newels, Handrails and Guards

Handrails run parallel to stairs and are designed to be grasped when ascending or descending. Guards surround openings to protect against falling over the edge. All stairways of three or more risers must have a handrail from floor to floor, and on both sides if the stair is 43 in. (1100 mm) or wider. For stairways with enclosing walls, the rail brackets are attached to the wall with at least two screws penetrating at least 1-1/4 in. (32 mm) into solid framing members. The supports are spaced no more than 4 ft. (1.2 m) apart, with the first and last supports no more than 1 ft. (300 mm) from the ends of the handrail. For stairs that are open on one or both sides, handrails are usually supported by balusters and end against newel posts. Handrails should be between 32 and 38 in. (800 and 965 mm) above the tread at the leading edge line, with at least 2 in. (50 mm) clearance from the wall, and be built so that there is no obstruction that could break a handhold. The start and end point of handrails must not obstruct pedestrian traffic or create a hazard.

Guards are required around openings at landings, decks and balconies that are more than 24 in. (600 mm) above the adjacent level, and alongside the open portions of stairways. Guards for stairs must be not less than 35⁷⁄₁₆ in. (900 mm) measured vertically from the leading edge. Guards around stair landings, within a dwelling they must be at least 36 in. (965 mm) high. Where one or both sides of a stairway are open, the guard may also be the handrail. Guards for exterior balconies or landings, porches or decks that are more than 2 ft. (600 mm) but less than 5 ft. 11 in. (1,800 mm) above the ground must be at least 36 in. (900 mm) high. For decks and landings higher than 5 ft. 11 in. (1,800 mm), guards must be at least 42 in. (1,070 mm) high. Spacing between balusters for all guards should not permit a 4 in. (100 mm) sphere from passing through. Guards must be strong enough to provide protection from falls for normal usage. The specific loads that guards need to resist to meet this requirement should be verified at the permit approval stage.

Basement Stairs

Ploughed stringers (Figure 106A) are commonly used supports for treads on basement stairs, but the tread may be supported on cut-out stringers (Figure 106B). Another method sometimes used is cut-out stringers nailed to a finish member (Figure 106C).

Exterior Steps and Stoops

Proportioning of risers and treads in laying out porch steps or approaches to terraces or decks should be as carefully considered as it is in the design of interior stairways. The riser-to-tread ratio should not exceed those for main stairs referred to previously.

Outside steps and stoops need good support. If they are supported independently of the house foundation, their foundation should extend below the frost penetration line and be carried down to undisturbed ground. Outside steps and stoops leading to entrances often consist of precast units that are designed to be highly resistant to moisture, frost and impact damage. Concrete for cast-in-place steps and stoops should be 5 to 8 per cent air-entrained and have a compressive strength of 4,600 psi (32 MPa).

RELATED PUBLICATIONS

Housing for Persons with Disabilities
Canada Mortgage and Housing Corporation

Housing Choices for Canadians with Disabilities
Canada Mortgage and Housing Corporation

Framing Details for Plumbing, Heating, Ventilating and Wiring

FRAMING DETAILS FOR PLUMBING, HEATING, VENTILATING AND WIRING

One advantage of wood-frame construction is that the space between the framing members in wood-frame walls, floors and roofs provides a safe and economical location to conceal the greater part of the heating, plumbing and electrical distribution system.

Most of the electrical wiring and many plumbing pipes and heating and ventilating ducts run parallel to the joists and studs and can easily be concealed in the space between the members. Where it is necessary to run pipes or wires at right angles to the joists and studs, the wood members may be notched or drilled. Within certain limitations, these notches or holes do not seriously reduce the structural strength of a framing member.

CUTTING THE FRAMING MEMBERS

Notching of Lumber Roof, Ceiling or Floor Joists. Notches made in the top at the end of lumber joists should be within one-half the joist depth from the edge of the bearing. The depth of the notch should be no more than one-third of the joist depth (Figure 107B).

If notches are necessary elsewhere in

Example of notch limitations

(A) Notch is located away from support.

(B) When applied to an 8 in. (184 mm) joist the depth of the notch at the support would be 2 3/8 in. (61 mm)

maximum and the length of the notch would not extend more than 3 5/8 in. (92 mm) from the joist support.

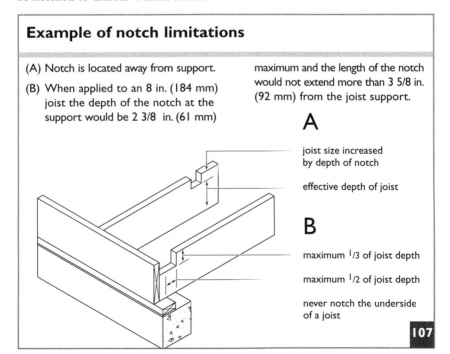

A

joist size increased by depth of notch

effective depth of joist

B

maximum 1/3 of joist depth

maximum 1/2 of joist depth

never notch the underside of a joist

107

CHECKING BACK

Framing Layouts for Plumbing, Heating and Electrical

When planning for plumbing, heating and electrical services in the dwelling, it is important to consider how the installation of these items may be affected by the layout of framing members. Check back to the Accommodating Ductwork and Piping note in the "Floor Framing" chapter for some helpful guidelines.

There may also be some special items such as large, one-piece tub and shower enclosures or hot tubs that may have to be located prior to the construction of walls. Check back to the Installing Special Items Prior to Wall Framing note in the "Wall Framing" chapter.

the span (Figure 107A), this should be considered when deciding the size of joist to use, so that the size of joist can be increased by the depth of the notch. The bottom edge of lumber joists should not be notched, since this may cause a joist to split when it deflects under load.

Notching of engineered wood products must conform to the product manufacturers' guidelines. The flanges of wood

I-joists and truss chord and web members must not be notched or cut.

Drilled Holes in Joists. Normally, holes drilled in joists should not be larger than one-quarter the joist depth or closer than 2 in. (50 mm) to either edge (Figure 108). Holes cut in the webs of wood I-joists must be in accordance with manufacturer's guidelines.

Maximum size of holes drilled in joists

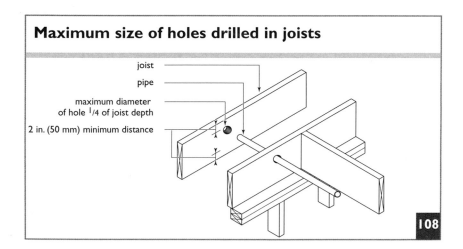

joist

pipe

maximum diameter of hole 1/4 of joist depth

2 in. (50 mm) minimum distance

108

Notched studs for plumbing

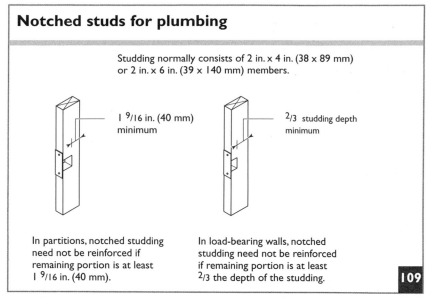

Studding normally consists of 2 in. x 4 in. (38 x 89 mm) or 2 in. x 6 in. (39 x 140 mm) members.

1 $^9/16$ in. (40 mm) minimum

$^2/3$ studding depth minimum

In partitions, notched studding need not be reinforced if remaining portion is at least 1 $^9/16$ in. (40 mm).

In load-bearing walls, notched studding need not be reinforced if remaining portion is at least $^2/3$ the depth of the studding.

109

Notching and Drilling of Studs. Load-bearing wall studs that have been notched or drilled to more than one-third of their depth must be reinforced, usually with 2 in. nominal (38 mm) lumber nailed to the side of the studs and extending about 24 in. (600 mm) each side of the notch or hole. Similar reinforcing is used when notched partition studs have less than 1 9/16 in. (40 mm) of solid wood remaining. (Figure 109)

Notching and Drilling of Top Plates. In load-bearing walls, top plates are also reinforced with 2 in. nominal (38 mm) lumber when the solid wood remaining in the plates is less than 2 in. (50 mm) in width. If the required reinforcing must be placed on the face of the plate or stud, sheet metal is normally used to support the wall finish and to protect the plumbing and electrical wiring from drywall fasteners.

FRAMING DETAILS FOR PLUMBING SYSTEMS

The installation of the plumbing system usually begins after the framing. This initial work is called "roughing-in." It includes putting in the plumbing vents and drains and all the hot and cold water piping that will be enclosed in the walls and ceilings and under the basement floor. Piping in outside walls should be insulated. Since the bathtub must be put in before the wall finish can be applied, bathtub installation is usually included in roughing-in. Plumbing fixtures and accessories are not connected until the installation of the interior finish has been completed. The design and installation of the entire plumbing system is usually regulated by provincial or municipal codes. (See Figures 110, 111 and 112 for details of a typical plumbing system installation.)

Kitchen and bathroom in proximity for minimum pipe length

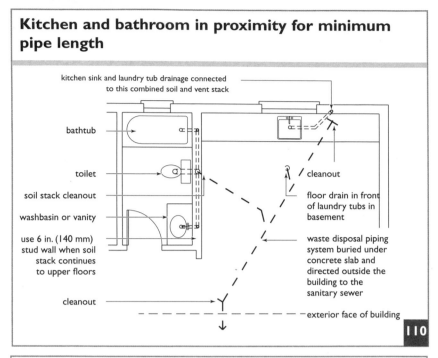

kitchen sink and laundry tub drainage connected to this combined soil and vent stack

bathtub

toilet

soil stack cleanout

washbasin or vanity

use 6 in. (140 mm) stud wall when soil stack continues to upper floors

cleanout

cleanout

floor drain in front of laundry tubs in basement

waste disposal piping system buried under concrete slab and directed outside the building to the sanitary sewer

exterior face of building

110

Washbasin and bathtub fixtures

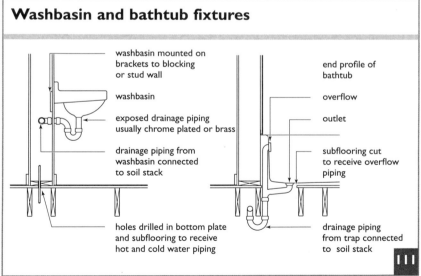

washbasin mounted on brackets to blocking or stud wall

washbasin

exposed drainage piping usually chrome plated or brass

drainage piping from washbasin connected to soil stack

holes drilled in bottom plate and subflooring to receive hot and cold water piping

end profile of bathtub

overflow

outlet

subflooring cut to receive overflow piping

drainage piping from trap connected to soil stack

111

When 3 in. (75 mm) copper or plastic piping is used, the stack wall may be made of 2 x 4 in. (38 x 89 mm) material. Sealing the area around the pipe is necessary to prevent air leakage into the attic space (Figure 113).

Where soil stacks or large pipes must run horizontally at right angles to the

Toilet fixture

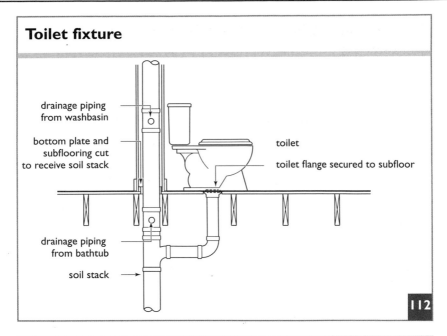

drainage piping from washbasin

bottom plate and subflooring cut to receive soil stack

toilet

toilet flange secured to subfloor

drainage piping from bathtub

soil stack

112

Venting for plumbing

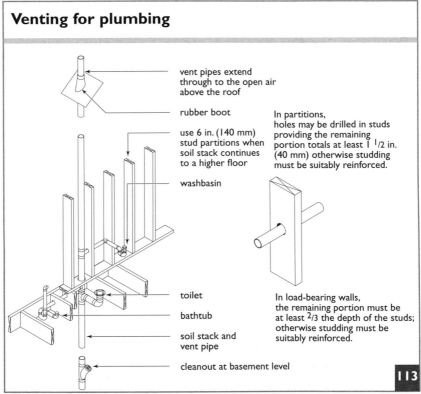

vent pipes extend through to the open air above the roof

rubber boot

use 6 in. (140 mm) stud partitions when soil stack continues to a higher floor

In partitions, holes may be drilled in studs providing the remaining portion totals at least 1 1/2 in. (40 mm) otherwise studding must be suitably reinforced.

washbasin

toilet

bathtub

soil stack and vent pipe

cleanout at basement level

In load-bearing walls, the remaining portion must be at least 2/3 the depth of the studs; otherwise studding must be suitably reinforced.

113

Framing for soil-stack pipes

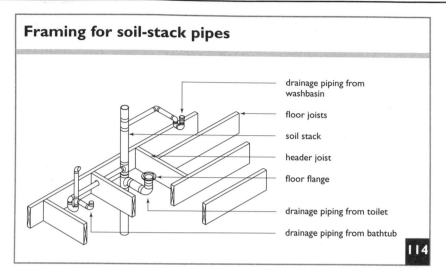

drainage piping from washbasin

floor joists

soil stack

header joist

floor flange

drainage piping from toilet

drainage piping from bathtub

114

HEALTHY HOUSING INSIGHT

Water-Efficient Fixtures and Appliances

Water conservation is one of the most important aspects of resource efficiency for Healthy Housing. The use of water-conserving fixtures and appliances not only saves this vital resource, but

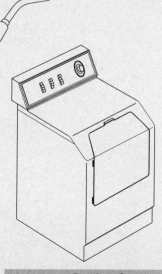

Continued on page 233

Continued from page 232

reduces the energy needed for providing potable water and treating waste water.

In recent years, manufacturers of water fixtures and water-consuming appliances have introduced water-conserving technologies in response to current requirements. This is especially true for clothes washers and dishwashers.

The critical fixtures and appliances to consider are typically toilets, showerheads and clothes washers. These account for most of the water used in a typical household. Low consumption (6 L) toilets (sometimes referred to as Ultra Low-Flush, ULF, Ultra and Lite by manufacturers) use the least amount of water for flushing. Water-saving showerheads can use about half the water of conventional types. Clothes and dishwashers that use between one-half to one-third as much water as conventional types are also available.

In the summer months, water consumption can double due to lawn watering. If lawns are still preferred over alternative landscaping options, then hardy strains of grass and in-ground irrigation systems should be considered.

joists, it will be necessary to frame out the joists. To do this, headers are installed between the joists (Figure 114). Alternatively, services are suspended and enclosed in a bulkhead or dropped ceiling.

FRAMING DETAILS FOR HEATING SYSTEMS

There are many ways to heat a house. Heating systems range from the multi-controlled electric or hot-water heating systems to the relatively simple single-space heater. In Canada, natural gas, oil and electricity are the most commonly used energy sources.

The three prevalent heating systems are: forced warm air, electric baseboards and forced-flow hot-water heating. Other less frequently used systems are: air, ground or water-source heat pumps with electric resistance back-up, heat pumps with natural gas back-up, and solid fuel-burning (wood or coal) furnaces. Figure 115 illustrates a typical heating layout, and Figure 116 shows an isometric view of a typical heating system.

All types of heating systems may be safely and easily installed in wood-frame houses. Certain clearances, however, must be maintained between parts of the system and combustible material. Installers of heating equipment should be aware of local regulations before starting work. Furnaces require a supply of combustion air from outside. The location of the air intake must be situated where snow and drifting snow will not affect air access and must not be within 6 ft. (1.8 m) of an exhaust vent. Earthquake vibrations can rupture fuel supply lines to heating and cooling appliances. In areas subject to earthquake vibration, appliances must be secured (strapped or braced) to the structure to resist overturning and displacement. Even in areas not subject to earthquakes, local regulations may require the securing of appliances.

For a warm-air heating system, the sheet metal ducts for supply and return air are usually located between studs in walls and between joists in floors. When planning the house, locating joists, beams and studs to suit the requirements of the duct system must be considered.

Provision must be made for controlled ventilation when planning the heat distribution system of the house. Assuming good, airtight construction, the ventilation system must be designed to exhaust house air (primarily from bathrooms and kitchen but also from other rooms) and draw in outside air so that the air quality of the house is maintained.

Warm-air and Ventilation Systems

Wall studs and joists can be located so that they do not have to be cut to install heating ducts. When ducts must pass up through a wall to heat the room above, a portion of the top and bottom plates must be removed and the ducts are then fitted between the studs.

Basement plan showing typical heating layout

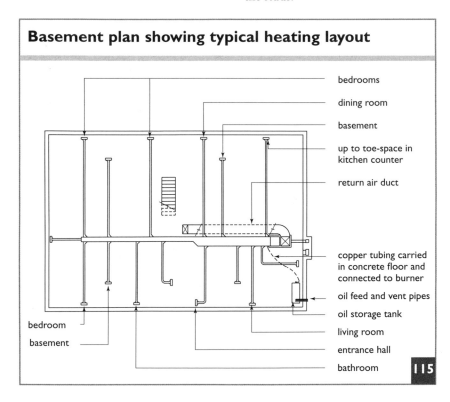

- bedrooms
- dining room
- basement
- up to toe-space in kitchen counter
- return air duct
- copper tubing carried in concrete floor and connected to burner
- oil feed and vent pipes
- oil storage tank
- living room
- entrance hall
- bathroom

bedroom
basement

115

When a partition is supported on doubled floor joists and a heating duct is to go in the partition, the joists are ordinarily spaced apart, with blocking, to allow room for the duct. This eliminates the need to cut framing members unnecessarily or to use intricate duct angles.

Return air grilles, usually located on inside walls near the floor level, can be connected to a duct or an enclosed stud space. At this point, the bottom plate and subfloor are cut to make a passage for the duct or air space. Blocks are nailed between the joists to support the ends of boards if diagonal subflooring has been used. Sometimes, the studs have to be cut to accommodate large return air grilles. Where this occurs, a lintel is used to support the studs that have been cut, and the opening is framed in the same way as the door opening shown in Figure 45, p. 113. When enclosed, the space between the floor joists may be used as a return air duct and other return air ducts may be connected to the same joist space. Non-combustible material, such as sheet metal, should be used to line the joist space within 24 in. (600 mm) of the furnace, under floor registers, and at the bottom of vertical ducts.

Warm-air registers are usually placed in the floor close to the outside walls, preferably under the windows. These registers are fitted with vanes to direct the warm air over the wide area of the

Isometric view of typical heating unit

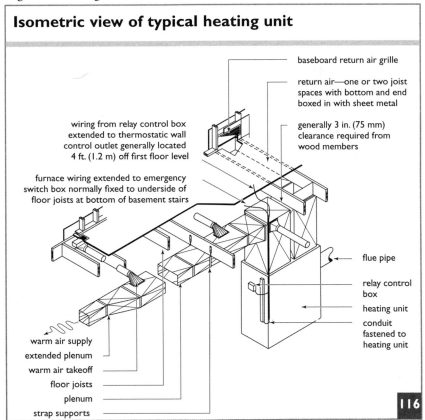

baseboard return air grille

return air—one or two joist spaces with bottom and end boxed in with sheet metal

generally 3 in. (75 mm) clearance required from wood members

wiring from relay control box extended to thermostatic wall control outlet generally located 4 ft. (1.2 m) off first floor level

furnace wiring extended to emergency switch box normally fixed to underside of floor joists at bottom of basement stairs

flue pipe

relay control box

heating unit

conduit fastened to heating unit

warm air supply
extended plenum
warm air takeoff
floor joists
plenum
strap supports

116

outside walls. Where possible, ducts leading to these registers are located between joists with a shaped "boot" connecting the duct and register. Then, only the subfloor and floor covering need to be cut. Diagonal subflooring must be supported by blocking at this point.

In houses with a crawl space, a warm-air furnace can either be put in a special compartment on the floor of the house, hung under the floor or mounted on a concrete base in the crawl space beneath the house. In the first two cases, the joists will have to be designed to carry the weight of the furnace.

Ventilation is often coupled to the warm air heating system of the house, using the heating ducts to also distribute ventilation air. In some cases, particularly for houses without forced air heating systems, dedicated, whole-house ventilation systems are used. The ducts are usually smaller than those required for heating purposes.

Hot-water Systems

Where the heating system requires only small pipes for a supply-and-return system, pre-planning the structural framing layout to accommodate the pipes is not usually necessary.

Baseboard-type convectors are usually located under windows along outside walls. In this manner, warm air rising through the convector blankets the outside walls. No cutting of the studs or joists is required with this type of installation as the baseboard type convector is positioned on the surface of the wall.

Carbon Monoxide Detectors

Carbon monoxide (CO) is a colourless, odourless gas that can accumulate in lethal concentrations in enclosed spaces without occupants being aware of it. Fuel-fired space or water heating equipment is a potential source of CO. Most well-tuned heat-producing appliances do not produce CO and even if they do, it is removed through the venting system. However, heating appliances can operate poorly and venting systems can fail. All residential buildings that have fuel-burning appliances need to have CO detectors located either in each bedroom, or located not more than 16 ft. (5 m) (measured along hallways) from each bedroom door. In addition, CO detectors are required where a bedroom shares a wall with a garage, or shares a wall with an attic space that abuts a garage.

Electric Baseboard Heating Systems

Because it is easy to conceal wiring in walls and floors, the accommodation of this type of electric heating system requires little or no planning in the structural framing. As with hot-water and warm-air systems, electric heating units are usually located along outside walls, so that the air warmed by the heating elements blankets the walls. Because the heating elements are mounted on the surface of the wall, there is no need to cut the wall studs. Radiant heating with the heating elements located in the ceiling is also used.

With hot-water systems and electric systems that use baseboard radiators, it is important, especially in a well-constructed, well-sealed house, to provide for room-air replacement and

HEALTHY HOUSING INSIGHT

Heating Energy and Equipment Choice

There exists a large and growing number of heating energy and equipment options. All of these options may not be available in a given area. Some choices are also more appropriate than others.

Energy Source

Most heating energy sources are non-renewable. Wood and solar energy are notable exceptions. Utilize these renewable sources to the greatest extent possible before tapping into a non-renewable energy source.

Equipment Type and Efficiency

Heating system options are numerous, but essentially these fall into two categories: central heating (furnaces and boilers), and unitary heating (individually controlled baseboard heaters, wall heaters, fireplaces and wood stoves). Central heating systems have the advantage that they may be combined with domestic water heating so that only a single piece of equipment needs to be purchased and maintained. Forced-air systems can easily incorporate air conditioning and ventilation, but cannot easily provide individual temperature control to each room or zone in the dwelling. Alternatively, when central hot water (hydronic) heating is employed, selected zones may be individually controlled, and the heating of floors in basements and bathrooms may be added. Unitary heating is useful in isolated or seasonal areas of the dwelling. Both hydronic and unitary heating systems require a separate ventilation system.

Affordability and Adaptability

Heating systems with low initial costs are not necessarily more affordable. Low-efficiency equipment and high-priced fuels can prove less affordable than heating system options with higher initial costs but lower operating costs. This is especially critical to entry level homebuyers and fixed-income households. The adaptability of heating systems also deserves consideration. Hot-water heating has proven to be one of the most durable and flexible options available. Forced-air systems are less flexible and will require special treatment such as fire dampers when dwellings are converted from single family to multi-unit.

Carefully research and plan heating energy and equipment choices.

Typical electrical equipment

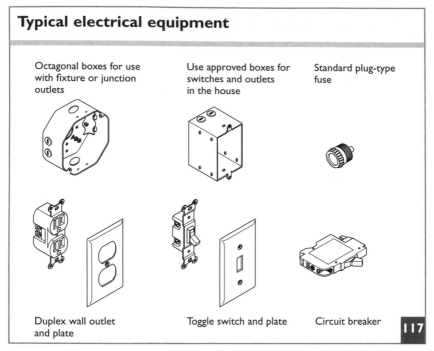

Octagonal boxes for use with fixture or junction outlets

Use approved boxes for switches and outlets in the house

Standard plug-type fuse

Duplex wall outlet and plate

Toggle switch and plate

Circuit breaker

117

not rely entirely on natural convection and infiltration. If measures for air circulation are not implemented, humidity levels may rise to the point where condensation will occur.

FRAMING DETAILS FOR WIRING

Wiring a house for electrical services is usually started after the house has been closed in, that is, after the exterior wall sheathing and roof have been completed.

This initial phase of wiring, also termed roughing-in, includes the installation of wiring and the boxes for the switches, lights and outlets. Figure 117 shows some typical electrical equipment.

Roughing-in is done before applying the inside finish and usually before placing the insulation in walls or ceilings. Lighting fixtures, switches, outlets and cover plates are installed after the interior finish and painting operations.

The design and installation of the entire wiring system is usually regulated by a provincial electrical code. All provincial codes are closely modelled on the *Canadian Electrical Code* published by the Canadian Standards Association. The provincial codes usually require installation to be done by a licensed electrician. Owners are advised to check with the local authority when planning a wiring installation.

Figures 118 and 119 show the typical arrangement of electrical service entrance equipment. The details of drilling structural members for wiring are shown in Figure 120.

Typical arrangement of service entrance

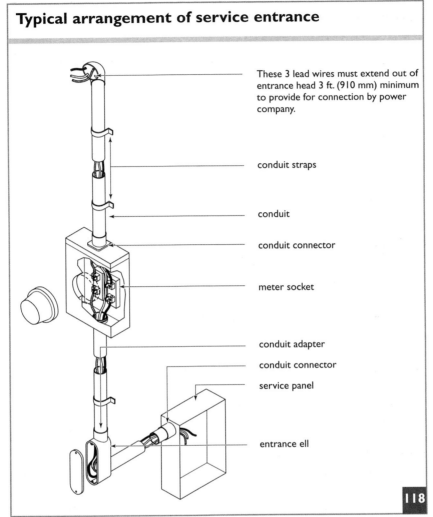

These 3 lead wires must extend out of entrance head 3 ft. (910 mm) minimum to provide for connection by power company.

conduit straps

conduit

conduit connector

meter socket

conduit adapter

conduit connector

service panel

entrance ell

118

Box Location

The location of switches and outlets is important. The wiring plans should be studied carefully to ensure that everything is included. Today's house uses electricity for a multitude of purposes from radios and televisions to major appliances that require their own circuits. The location of outlets for all these purposes should be carefully planned.

The amperage of the electrical service and the number of circuits and outlets installed should also take into account future needs after the house is finished. Alterations and additions to electrical systems are expensive. To accommodate the multitude of electrical appliances in a modern house, electrical services are usually 200 amps.

Service entrance equipment

pot head

overhead wires

service mast

meter base and meter on exterior

3-wire 120-240V

15 ft. (4.6 m) above grade
9 ft. (2.75 m) minimum on low building

stud wall with insulation and
air/vapour barrier

drywall

grounding wire

main breaker

distribution panel

1/2 in. (12.7 mm) back-up
panel fixed to wall

Note: Capacity 100 to 200 amps.
The service wires are brought
to the main breaker located in
the basement through a rigid
conduit. The main breaker and
distribution panel containing
fuses for the branch circuits
are mounted on a plywood
or OSB back-up panel.

floor joists

water supply pipe fixed to
back-up strip

combination service
entrance panel

water meter

ground wire clamped below
shut-off valve

finished basement floor

Note: Service equipment must be grounded.

Note: Ground wire from main entrance
panel must be clamped to the water
service entrance pipe below shut-off
valve as shown (metallic pipe only).

119

Drilling of structural members for wiring

blocking

caulking sealant or
rubber grommet

truss chord

air/vapour barrier

drywall ceiling finish

surface mounted receptacle

pendant fitting recommended
to reduce heat build-up

double studs at
door opening

switch box to door framing
with two 4 in. (100 mm) nails

wires stapled as shown

metal protection plate
fixed to edge of stud
member when required

1 1/4 in. (30 mm)

holes drilled to receive wires

Note: When holes are drilled
closer than 1 1/4 in. (30 mm)
to the edge of a stud,
metal protection plates
are required.

holes drilled in double
top plate

to ceiling fixture

4 ft.–6 in. (1,400 mm)

holes drilled in studs
to receive wires

outlet boxes fixed to studs
with two, 4 in. (100 mm) nails

holes drilled in bottom plate
and joists

to service panel

120

When planning the location of outlets and fans, remember that electrical boxes in insulated ceilings and exterior walls can be a major source of air leakage. At all times these should be carefully sealed.

SWITCHES

Switches are commonly located just inside the door of a room so that they may be easily reached upon opening the door. Switches may activate a wall outlet for a table or a floor lamp as well as the usual ceiling or wall lights. It is common practice to locate the switch boxes about 4½ ft. (1.4 m) above the floor, and 3½ ft. (1.1 m) above the floor when the occupant has a disability.

HEALTHY HOUSING INSIGHT

Energy-Efficient Lighting and Appliances

Appliances and lighting represent a significant proportion of energy consumption in the typical household. Appropriate choices of appliances and lighting is a cost-effective way of reducing the amount of energy consumed.

Appliances

➔ When purchasing appliances, always refer to the EnerGuide rating. Select appliances that are closest to the lowest rating available for the type of appliance being considered.

➔ For water-consuming appliances such as clothes and dishwashers, check the amount of water these require. Water conserving appliances also save energy.

Electric Lighting

➔ A large number of electric lighting options are available, but these vary considerably in their energy efficiency.

➔ Incandescent lighting is the least efficient and should be reserved for lighting that is only used occasionally. Tungsten-halogen lighting is an efficient alternative to incandescent lighting.

➔ Fluorescent lighting is preferred where lighting will be used extensively. Compact fluorescent and energy-saving fluorescent lamps are the most efficient alternatives.

Continued on page 243

Continued from page 242

→ Exterior lighting with photocell controls is recommended since the photocell prevents the lights from operating until dark. This avoids wasting energy when occupants forget to shut off outdoor lights.

Natural light

→ The size and arrangement of windows and skylights can promote good natural light and reduce the use of electric lighting.

→ Natural light and passive solar heating are entirely compatible, and represent cost-effective means of reducing energy consumption.

Having made appropriate choices for appliances and lighting, recognize that the cleaning and maintenance of appliances, light fixtures and windows are important factors in realizing the full potential of these investments in energy efficiency.

Multiple-control switches are convenient in many locations so that lights may be controlled from more than one switch. A living room light could have a switch near the outside entrance and another at inner doors leading to the kitchen or to a hallway. In two-storey houses, three-way switches should be provided at the bottom and at the top of the stairway to control stairway lighting. Three-way switches can control power from more than one location. Three-way switches at the head and foot of the stairs should also control basement stair lights, particularly if there is living accommodation in the basement, or if there is an outside exit from the basement.

RELATED PUBLICATIONS

Canadian Plumbing Code
National Research Council of Canada

Canadian Electrical Code
Canadian Standards Association, CAN3-C22

Chimneys
and Fireplaces

CHIMNEYS AND FIREPLACES

Chimneys and fireplaces can be of masonry construction supported on a suitable foundation. Lightweight, factory-built chimneys and fireplaces requiring no foundation are becoming more common. A chimney must be capable of producing sufficient draft to maintain the fire and carry off the products of combustion.

Since an ordinary fireplace has a very low heating efficiency, its chief value is decorative. Its efficiency can be increased, however, by use of a factory-made metal unit incorporated in the fireplace structure. In addition to direct heat from the fire, the room is also heated by air circulating through the unit. To be most effective, the unit should have draft-tight doors and a separate air supply directly from the exterior to support combustion.

The inefficiencies of wood burning and the air leakage characteristics of fireplaces are somewhat offset when wood stoves are used. The fire safety requirements for wood stoves are different from those for fireplaces, and should be reviewed with the building official.

Both the chimney and the fireplace must be carefully built to minimize fire hazards. Where possible, chimneys and fireplaces should not be located on outside walls. Locating the chimney within the house, offers the following advantages:

- heat that would otherwise be lost up the chimney and outdoors stays in the house;

- there will be less deterioration of the masonry from condensation of flue gases;

- if located near south-facing windows and of masonry construction, the chimney will contribute to the thermal inertia of the house by storing solar energy gained during the day, and releasing it to the house during the night; and

- due to its warmer temperature, the chimney will have a better draft and thus exhaust flue gases more efficiently.

CHIMNEYS

Masonry chimneys must be built on a concrete footing, properly designed to support the load. Because a chimney may contain more than one flue, the minimum dimensions depend on the number of flues, and their arrangement and size. The wall thickness of a masonry chimney should not be less than 3 in. (75 mm) of solid masonry units.

The flue is a vertical shaft through which smoke and gases are carried to open air. A single flue may serve one or more appliances located on the same floor, for example, a furnace and water heater. In this case, both connections to the flue should be located one above the other to ensure a good draft. In general, the flue from a solid-fuel burning appliance such as a wood stove should not be connected to the flue from an oil burning appliance. As well, installing a certified chimney liner is recommended. The size of the flue, and the placement of multiple connections, depends on the requirements of the appliances connected to it. A fireplace must always have a separate flue.

The flue lining for masonry fireplaces usually consists of rectangular glazed clay pipe in sections, which are about 24 in. (600 mm) long and installed when the surrounding masonry is being placed. Care should be taken to set the linings close and flush on top of one another with full mortar beds. If more than one flue is used in a chimney, flues should be separated from one another by at least 3 in. (75 mm) of solid masonry or concrete, or 3½ in. (90 mm) of fire brick where fire-brick liners are used (Figure 120). The linings usually start about 8 in. (200 mm) below the flue pipe connection and extend 2 to 4 in. (50 to 100 mm) above the chimney cap.

The top of masonry chimneys should be capped to keep water away from masonry joints. Concrete is generally used for this purpose. The top of the cap should be sloped away from the flue lining and

extend beyond the chimney wall at least 1 in. (25 mm) to form a drip edge. A saw cut or groove should be provided under the cap to act as a capillary break.

Most factory-built metal chimneys are fabricated in sections and connected during installation. They are comparatively light in weight, and can be supported by special anchors that are attached to the floor joists when the chimney is erected. Two precautions should be taken in the use of a factory-built chimney:

- make sure the model has been tested and approved by Underwriters' Laboratories of Canada; and

- ensure that it is installed in strict accordance with the manufacturer's instructions and the conditions of approval set out by Underwriters' Laboratories of Canada.

The chimney flue should be carried high enough above the roof to avoid downdrafts caused by wind turbulence. The height should never be less than 3 ft. (900 mm) above the highest point where the chimney intersects the roof and should extend at least 2 ft.

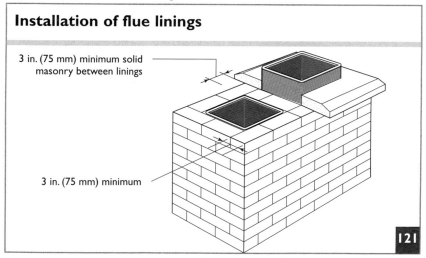

Installation of flue linings

3 in. (75 mm) minimum solid masonry between linings

3 in. (75 mm) minimum

121

(600 mm) above the ridge or any other roof surface within 10 ft. (3 m) of the chimney (Figure 122).

In masonry chimneys, a metal cleanout opening and door shall be provided near the bottom of the flue so that soot can easily be removed from the chimney.

Chimneys may be used to vent gas-burning equipment provided the lining complies with gas appliance installation codes. Alternatively, the equipment may be vented through special gas vents approved for this purpose.

SITE-BUILT FIREPLACES

A fireplace must be designed properly and the building must be sited correctly for good performance. Fire-places must have an external air supply to improve combustion. The fireplace flue should have a liner. Its size depends on the size of the fireplace opening. One rule commonly used is to take one-tenth of the area of the fireplace opening to find the minimum size of the flue; however, the outside dimension of the flue should never be less than 8 x 12 in. (200 x 300 mm). The terminology and locations of the various parts of a fireplace are illustrated in Figure 123.

Other design principles commonly used in the construction of a fireplace with a single face are:

- the front of the fireplace should be wider than the back and the upper part of the back should tilt forward to meet the throat for better burning performance;

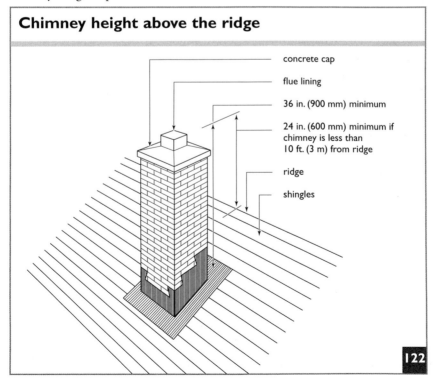

Chimney height above the ridge

concrete cap

flue lining

36 in. (900 mm) minimum

24 in. (600 mm) minimum if chimney is less than 10 ft. (3 m) from ridge

ridge

shingles

122

- the back, which should rise one-half the height of the opening before sloping forward, is usually about two-thirds of the opening in width;

- a smoke shelf, to reduce back drafts, is formed by projecting the throat forward as much as possible. The throat should be as wide and shallow as possible, but in total area it must equal the area of the flue; and

- the sides of the fireplace above the throat are drawn together to form the flue, which usually starts over the centre of the width of the fireplace; the slope, however, should not exceed 45˚ to the vertical.

The lining of the fire box must be built with materials having a high resistance to heat. A steel liner designed for this purpose or 2 in. (50 mm) of firebrick meet this requirement. When firebrick

Terms used in fireplace construction

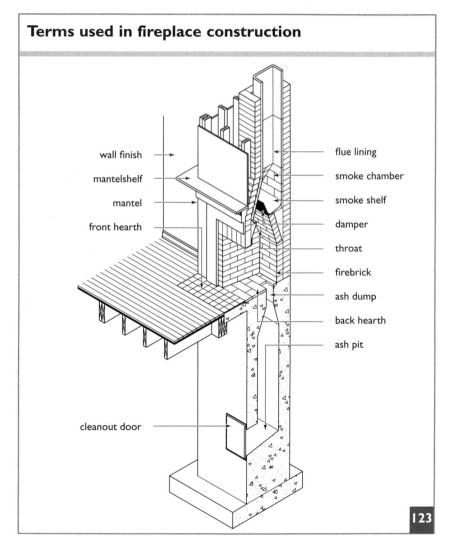

wall finish
mantelshelf
mantel
front hearth

flue lining
smoke chamber
smoke shelf
damper
throat
firebrick
ash dump
back hearth
ash pit

cleanout door

123

is used, it should be laid with fireclay mortar or high-temperature cement.

If a 2 in. (50 mm) firebrick liner is used, the back and sides of the fireplace should be at least 8 in. (190 mm) thick including the thickness of the masonry liner. Portions of the back exposed to the outside may be 5 ½ in. (140 mm) thick. Where a steel fireplace liner with an air circulating chamber surrounding the fire box is used, the back and side may be solid masonry units 3 1/2 in. (90 mm) thick or 8 in. (190 mm) hollow units.

The damper is a large valve set in the throat of the fireplace that can be adjusted from the front to regulate the draft. Many types of damper units are available. By choosing one with a correctly proportioned throat passage, the risk of failure in the function of the fireplace is reduced. The damper should be capable of being fully closed, and should be as tight-fitting as possible in the closed position to minimize heat loss up the chimney when the fireplace is not in use.

The hearth may be set even with the floor, or raised above the floor level. It consists of two parts: the front or finish hearth, and the back hearth under the fire. Because the back hearth must withstand more heat, it is usually built of firebrick. The front hearth is simply a precaution against flying sparks and is often built of 4 in. (100 mm) rein-forced concrete finished with ceramic tile. The front hearth should extend at least 16 in. (400 mm) in front of the fireplace opening and 8 in. (200 mm) on each side.

At the back of the fireplace, it is customary, but not essential, to have an ash dump through which ashes can be dropped into an ash pit. A cleanout door to the ash pit can be provided in the basement for periodic removal of ashes.

If a factory-built fireplace is used (Figure 124), the same precautions should be observed as indicated for a site-built fireplace.

In all cases, chimney flues should be as straight as possible to properly vent the fireplace.

A popular alternative for wood-burning fireplaces is a gas-burning appliance (both natural gas and propane). Some of these are purely decorative and manufactured for installation into existing masonry fireplaces. However, gas fireplaces with higher combustion efficiencies and fans for distribution of the heat are also available. Ensure that these are installed according to the manufacturer's instructions and conform to all applicable requirements of the natural gas or propane appliance installation code.

A fireplace is a fuel-burning appliance and requires the installation of CO detectors.

Factory-built fireplace

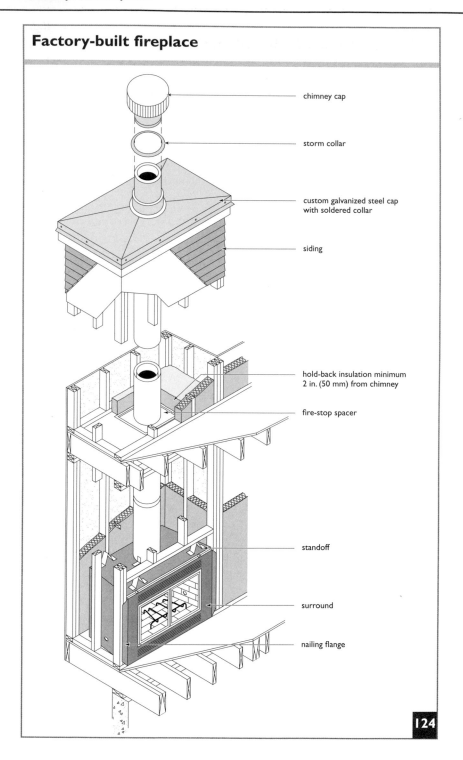

chimney cap

storm collar

custom galvanized steel cap with soldered collar

siding

hold-back insulation minimum 2 in. (50 mm) from chimney

fire-stop spacer

standoff

surround

nailing flange

124

HEALTHY HOUSING INSIGHT

Wood-burning Appliance Selection

Wood-burning appliances can provide effective and affordable home heating using a renewable energy resource. It is important to select appropriate appliances that function safely, cleanly and efficiently.

Wood-burning Appliance Considerations

➜ When selecting any wood-burning appliance, in addition to Underwriters' Laboratory certification, check that the appliance is also EPA-certified. The U.S. Environmental Protection Agency was the first jurisdiction in North America to establish emission standards for wood-burning appliances in response to concerns over air pollution from the burning of wood fuels. EPA certification ensures that the appliance is clean burning, and that as a result, it is also highly efficient.

➜ Locate the appliance in an area of the home where its immediate heating output is needed and welcome. Rooms where occupants spend a great deal of time, such as family rooms or living rooms, will benefit most from a wood stove or fireplace. Selecting appliances with glass doors affords a welcome view of the fire and improves heating efficiency.

Wood-burning appliances are also useful in areas such as unheated sunrooms and workshops.

➜ Distribute the heat to other parts of the home using a forced-air heating system or a ventilation system with a recirculating mode of operation.

➜ Only use the type of chimney that has been certified for use with the appliance. Follow the manufacturer's certified installation instructions and have the completed installation inspected by the local building inspector prior to closing it in.

➜ Use wood that has been harvested from managed woodlots. Avoid supporting sources of firewood that do not observe sustainable resource management of the forests. Wood that has been drying for at least two years is the best and cleanest-burning fuel. Hardwoods are generally preferred because they provide more heat per volume than softwoods. However, any suitable, well-seasoned species will burn properly in a properly installed wood-heating system.

Thermal Insulation

THERMAL INSULATION

The effectiveness of a building assembly such as a wall or ceiling in resisting the flow of heat is measured as its thermal resistance or R-value (RSI-value). Although most materials have some resistance to the flow of heat, the materials used for structure, cladding and finish generally have relatively low resistance. Insulation is, therefore, added to reduce the loss of heat from the house. Wood-frame construction is quite easy to insulate since it incorporates many cavities that can be readily filled with relatively inexpensive types of insulation. The cavities or air spaces themselves have appreciable resistance to heat flow, but it is greatly increased by placing insulation in the space.

In the past, due to low energy prices, it was not common to completely fill wall stud spaces with insulation, or to insulate attics to a depth greater than that of the truss bottom chords or ceiling joists. Neither was it common to insulate foundation walls. Now, however, higher energy prices and our increasing realization of the need for energy conservation make it apparent that insulation should at least fill all available cavities within the building shell and that perhaps the shell construction should be altered to accommodate even more insulation. It has also become apparent that uninsulated foundation walls are a major source of heat loss.

TYPES OF INSULATION

Insulation is manufactured from a variety of materials and in a variety of forms. These forms can be grouped into five basic types.

Batts

Batts consist of fibres of glass or steel-mill slag spun together with a binding agent into a blanket-like strip of convenient length and width to fit standard framing spaces and in a range of thicknesses. This type is called "friction fit" because it is made slightly wider than the standard stud space and held in place by friction.

It is often necessary to use insulation batts in cavities that are not as deep as the batts are thick. For example, 6 in. (150 mm) batts might be used in a wall built with 2 x 6 in. (38 x 140 mm) studs. Slight compression causes a small reduction in the thermal resistance of the batts. The batts should not be compressed, if possible.

Loose Fill

Many types of insulation are made in loose form for pouring or blowing into place. Common materials include glass and mineral wool fibre and cellulose fibre.

Rigid

Rigid insulation is manufactured in sheets or boards using materials such as wood fibre and expanded or extruded foamed plastic.

Semi-rigid

Semi-rigid insulation boards are relatively flexible compared to rigid insulation products, and are not as easily damaged by impact or bending. Usually, these are formed from glass and mineral wool fibres.

Foamed-in-place

Processes are available for spraying or injecting under pressure materials such as polyurethane and isocyanurate in a foamed liquid state. The foam sets into a rigid mass within minutes of installation. Because this foaming operation is, in effect, the last stage of manufacturing the product, and it occurs at the building site, the installer must be highly skilled and very conscientious to provide a product of uniform quality and consistency. Ensure that the products being installed are approved for use in houses and hire a qualified contractor to perform the installation.

Amount of Insulation

The amount of insulation required for various parts of houses can be found in the Model National Energy Code of Canada for Houses (MNECH). The amount of insulation is related to the severity of the climate as categorized in zones for each province, and to the cost of space-heating fuel. The zones in each province are established using the degree-day method. Degree-days are calculated for a given location by accumulating the differences between 64°F (18°C) and the mean temperature for every day in the year when the mean temperature is below 64°F (18°C). Degree-day values for a number of locations in Canada are listed in the National Building Code.

It should be recognized that the R-values (RSI–values) recommended in the MNECH are minimum effective thermal resistance values. *Effective thermal resistance* values are different than *nominal thermal resistance* values in that the former take into account thermal bridging through framing members, whereas the latter relate to the sum of installed insulation R-values (RSI-values). It is worth considering when designing and building a new house to allow for more than the minimum R-values (RSI values). It is much easier to incorporate extra insulation when building than to add it afterwards. It is also likely that the cost of energy will continue to increase.

All walls, floors and ceilings that separate heated space from unheated space or the outside air should be insulated. Foundation walls separating heated basements or crawl spaces from the outside air or soil should also be insulated to at least 24 in. (600 mm) below grade level on the inside of the basement, or full height on the outside. Methods of insulating these different areas are given in the following sections. The figures illustrate a number of possible methods of insulating building elements. It is not intended to imply that these are the only acceptable methods. Specific materials, thicknesses and spacings are shown in the illustrations in order to correlate these with their effective thermal resistance values. In most cases, the material, thickness or spacing illustrated is only one of a number of equally acceptable alternatives. However, if elements other than those illustrated here, or listed in tables in the MNECH are used, the effective thermal resistance of the assembly must be recalculated according to the method shown in the MNECH.

CHECKING BACK

Foundation and Framing Detailing

The selection of the type and amount of insulation cannot be made without due consideration of appropriate foundation and framing details. Check back to the parts of this publication, mentioned below, to ensure that the required amount of insulation can be accommodated within the structure of the house.

→ Review the Foundations section in "Footings, Foundations and Slabs."

→ Review the "Floor Framing," "Wall Framing" and "Ceiling and Roof Framing" chapters.

Concrete wall with rigid insulation on outer face

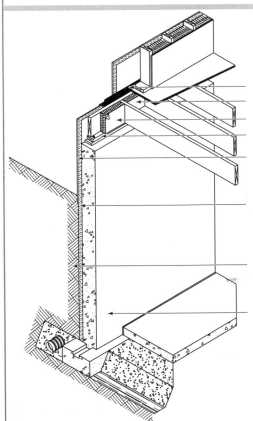

base flashing

R-12 (RSI 2.1) batt insulation

vapour retarder

sill plate

1/2 in. (12 mm) cement parging on wire lath nailed to sill plate and concrete

2 in. (50 mm) type 4 extruded polystyrene, or type 2 expanded polystyrene, or rigid glass fibre insulation bonded to concrete

granular backfill around insulation to protect against damage due to frost heave

8 in. (200 mm) concrete wall

Effective Thermal Resistance R-11.2 (RSI-1.97)

125

INSULATION OF FOUNDATIONS

Foundation walls enclosing heated space should be insulated full height. The preferred way to insulate basement walls is to apply rigid insulation to the exterior of the foundation wall.

When insulation is applied on the outer surface of a wall or a slab perimeter, it should be of a type not susceptible to water damage, such as expanded or extruded polystyrene, or insulation capable of draining water, such as high density, rigid glass-fibre insulation. In addition, the insulation should be protected above grade with ½ in. (12 mm) cement parging on wire lath applied to the exposed face and edge (Figure 125). Insulation may also be applied to the interior surfaces of foundation walls. The method of applying polyethylene sheet against the concrete wall up to grade as an interior damp-proofing may trap moisture in the wall and result in moisture problems in some situations. One alternative to the polyethylene sheet is to install at least 1 in. (25 mm) of rigid insulation against the concrete foundation wall prior to the installation of the framing, batt insulation, air barrier and vapour retarder (Figure 126). The rigid insulation can serve as the air barrier if extruded polystyrene is used and the seams and joints are sealed to the adjoining air barrier above and below. Another alternative is to simply

Concrete wall insulated with rigid insulation and batts

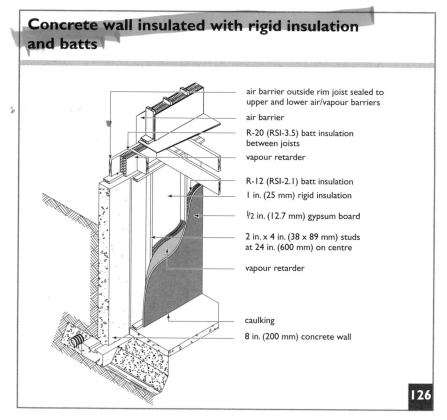

air barrier outside rim joist sealed to upper and lower air/vapour barriers

air barrier

R-20 (RSI-3.5) batt insulation between joists

vapour retarder

R-12 (RSI-2.1) batt insulation

1 in. (25 mm) rigid insulation

½ in. (12.7 mm) gypsum board

2 in. x 4 in. (38 x 89 mm) studs at 24 in. (600 mm) on centre

vapour retarder

caulking

8 in. (200 mm) concrete wall

126

space the wood framing 1 in. (25 mm) away from the wall to avoid the need for interior damp-proofing. The problem with this approach is that it usually permits air movement behind the insulation, reducing the benefit of the insulation and sometimes encouraging condensation.

Rigid, board-type insulation should be bonded to the wall with cement grout or synthetic adhesive applied in bands forming a grid pattern. This pattern of bonding is recommended to limit warm moist air movement behind the insulation since this can cause condensation and ice build-up between the wall and the insulation. If a protein-based adhesive is used to bond the insulation to the wall, the adhesive should contain a preservative.

Due to its high potential for contributing to the rapid spread of fire, any plastic insulation applied to the inside of basement walls must not be exposed, but should be protected with an acceptable finish, such as drywall. Other types of insulation must also be covered to protect them from damage. Where fire protection covering is required, insulation should be held in place by mechanical fastening to framing members at least at the top and bottom of the insulation and around all openings.

Insulation is normally placed between the studs of preserved wood foundations. Preferably, the cavity should be filled to prevent air pockets and the possibility of convection loops being set up within the cavity.

Normal weight concrete, that is, concrete with a density of about 150 lb./cu. ft. (2,400 kg/m³) is commonly used in basement construction.

Lightweight concrete may be used to achieve higher thermal resistance but should have a 28-day compressive strength of at least 2,000 psi (15 MPa).

In Figures 125 and 126, the insulation is shown extending the full height of the basement wall. With hollow core concrete block walls, convection currents may occur if the wall is not insulated over its full height. The bottom edge of the insulation should be sealed by caulking and, in the case of batt-type insulation, by solid blocking.

INSULATION OF FLOORS

Floors over unheated crawl spaces or over heated or unheated garages should be insulated.

Where there is no finished ceiling on the underside of the floor, some material must be added to support the insulation. For friction-fit type batts or for rigid insulation (Figure 127), wire lath or "chicken wire" tacked to the bottom of the joists may be the most economical method. For loose, fill-type insulation (Figure 128), the support must be provided by a material that is solid (to prevent the insulation from falling through) but permeable (to avoid trapping water vapour that happens to penetrate the vapour retarder).

The vapour retarder must be installed on the upper or warm side of the insulation. No additional vapour retarder need be installed where a plywood subfloor with tight-fitting or sealed joints is used, because it is generally a good air barrier and a very good vapour retarder.

Floor over unheated crawl space insulated with friction-fit batts

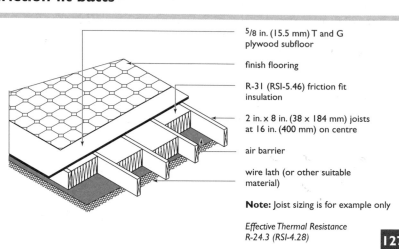

5/8 in. (15.5 mm) T and G plywood subfloor

finish flooring

R-31 (RSI-5.46) friction fit insulation

2 in. x 8 in. (38 x 184 mm) joists at 16 in. (400 mm) on centre

air barrier

wire lath (or other suitable material)

Note: Joist sizing is for example only

Effective Thermal Resistance R-24.3 (RSI-4.28)

127

Floor over unheated crawl space insulated with loose-fill insulation

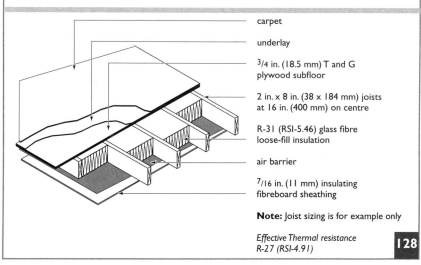

carpet

underlay

3/4 in. (18.5 mm) T and G plywood subfloor

2 in. x 8 in. (38 x 184 mm) joists at 16 in. (400 mm) on centre

R-31 (RSI-5.46) glass fibre loose-fill insulation

air barrier

7/16 in. (11 mm) insulating fibreboard sheathing

Note: Joist sizing is for example only

Effective Thermal resistance R-27 (RSI-4.91)

128

The insulation must be tightly fitted around cross bridging or blocking between joists. This requires particular care with batt and rigid insulation. It is also important not to omit insulation in small spaces such as between blocked double joists or between a wall and the first joist. In such cases, the insulation should be cut slightly oversize and carefully installed to avoid bunching and excessive compression.

When the insulation is installed only at the bottom of the joist space, the area at the ends of the joist must be carefully considered. The area of the joist header is, in effect, a wall and should be insulated accordingly. Also a well-sealed air barrier must be provided around the perimeter and beneath the insulation to minimize the possibility of cold air leaking into the joist space and bypassing the insulation.

Insulating a floor over unheated space reduces the heat loss through it, but may not prevent it from feeling cold. Filling the floor cavity with a sprayed-in-place foam-type or blown-in-place blanket-type insulation is an effective alternative to providing radiant floor heating. The use of carpeting or rugs may also improve the comfort of floors over unheated spaces.

Another effective alternative is to build an insulated dropped ceiling below the floor joists and supply inside air to the joist space. It is important to insulate the exterior walls of the joist space to prevent heat loss.

INSULATION OF WALLS

With normal 2 x 4 in. (38 x 89 mm) stud framing, the maximum effective thermal resistance that can be achieved by filling the cavity with batt-type insulation and using normal finishing, sheathing and cladding materials is approximately R-12 (RSI-2.1). By careful selection of the sheathing and cladding, this can be increased to about R-13 (RSI-2.3). This assembly, while suitable for seasonal buildings, does not meet the requirements of the MNECH. Going beyond this level requires special measures. One approach is to use deeper studs, such as 2 x 6 in. (38 x 140 mm), in order to accommodate thicker batt insulation (Figure 129). Insulation products with higher thermal resistance values are a simple alternative for enhancing the efficiency of the wall assembly (Figure 130). Another approach is to use 2 x 4 in. (38 x 89 mm)

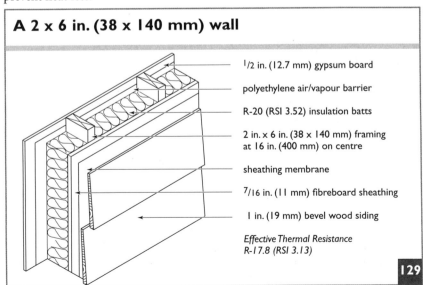

A 2 x 6 in. (38 x 140 mm) wall

1/2 in. (12.7 mm) gypsum board

polyethylene air/vapour barrier

R-20 (RSI 3.52) insulation batts

2 in. x 6 in. (38 x 140 mm) framing at 16 in. (400 mm) on centre

sheathing membrane

7/16 in. (11 mm) fibreboard sheathing

1 in. (19 mm) bevel wood siding

Effective Thermal Resistance R-17.8 (RSI 3.13)

129

studs with the cavities filled with batt insulation, and rigid insulation applied to the outside either in place of, or in addition to, the normal sheathing (Figure 131). This latter method has the merit of providing a significant proportion of the wall's thermal resistance in a form that is continuous over the framing, thus reducing thermal bridging through the framing members.

Some types of semi-rigid insulation come with a spunbonded polyolefin sheet attached to one surface.

A 2 x 6 in. (38 x 140 mm) wall with higher efficiency insulation

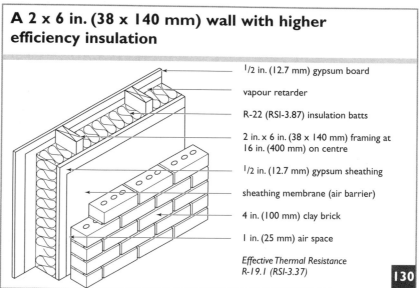

$^1/2$ in. (12.7 mm) gypsum board

vapour retarder

R-22 (RSI-3.87) insulation batts

2 in. x 6 in. (38 x 140 mm) framing at 16 in. (400 mm) on centre

$^1/2$ in. (12.7 mm) gypsum sheathing

sheathing membrane (air barrier)

4 in. (100 mm) clay brick

1 in. (25 mm) air space

Effective Thermal Resistance
R-19.1 (RSI-3.37)

130

A 2 x 4 in. (38 x 89 mm) wall with exterior insulation

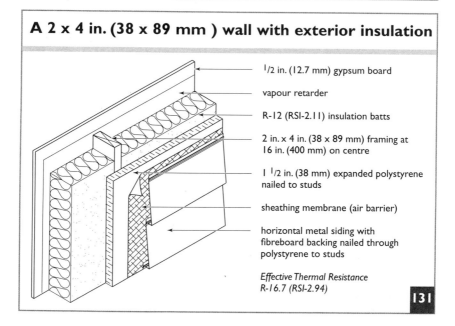

$^1/2$ in. (12.7 mm) gypsum board

vapour retarder

R-12 (RSI-2.11) insulation batts

2 in. x 4 in. (38 x 89 mm) framing at 16 in. (400 mm) on centre

1 $^1/2$ in. (38 mm) expanded polystyrene nailed to studs

sheathing membrane (air barrier)

horizontal metal siding with fibreboard backing nailed through polystyrene to studs

Effective Thermal Resistance
R-16.7 (RSI-2.94)

131

This material is vapour permeable but air impermeable, and can constitute a good air barrier if the joints between the sheets are taped. Materials such as spun-bonded polyolefin or perforated poly-ethylene are available in 4 and 9 ft. (1.2 and 2.7 m) rolls, and can be applied to the exterior of any wall assembly to create an effective air barrier.

Other types of insulation, such as rigid plastics, can be air impermeable and constitute a good air barrier if they are placed with the joints butted and caulked. However because some of these insulations have low vapour-permeability, they can also behave as a vapour retarder. To prevent condensation forming within the wall assembly, these sheet and panel insulation materials must be a certain thickness and be situated in the wall assembly in such a way that moisture moving from the inside to the outside does not become trapped in the wall assembly. This is accomplished by locating the insulation:

- On the warm side of the wall

- At a location where the ratio between the total thermal resistance of all materials outside of the innermost impermeable surface of the insulation to the thermal resistance of materials inside the innermost impermeable surface of the insulation is sufficient to prevent condensation from form-ing. This required ratio depends on the local climate—the colder the climate the thicker the insulation panel must be if placed on the cold side of the wall (refer to your local building official for assistance).

- Outside a vapour-permeable moisture barrier that is drained to the exterior of the wall assembly.

- Outside an air space that is vented to the outside and drained. However, this arrangement diminishes the effectiveness of the insulation due to short-circuiting of the insulation.

The use of a sheathing membrane on top of the insulating sheathing is required as a rain-shedding device, unless the joints in the sheathing are sealed or designed to shed water.

Where blown-in insulation is installed in wood-frame walls, it must be a type that is not prone to settlement, and the insulation needs to be installed behind a membrane that permits visual inspection prior to the installation of the interior finish.

Except where unavoidable, electrical and mechanical facilities, such as boxes, pipes and ducts, should not be installed in exterior walls. Where this cannot be avoided, insulation should be fitted between the item and the outside surface in a manner that will minimize compression of the insulation.

Insulation for small spaces at intersections, corners and around openings should be cut only slightly oversize and carefully installed to avoid bunching and excessive compression.

Walls between dwelling units and garages should be insulated to the same degree as exterior walls whether the garage is heated or not, since garages may be left open for extended periods.

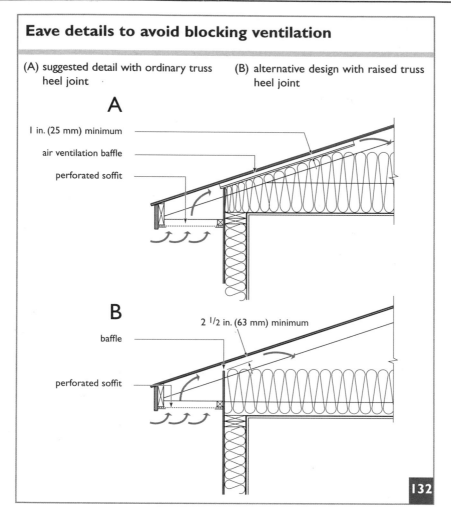

Eave details to avoid blocking ventilation

(A) suggested detail with ordinary truss heel joint

(B) alternative design with raised truss heel joint

A

1 in. (25 mm) minimum

air ventilation baffle

perforated soffit

B

2 1/2 in. (63 mm) minimum

baffle

perforated soffit

132

INSULATION OF TRUSS OR RAFTER-TYPE ROOF-CEILINGS

The thicker batts now available for insulating roofs are made in widths equal to the full centre-to-centre distance of standard roof framing. The lower portion is slightly compressed when installed between the framing, but the upper portion retains its width and covers the tops of the framing, thus reducing thermal bridging (heat loss) through the framing.

Loose-fill insulation can also be used to cover the framing and, unlike the standardized batts, offers the advantage that only the amount desired need be installed. On the other hand, care must be exercised to ensure it is installed at the correct density or settling may occur. Loose-fill insulation must also be prevented from spilling onto eave vents and from being displaced by wind entering the vents. Where loose

Insulating joist-type roof-ceiling between the ceiling and sheathing

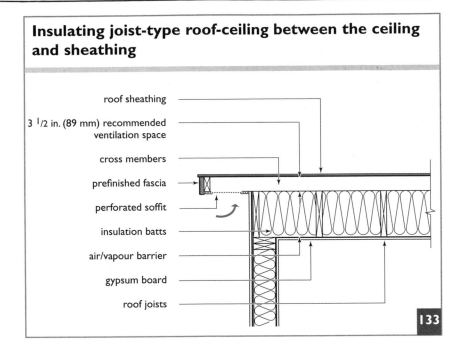

roof sheathing

3 $^1/_2$ in. (89 mm) recommended ventilation space

cross members

prefinished fascia

perforated soffit

insulation batts

air/vapour barrier

gypsum board

roof joists

133

Alternative method of insulating joist-type roof-ceiling between the ceiling and sheathing

This method can be used where the slope is at least 1:6, the joists run in the same direction as the slope, and the ventilation space is continuous from eave to ridge and is vented in both directions.

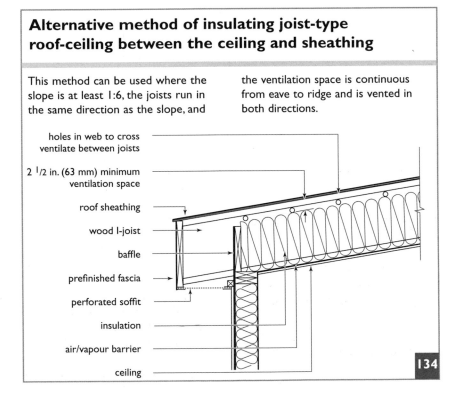

holes in web to cross ventilate between joists

2 $^1/_2$ in. (63 mm) minimum ventilation space

roof sheathing

wood I-joist

baffle

prefinished fascia

perforated soffit

insulation

air/vapour barrier

ceiling

134

Insulation of nominally flat joist-type roof-ceiling above the sheathing

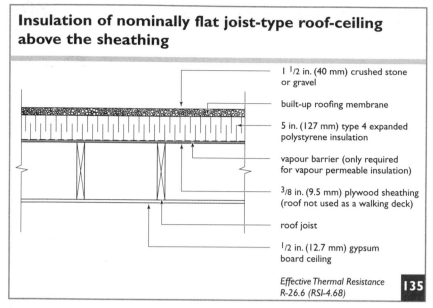

1 1/2 in. (40 mm) crushed stone or gravel

built-up roofing membrane

5 in. (127 mm) type 4 expanded polystyrene insulation

vapour barrier (only required for vapour permeable insulation)

3/8 in. (9.5 mm) plywood sheathing (roof not used as a walking deck)

roof joist

1/2 in. (12.7 mm) gypsum board ceiling

Effective Thermal Resistance R-26.6 (RSI-4.68)

135

fill insulation is installed in an unconfined slope such as a roof space over a sloped ceiling, the slope of the surface must not exceed 4.5:12 for mineral fibre or cellulose fibre insulation, and 2.5:12 for other types of loose-fill insulation.

If is essential that eave baffles be installed, both to vent the eaves and to prevent the loose-fill insulation from being blown away from the edges of the attic space.

Batt and rigid type insulation should be installed so that it fits tightly against framing members. Care should be taken to ensure that air circulation to and from eave vents is not blocked, and to ensure wind-driven snow cannot enter through vent openings. Air ventilation baffles such as those shown in Figure 132 must be used to avoid loose insulation from blocking air circulation.

INSULATION OF JOIST-TYPE ROOF-CEILINGS

When the ceiling finish is applied directly to its bottom surface, a roof framing member is called a joist rather than a rafter. This type of construction is found in low-slope roofs and some cathedral or sloping ceilings. When such roofs are insulated between the ceiling and the sheathing, condensation problems can occur because the space between the insulation and the sheathing is divided into small compartments which are difficult to ventilate. Thus, any moisture that leaks through imperfections in the air barrier and vapour retarder is not dissipated but accumulates and condenses. Measures to prevent this are shown in Figures 133 and 134.

HEALTHY HOUSING INSIGHT

Insulation Selection

There are many insulation products available, and the number is growing as manufacturers seek to provide better performing and easier-to-install products. Some important factors to consider when selecting insulation products are summarized below.

➜ Occupant Health: Never use insulation products that may adversely affect the health of the house occupants. This may occur when insulation is left exposed, or particulates enter ductwork.

➜ Energy Efficiency: The energy efficiency of insulation products may vary significantly for a given unit of thickness. For example, glass fibre insulation batts for installation in 2 x 6 in. (38 x 140 mm) cavities can vary from R-19 to R-22 (RSI-3.3 to R-3.9). Obtain the highest thermal efficiency where possible.

➜ Resource Efficiency: Where possible, use insulation materials made from industrial by-products or recycled waste. Most glass and mineral fibre products, as well as cellulose products, meet these criteria. Appropriate selection of insulation materials is an important step toward greater resource efficiency in house construction.

➜ Environmental Responsibility: Avoid using insulation products that use processes or chemicals that degrade the environment. For example, some foam insulations use blowing agents that cause damage to the ozone layer. Also, some products produce toxic effluents during the manufacturing process. Research insulation products carefully to ensure that your purchasing power is promoting environmental responsibility.

➜ Affordability: The stability and longevity of insulation products ensures that their stated thermal performance is sustained over the useful life of the house. Using innovative products should be balanced against proven performance, since the heating costs of housing can significantly affect its affordability, particularly for fixed-income households.

Insulation is a passive, energy-conserving element in the house and should be selected with careful consideration.

Another approach to avoid condensation problems in joist-type roof-ceilings is to place the insulation above the sheathing, as is commonly done with low-slope roofs (Fig. 135).

RELATED PUBLICATIONS

Model National Energy Code of Canada for Houses 1997
National Research Council of Canada

CHBA Builders' Manual
Canadian Home Builders Association

Vapour Retarders and
Air Barrier Systems

VAPOUR RETARDERS AND AIR BARRIER SYSTEMS

Many normal activities that take place within a house, such as cooking, dishwashing, laundering and bathing, release considerable amounts of water vapour into the air and increase its humidity. If, during cold weather, this water vapour is allowed to pass into the outer walls and ceiling of the building (called the "building envelope"), the low temperature within the thickness of the building envelope can cause the water vapour to condense into liquid or frost. Since wetting of the structure, cladding and insulation is undesirable, some means must be used to keep the water vapour from escaping into the building envelope (wall and ceiling cavities). This is the function of the "vapour retarder," which many people refer to as the "vapour barrier." Because it reduces, but does not stop movement of water vapour through the building envelope, the term "vapour retarder" is a more accurate description of the function of this component, and the term that will be used in this guide.

Two mechanisms drive water vapour through the building shell: vapour pressure and air movement.

In the winter, there is more water vapour in the air inside the house than in the outside air. As a result, the difference in vapour pressure forces the water vapour to diffuse through the materials making up the building envelope. Most building materials are, to some degree, permeable to the passage of water vapour, but those classified as vapour retarders , such as polyethylene, have very low permeability and are thus very resistant to this diffusion mechanism.

The second mechanism by which water vapour is forced through the building envelope is air movement. There are often differences in air pressure from inside to outside the house caused by stack effect, the operation of fans or the action of the wind. When the air pressure inside is greater than that outside, air will flow outwards through any holes or cracks in the building envelope, carrying with it any water vapour it contains. It has been recognized that this air movement plays a much greater role in the transmission of water vapour than the diffusion mechanism.

The potentially damaging movement of water vapour through the building envelope can be stopped by applying a continuous air barrier system to the exterior walls, roofs and floor overhangs. An air barrier system is composed of several structurally supported components, such as drywall, polyethylene, rigid insulation, plywood or OSB sheathing, metal and glass, which are carefully sealed together to produce an air-impervious shell between the interior and exterior environments. The most important aspect of an air barrier system is continuity— an air barrier is only good if it is continuous. An air barrier system relies on several materials that are connected with airtight joints, and properly supported so that they won't deform or tear. Polyethylene can be made to perform the functions of both an air barrier system and a vapour retarder if it is continuous, well supported and sealed with caulking at all joints and penetrations. Many places in the building envelope, such as headers, openings, services, vent stacks, chimneys, electrical, plumbing and mechanical system penetrations and unusual framing details are prone to air leakage and must be carefully sealed for the life of the building.

Air barrier systems are usually placed on the exterior of the stud wall sheathing because this surface is more uniform and has fewer penetrations and interruptions than the interior. A moisture barrier placed over the sheathing and carefully sealed at all joints and connections to windows, doors and service penetrations, can provide an effective air barrier.

Once it is well understood that there should not be a direct path from the house interior to the exterior through the wall

cavity, additional precautions should be taken to ensure that the air barrier system performs properly. The air barrier components must be able to resist powerful wind pressures and, therefore, must be supported. Vapour pressure, on the other hand, is not as forceful and can be easily resisted by lightweight materials, such as polyethylene.

LOCATION OF THE AIR BARRIER SYSTEM

The air barrier system can be located on the warm or cold side of a wall, or in between. However, when the air barrier system also performs the function of the vapour retarder, as in the case of sealed polyethylene, it must be located on the warm side of the insulation to discourage the deposition of condensed water vapour

Applying polyethylene air barrier/vapour retarder

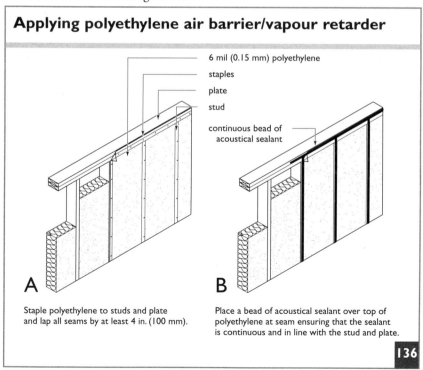

6 mil (0.15 mm) polyethylene

staples

plate

stud

continuous bead of acoustical sealant

A
Staple polyethylene to studs and plate and lap all seams by at least 4 in. (100 mm).

B
Place a bead of acoustical sealant over top of polyethylene at seam ensuring that the sealant is continuous and in line with the stud and plate.

136

in the wall cavity. A deviation from this rule is permitted with walls, where no more than one-third of the total thermal resistance or R-value (RSI value) is located on the interior side of the vapour retarder. This will prevent condensation in the insulated cavity in most Canadian climate zones. For the polyethylene to perform as an air barrier, it must be structurally supported. Polyethylene is not a good air barrier component when placed directly over studs, joists and trusses, because it is not supported in the space between framing members. Polyethylene is a better air barrier component when placed between two stiff surfaces, such as rigid insulation and drywall, where it is supported on both sides.

The ceiling air barrier must be sealed to the wall air barrier, and both should be continuous on top of and behind intersecting interior partitions. Since interior partitions are usually framed before the insulation and air barrier are installed, an air barrier can be achieved by covering the top and ends of the interior partitions with strips of polyethylene or polyolefin at least 18 in. (450 mm) wide, which are subsequently lapped and sealed to the wall and ceiling air barriers. It is often necessary to use the tops of interior partitions as a walking surface when installing roof framing. In such cases, in order to avoid damage to the polyethylene or polyolefin strips and to provide better footing, they are installed between the two top plates (Figure 137). When the air barrier is on the exterior of the wall framing, it can be lapped under and taped to the strip of polyethylene at the top of the wall, which is then sealed to the polyethylene attached to the underside of the roof framing. This ensures that the air barrier system is continuous at the junction between the walls and roof.

When the air barrier is on the interior of the wall framing, it can be easily sealed to the polyethylene attached to the underside of the roof framing.

To ensure air barrier continuity at the floor framing, it is common to wrap a vapour-permeable sheet material, such as spunbonded polyolefin, around the outside face of the floor header and extend it at least 4 in. (100 mm) inside

Installation of polyethylene or polyolefin air barrier/vapour retarder strips in interior wall framing

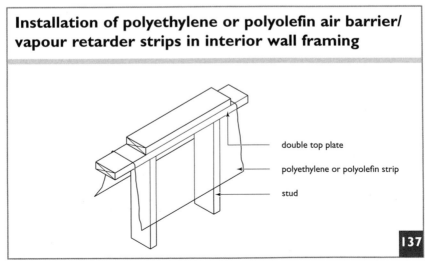

double top plate

polyethylene or polyolefin strip

stud

137

the wall framing above and below the floor. The air barrier inside the walls is then sealed to the ends of the header strips to ensure continuity at the junction between the walls and floor. (Do not wrap the floor header with polyethylene, because it might trap water vapour against the framing and insulation.)

The air barrier should overlap and be sealed to door and window frames, and be taped or caulked to any wires or pipes that penetrate it. It must also be continuous behind electrical boxes located in the exterior walls. When using polyethylene as an interior air barrier component, the electrical boxes should be wrapped with 6 mil (0.15 mm) polyethylene, which is later lapped over the polyethylene on the wall and taped or caulked to it. The lap should be at least 4 in. (100 mm) and occur over framing members. Alternatively, special polyethylene box covers can be used. All wires should be

caulked where they enter the box to prevent air leakage. Ideally, it is best to avoid locating electrical outlets on exterior walls.

LOCATION OF THE VAPOUR RETARDER

The most common vapour retarder used in Canadian houses is polyethylene film. The film is available in large, room-height sheets that can be applied with a minimum of joints, thus reducing the chance of openings through which vapour can move. Any joints that do occur should be lapped over two adjacent framing members. The National Building Code requires that when polyethylene is used as an air barrier, or as a vapour barrier where a high resistance to vapour movement is required, such as in wall construction that incorporates exterior cladding or sheathing having a low water vapour

Placement of air barrier over joist headers

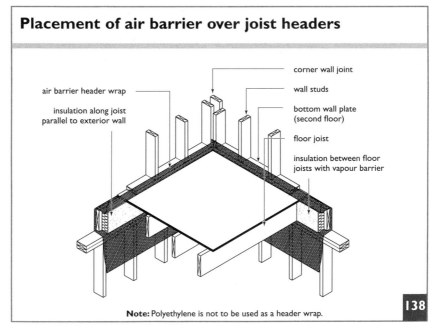

corner wall joint

air barrier header wrap

wall studs

insulation along joist parallel to exterior wall

bottom wall plate (second floor)

floor joist

insulation between floor joists with vapour barrier

Note: Polyethylene is not to be used as a header wrap.

138

permeability, it must be a minimum thickness of 6 mil (0.15 mm), and comply with applicable material standards (Figure 136). Avoid storing polyethylene in any manner that may lead to sustained exposure to sunlight or heat. Ultraviolet radiation and high temperatures can degrade the integrity of polyethylene.

It is also important to provide vapour retarder protection to insulation installed between the ends of floor joists in the header space. It is usually very difficult to achieve an effective vapour retarder at this location because the materials must be cut and fitted between the joists (Figure 138). Extra care is therefore required, especially on the higher floors where air exfiltration is more likely to occur due to stack effect. When the exterior wall has insulating sheathing, it should be carried over the header; however, it is generally preferable to use an air barrier membrane, such as spunbonded polyolefin or perforated polyethylene, at this location. If additional insulation is placed on the inside, a vapour retarder will be necessary on the inside face of the insulation to ensure that no moisture-laden air reaches the header and condenses on it.

The edges of the polyethylene covering the fitted insulation should be caulked to the framing, in order to seal the joints and prevent exfiltration. Rigid-board insulation is suitable in this location, and some semi-rigid or soft insulation materials that come with a reinforced aluminum backing can be used effectively. Extra care in ensuring continuity of the sheathing and sheathing membrane at this point will also help to minimize air leakage.

The attic hatch is a potential weak point in the air barrier system and should be carefully weatherstripped.

RELATED PUBLICATIONS

The Details of Air Barrier Systems for Houses

Ontario New Home Warranty Program

CHBA Builders' Manual

Canadian Home Builders' Association

Best Practice Guide: Wood-Frame Envelopes

Canada Mortgage and Housing Corporation

HEALTHY HOUSING INSIGHT

Airtightness and Building Envelope Integrity

There is no such thing as an airtight building; however, achieving a high degree of airtightness is important to the integrity of the building envelope. The durability of buildings is a key aspect of resource-efficient and environmentally responsible healthy housing.

Research has shown that moisture can migrate into the building envelope through two mechanisms, vapour diffusion and air leakage. During the heating season, vapour diffusion is a relatively slow process that involves a high concentration of water vapour from the air inside a building, diffusing through building materials toward a lower humidity level outdoors. A vapour retarder is required to adequately control vapour diffusion.

Air leakage from the inside of the building to the outside (exfiltration) will transport the water vapour it contains. Air leakage can transport more than 30 times as much moisture as vapour diffusion, depositing water within the building assembly in areas concentrated around air leakage points. This must be avoided since most building materials are highly susceptible to moisture damage. Only a continuous air barrier system can prevent airborne moisture migration.

Key Points

→ The higher the level of airtightness the better. In addition to protecting the building envelope, airtightness promotes energy efficiency, allows for better control of natural and mechanical ventilation and reduces the transmission of outdoor noise.

→ Properly located and sealed, polyethylene can serve as an effective air barrier and vapour retarder, but must be kept on the warm side of the insulation.

→ An exterior air barrier membrane is also recommended, particularly if the insulation being used in the walls is air permeable. Ensure that the air barrier membrane is also not a vapour retarder when it occurs on the cold side of the insulation.

→ Airtightness is cumulative—good workmanship in the construction of the entire building envelope is essential to its proper performance. Properly installed air barrier systems are not a cure-all for poor construction practices.

Fire and Sound Control

FIRE AND SOUND CONTROL

All buildings need to provide the degree of fire safety required by the building code. There are many strategies to reduce fire risk; to warn occupants of fire; to improve the likelihood of occupants moving to a safe place in a fire; and to reduce the risk of collapse of physical elements due to a fire. Code requirements for clearances around heating and cooking appliances are intended to prevent fires from starting. Smoke alarms are the common method in residential buildings for making occupants aware of fire. Code requirements specify the size and operability of a bedroom window as an emergency exit route. The building code does not explicitly require fire rated floor or wall assemblies in single-family houses, but normal wood-frame construction is considered to provide an acceptable level of fire safety. Gypsum board is not only an economical way of providing smooth wall surfaces; it also provides essential protection to structural components for a certain period of time. In the same way, normal wood-frame construction provides a level of sound resistance between floors and rooms that is adequate for single-family applications.

The situation becomes more complex for attached housing like duplexes, townhouses and apartments because a fire in one unit could spread to an adjacent unit without the occupants in the affected unit being aware of a problem. In a similar fashion, noise that penetrates walls and floors is much less tolerable when it is originating from outside a living unit (coming from neighbours rather than family members). For these reasons, additional building code requirements apply to multi-family housing for fire safety and sound control. For example, rated fire separation walls and floors are required between units and they need to provide a minimum level of protection against the transmission of airborne noise. Wood-frame construction is accepted for multi-unit residential buildings up to three storeys in height (four storeys with sprinklers) and is required to provide the same level of protection as other types of construction. Recent research has developed a much better understanding of the ability of many types of walls and floors to resist fire and control sound.

SMOKE ALARMS

The National Building Code and most local building codes require early-warning, fire-detecting devices in dwellings, usually a self-contained combined smoke detector and an alarm that is wired into the electrical system. The two basic types of smoke alarms are: ionization (or "products-of-combustion") and photoelectric.

Location and Installation

Smoke alarms should be located in or near each bedroom and on each storey including basements. Smoke alarms should be mounted on the ceiling or on a wall between 8 and 12 in. (200 and 300 mm) from the ceiling.

Building codes usually require smoke alarms to be permanently connected (hard-wired) to an electrical circuit. There should be no disconnect switch between the smoke alarm and the electrical service panel, and the circuit should not be connected to a wall outlet.

Where electric power is not available, battery-powered smoke alarms may be used. These units are designed to operate for at least one year, followed by a seven-day trouble signal when the battery runs down.

Only install smoke alarms that are certified by a recognized testing agency, such as the Underwriters' Laboratories of Canada.

RELATED PUBLICATION

2005 National Building Code of Canada
National Research Council of Canada

Ventilation

VENTILATION

Ventilation of a house, and for that matter, any occupied building, is needed to maintain acceptable indoor air quality (IAQ), and to control indoor moisture levels. IAQ is important for human health and well being, which may be maintained by the ventilation of contaminants and odours. Failure to control interior moisture levels within the house can affect human health if conditions that promote the growth of molds and mildew are not prevented. Further, the control of internal moisture levels is important to the integrity of the building envelope. Moisture migrating from the interior of the house to the outdoors may accumulate within the building envelope, causing damage and mold growth to the wood structure, insulation, drywall and finishes. Ventilation may also be used to cool the interior when high humidity levels occur.

Ventilation is provided in buildings by two primary means: natural ventilation, typically through operable windows; and mechanical ventilation, through some kind of mechanical ventilation system that exhausts indoor air or supplies outdoor air to the house, or both. The sections that follow describe these two means and their key requirements under the National Building Code.

NATURAL VENTILATION

Natural ventilation through operable windows occurs primarily during the non-heating season when the air entering the house is at a comfortable temperature. During the heating season, the National Building Code assumes that occupants will be discouraged from opening windows that will admit cold drafts and lose heating energy—hence a controlled mechanical ventilation system is required. In some cases, windows opened during extreme cold weather lose energy and may not close properly due to ice build-up. At such times, only a suitable mechanical ventilation system will provide the required ventilation properly.

The minimum unobstructed area of ventilation openings specified in the National Building Code applies to rooms that are not mechanically ventilated. This means that in situations where air is exhausted from, or supplied to, a room by mechanical means, no operable windows are required. In practice, however, occupants normally expect operable windows in most rooms, and in some cases, operable windows are required as a means of egress in case of fire.

By carefully planning the type, location and orientation of operable windows, it is possible to provide highly effective natural ventilation and cooling. Windows that open into prevailing summer winds can serve as scoops that capture and direct the breezes through the house. Providing both low and high openings can promote natural ventilation during calm periods.

MECHANICAL VENTILATION

The National Building Code requires the installation of a mechanical ventilation system with a prescribed capacity, which is capable of operating on a continuous basis, in all houses intended for year-round occupancy. It is not necessarily intended that house occupants operate the system at peak capacity on a continuous basis. In households with frequent moisture-generating activities such as cooking, bathing and floor washing, continuous mechanical ventilation at a low speed may be needed to control indoor humidity. There may be occasions when operating the mechanical ventilation system at its peak capacity on a continuous basis is needed to control contaminants arising from activities such as painting or social events. In households with sedentary occupants, or when the house is not occupied for extended periods of time, intermittent operation of the mechanical ventilation system may be all that is required to maintain acceptable indoor air quality. Mechanical ventilation systems should be viewed as appliances intended for occupant health and comfort, as well as the integrity of the building envelope. Ideally, these systems should comfortably accommodate the full range of normal household activities without over-or under-ventilating the home.

Mechanical Ventilation System Options

There are essentially two mechanical ventilation system options for housing. The first option consists of a number of alternatives that are prescribed in the National Building Code. The second option involves competent mechanical design and installation in accordance with the requirements of "CAN/CSA-F326, Residential Mechanical Ventilation Systems". The discussion that follows focuses on the prescribed alternatives noted in the National Building Code. Further information may be obtained from the reference publications listed at the end of this chapter.

Stand-alone ventilation systems, which are not coupled to a forced-air heating system, consist of fans, ducts, grilles and controls that exhaust air from selected rooms in the house and supply air to rooms that are not being exhausted. These systems have the advantage of being designed especially for ventilation only, independent of the need to deliver heating or cooling. Incoming outdoor air should be tempered to maintain a comfortable air supply temperature. Stand-alone ventilation systems are usually installed in houses with heating systems that do not rely on forced-air distribution of heat.

Ventilation systems coupled to a forced-air heating system are similar to stand-alone ventilation systems, but share ductwork with the heating system for the supply of fresh air to

CHECKING BACK

Accommodating Ductwork During Framing

When planning the installation of the ventilation system, it is important to provide passageways, or chases, for ducts. Otherwise, these may have to be concealed with dropped ceilings or bulkheads in finished areas of the house. Refer to the Planning Ahead note in the "Floor Framing" chapter for helpful planning tips.

---

heated rooms. It is necessary to interlock ventilation system and heating system controls, so that the furnace fan mixes and circulates the outdoor air that is delivered to the distribution ductwork. Coupled ventilation systems are generally less expensive to install since much of the ductwork is already provided by the forced-air heating system. Operating costs may be higher depending on the efficiency of the furnace circulating fan. There are various classes of heating equipment that do not rely on a chimney for venting. Many of these systems are more resistant to accidental backdrafting of exhaust fumes or gases into a building than naturally ventilated systems. A combustion device whose operation is independent of house pressures is a good choice if the house is commonly depressurized by exhaust appliances. Houses that experience depressurization should not have appliances that rely on natural ventilation for exhaust, such as most wood fireplaces, naturally aspirated gas furnaces with draft hoods and oil furnaces with barometric dampers.

If the ventilation system supplies outdoor air to the return air ducting of a forced-air furnace, there may be times where the outdoor air significantly chills the circulating air. Furnace-heat exchanger life may be affected by very cold return air. Proper design is necessary to ensure that outside air is mixed and adequately warmed before entering the heat exchanger.

Heat Recovery Ventilators

A heat recovery ventilator (HRV) is a packaged type of ventilation system that is engineered to recover heat from the air being exhausted from the house, and transfer this heat to the incoming outdoor air. Numerous studies have concluded that in the long term, HRVs are a cost-effective alternative whose energy savings more than offset their higher initial capital costs. They also have the advantage of tempering the incoming air such that the need for auxiliary heating is avoided.

Canadian heat recovery ventilator technology is improving in affordability, effectiveness and sophistication. At present, there are two types of heat recovery ventilators manufactured in Canada: plate heat exchangers, and heat wheel exchangers.

Plate heat exchangers function using either a parallel flow or counter flow

(Figure 139) of air streams through a plastic or metal core of plates. Outside air and indoor streams flow through alternate, adjacent plates. During the exchange of heat between adjacent plates, moisture from inside air condenses out and is drained to the plumbing system. As a result of this phenomenon, when plate heat exchangers are used, humidification of the house is often required to maintain suitable indoor relative humidity levels.

Heat wheel exchanger types use a heat wheel made from a desiccant material (Figure 139). Inside air passing through the heat wheel deposits the moisture it contains within the desiccant material, and as the wheel rotates into the outside air stream, the moisture and heat are released into the air supply. Humidification of the house air is usually not required with these HRVs, nor do they require a condensate drain.

Both types of HRV may be installed as a stand-alone ventilation system or as

Common types of heat recovery ventilators

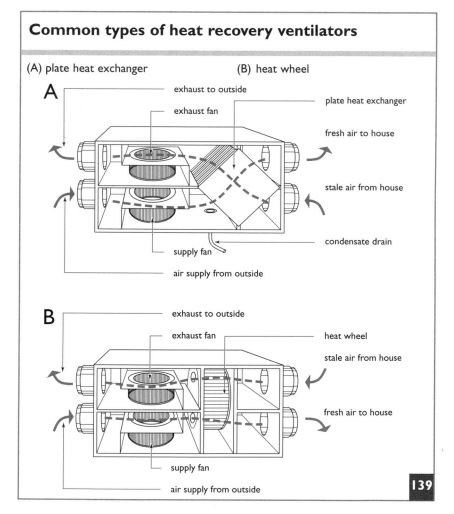

(A) plate heat exchanger   (B) heat wheel

A

exhaust to outside
exhaust fan
plate heat exchanger
fresh air to house
stale air from house
condensate drain
supply fan
air supply from outside

B

exhaust to outside
exhaust fan
heat wheel
stale air from house
fresh air to house
supply fan
air supply from outside

139

a ventilation system coupled to a forced-air heating system. Properly installed, HRVs deliver a balanced flow of supply and exhaust air, neither pressurizing nor depressurizing the house. This makes them ideally suited for installation in homes with spillage-susceptible combustion appliances such as fireplaces and wood stoves. As well, some types of HRVs can operate in a recirculation mode to distribute heat from wood-burning appliances throughout the house.

Mechanical Ventilation System Operation and Maintenance

Some of the most important aspects of mechanical ventilation systems are their operation and maintenance. To be effective, mechanical ventilation systems must not only be properly designed and installed, but also be appropriately operated by the occupants.

Maintenance of the mechanical ventilation system typically includes cleaning screens and filters, as well as servicing the equipment according to manufacturer's instructions. Accessibility to the equipment is important.

Consult with the heating contractor prior to finalizing the house design so that the mechanical ventilation system may be properly integrated within the house, and the work coordinated accordingly.

HEALTHY HOUSING INSIGHT

Ventilation, Moisture Control and Indoor Air Quality

The relationship between ventilation, moisture control and indoor air quality is important to understand when designing and building a house.

Ventilation

➔ Ventilation is needed as much in leaky houses as it is in tightly constructed houses, because the wind, the indoor-to-outdoor temperature difference and the location and distribution of leaks cannot always be fully controlled.

➔ Ventilation may be provided naturally or mechanically, however, it should be recognized that natural ventilation cannot be controlled effectively at all times. Mechanical ventilation that exhausts air from kitchens, bathrooms and other moisture generating rooms, and supplies outside air to the other habitable rooms, is most effective in controlling indoor moisture levels.

Moisture Control

➔ Moisture control is essential in any home, but especially in those that are built in cold climates, such as in Canada. If moisture levels are too high in the home and air barriers and vapour retarders are inadequate, it is possible for the moisture to migrate into the building assemblies. This may result in condensation within insulated assemblies, and the accumulation of moisture that may damage the structure and components of the home. Condensation on windows may also result, leading to the deterioration of window and sill finishes.

➔ High moisture levels in the home may also promote the growth of molds and mildew. Many of these have been found harmful to human health, in addition to permanently staining finishes.

Indoor Air Quality

➔ Indoor air quality is best controlled by eliminating sources of contamination - select appropriate building materials and carefully consider products and lifestyle in the home.

➔ Operating mechanical ventilation sensibly to control moisture and odours is all that is normally required to maintain acceptable indoor air quality in a home where sources of contaminants have been eliminated or reasonably minimized.

Interior Wall and Ceiling Finishes

INTERIOR WALL AND CEILING FINISHES

Interior finish means any material used to cover the interior wall and ceiling framing. The principal type of interior finish is gypsum board (commonly referred to as "drywall"), although plywood, hardboard, simulated veneer hardboard and lumber can also be used.

GYPSUM BOARD FINISH

Gypsum board is the most widely used interior finish because of its speed of installation, low cost, consistent result and fire resistance. In addition, gypsum board is manufactured in a variety of types for different uses, such as fire-rated, foil-backed, water-resistant and prefinished. Various fasteners and glues, finishing accessories, wall systems and wall furring are also available. Thin sheet materials such as gypsum board require that studs and ceiling joists be well aligned. This is normally achieved by the use of good lumber, its proper placement (for example, crowns up for joists), and the use of additional bracing and blocking.

Gypsum board is a sheet material composed of gypsum filler between two layers of paper. Sheets are 4 ft. (1.22 m) wide and are supplied in various lengths, 8 ft. (2.44 m) and longer. The edges along the length of the sheet are tapered on one face to receive joint compound and tape. Although gypsum board on walls may be used in ⅜ in. (9.5 mm) thickness on support spacings up to 16 in. (400 mm) on centre, a 1/2 in. (12.7 mm) board is more commonly used for its extra stiffness and strength. Where supports are spaced at 24 in. (600 mm) on centre, the minimum thickness should be 1/2 in. (12.7 mm). A new gypsum ceiling board, especially designed to resist sagging when water-based textured finishes are applied to a ceiling, is available. Its properties allow the use of a thinner 1/2 in. (12.7 mm) panel when installed perpendicular to supports at spacings up to 24 in. (600 mm).

Gypsum drywall is usually applied in single sheets directly on the framing members. On ceilings, the board is generally applied with the long dimension at right angles to the trusses or joists. Ceilings can also be strapped with 1 x 4 in. (19 x 89 mm) lumber, and in this case, the long dimension would run parallel to the trusses or joists. On walls, it is more common to apply the sheets horizontally rather than vertically because it reduces the amount of nailing and the length of joints. Horizontal joints at 4 ft. (1.2 m) above the floor are below eye level, making them less conspicuous. Horizontal joints are also easier to tape than vertical joints, as they are continuous and at a convenient tapered height. Ends of sheets, which are not recessed, should terminate at a corner and always on a support. This method provides a secure attachment and reduces nail-popping.

Gypsum board panels are applied and attached with a minimum number of supplementary fasteners. Gypsum board can be attached to wood members by single-nailing, double-nailing, glue and nailing, or screwing. In the glue-and-nailing application, a continuous bead of adhesive is applied to the face of the wood framing.

Drywall screws are the most common method of attachment and should slightly depress the drywall surface without breaking the paper face.

Nails used to fasten gypsum board should be ringed, with 3/32 in. (2.3 mm) shanks and 7/32 in. (5.5 mm) diameter heads. The nails should be long enough

to penetrate 3/4 in. (20 mm) into the support. Where higher than normal, fire-resistant ceilings are required, special gypsum board and greater penetration of fasteners may be necessary.

The fastener heads are set slightly below the surface without damaging the paper so that a slight dimple is formed in the face of the board (Figure 140A). The fasteners at the recessed edge of the sheet may be driven with the heads flush since they will be covered with tape and joint compound.

Gypsum board may be "double-nailed," that is, nails are driven in pairs about 2 in.

Finishing of gypsum board

(A) nail set with crowned hammer or special drywall screw

(B) cementing and taping of joint

(C) taping at inside corners

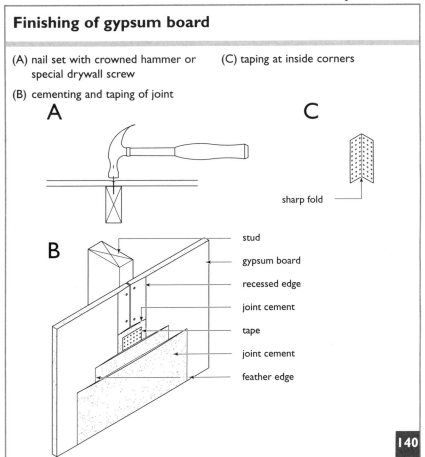

A

C

sharp fold

B

stud

gypsum board

recessed edge

joint cement

tape

joint cement

feather edge

140

Application of drywall finish

(A) vertical application of gypsum board showing single-nailing method

(B) horizontal application of gypsum board showing double-nailing method

Where the ceiling sheets are supported by the wall sheets around the perimeter of the ceiling, the nails along the upper edge of the gypsum board may be omitted, with the uppermost nails being not more than 8 in. (200 mm) below the ceiling. Fastening of the ceiling boards should begin approximately 8 in. (200 mm) from the wall face to allow for differential movement.

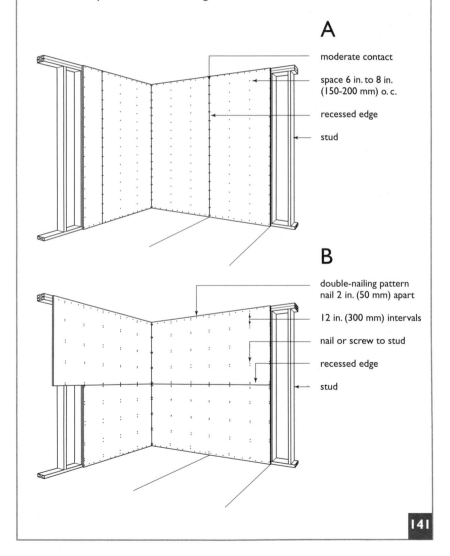

A

moderate contact

space 6 in. to 8 in. (150-200 mm) o. c.

recessed edge

stud

B

double-nailing pattern nail 2 in. (50 mm) apart

12 in. (300 mm) intervals

nail or screw to stud

recessed edge

stud

141

(50 mm) apart at the required intervals (Figure 141B). For ceilings, double nails are placed at intervals of 12 in. (300 mm) along the supports and for walls, at intervals of 12 in. (300 mm) or less. For single-nailing (Figure 141A), the ceiling nails are placed at 7 in. (180 mm) or less and for walls, at 8 in. (200 mm) or less. The double-nailing method is more commonly used because nail-popping is less likely to occur.

Special drywall screws are often used to fasten gypsum board using screw guns. Screws are usually spaced 12 in. (300 mm) on centre at both the edge and intermediate supports. The distance can be increased to 16 in. (400 mm) on walls when the supports are not more than 16 in. (400 mm) on centre. The screws should be long enough to penetrate the support at least 5/8 in. (15 mm).

If two layers of gypsum board are needed, such as for sound control or additional fire rating, the boards can be fastened in the usual manner with nails or screws, however, the penetration into the support of fasteners for the second layer must be the same as that for the first layer.

Before the joints are taped, all loose paper must be removed and the joints cleaned. All joints wider than 1/8 in. (3 mm) are then filled with joint compound and allowed to dry. External corners are protected with corrosion-resistant corner beads or wood mouldings, and at interior corners the tape is folded as shown in (Figure 140C).

Joint compound is supplied premixed or in powder form which is mixed with water to a soft putty consistency. Joint compound may be applied with hand tools, but mechanical applicators are now commonly used for both taping and filling.

The first layer of joint compound is applied in a band 5 in. (125 mm) wide along the joint. The tape is then applied and pressed into the wet compound with a trowel or wide-blade putty knife. Care should be taken to remove the excess compound, smooth the tape and feather the compound band to zero thickness at its outer edges (Figure 140B).

After the first layer has set, a second layer is applied in a band 8 in. (200 mm) wide on recessed joints and 10 in. (250 mm) wide where the edges of the board are not recessed. Once again, the edges are feathered.

A third layer is applied and feathered to a band 10 to 12 in. (250 to 300 mm) wide on recessed joints and 16 in. (400 mm) on joints that are not recessed. Special care should be taken with this final layer so that the joint surface is smooth, and does not form a noticeable bulge in the wall. When the third layer has set, the feathered edges should be sanded lightly with fine sand paper, care being taken to avoid damaging the paper surface of the gypsum board.

Nail heads and indentations in the centre of the board are filled with two layers of joint compound. Taping and finishing of gypsum board should be done at a temperature of 10°C or higher.

OTHER FINISHES

Other products used for finishing walls and ceilings are plywood, hardboard, simulated veneer hardboard and lumber.

Plywood is usually installed vertically in panels or in strips. The minimum thickness should be 3/16 in. (4.7 mm) for supports at 16 in. (400 mm) centres and 5/16 in. (8 mm) for 24 in. (600 mm) centres. Where blocking is provided at mid-height in the walls, however, 3/16 in. (4.7 mm) thickness is used at 24 in. (600 mm) centres or less. Panels or strips are nailed on all edges with 1½ in. (38 mm) finishing nails, spaced 6 in. (150 mm) along the edges and 12 in. (300 mm) at intermediate supports. Panels are available unfinished or with a factory-applied finish. For a paneled effect, plywood may be installed in strips, with a ¾ in. (20 mm) space between strips, and supported on a backing course nailed to the framing members.

Hardboard finish is supplied in panels, and is usually installed vertically. Thin sheets ⅛ in. (3.2 mm) thick need continuous backing. Sheets may be nailed directly to the studs, provided ¼ in. (6 mm) thick sheets are used for supports up to 16 in. (400 mm) centres and ⅜ in. (9 mm) sheets on supports up to 24 in. (600 mm) centres. Hardboard should be supported on all edges and nailed as recommended for plywood. Both finished and unfinished panels are available.

HEALTHY HOUSING INSIGHT

Wall and Ceiling Finish Selection

With the many choices of wall and ceiling finishes available, it is important to consider the implications for occupant health and environment of material and finish choices. The long-term upkeep and adaptability of the building should also be considered. Walls and ceilings that are difficult to clean and maintain, and that do not wear well, may become an ongoing burden for house occupants. Finishes that cannot be easily changed by painting, wallpapering or panelling may encourage replacement long before their useful service life is over. Some criteria to be considered when selecting wall and ceiling finishes are summarized below.

Appropriate Choices

➔ The use of local materials should be encouraged where possible. These stimulate the local economy and reduce the environmental impacts associated with long-distance transportation.

➔ Synthetic materials made from non-renewable materials and materials that are not reusable or recyclable should be avoided. These materials eventually end up in landfills as waste.

Continued on page 298

Continued from page 297

→ Select materials based on their durability and ease of maintenance. Experience has shown that finishes such as solid wood panelling and ceramic tile deliver long service. Plaster and drywall are easy to maintain, repair and refinish. Wallpaper that is not recyclable should be avoided.

→ Certain interior finishes for walls and ceilings must be attached using adhesives. Others may require special coating-type finishes. Check that these adhesives and coatings are non-toxic, and that they do not continue to off-gas for long periods of time. Fumes and vapours from such materials are known to cause discomfort, and in some cases, health problems.

There is no ideal interior finish for walls and ceilings; however, there is strong evidence of inappropriate finishes accumulating in landfill sites across the country. It should be recognized that the interior skin of the house will be exposed to wear and tear, require cleaning, and even renewal from time to time. This process should not strain the environment or the occupants, rather, it should be a natural extension of a healthy house.

Hardboard is also supplied in tile form and used principally on ceilings. Tile size may vary from about 12 in. (300 mm) square to 16 x 32 in. (400 x 800 mm). The tile is tongue-and-grooved and is supported by concealed nails, clips or staples. It should be ½ in. (12.7 mm) thick when supported not more than 16 in. (400 mm) on centres.

Lumber is sometimes used as a decorative finish to walls and ceilings. Lumber is supplied in tongue-and-grooved boards about 4 to 8 in. (100 to 200 mm) wide and ⅝ to ¾ in. (15 to 20 mm) thick. Softwood species include cedar, pine or hemlock; hardwoods include maple, birch or cherry. Some of these species are used in plywood form as well.

Floor Coverings

FLOOR COVERINGS

Any material used as the final wearing surface on a floor is called finish flooring. There are many such materials on the market, each with specific advantages for a particular use. Two essential properties of any kind of finish flooring are durability and ease of cleaning.

Hardwoods such as birch, maple, beech and oak are used in a variety of widths and thicknesses as strip flooring. Some species are also available in parquet form. Vertical-grain strips of soft woods such as fir or hemlock are sometimes used. Wood-finish flooring is widely used in living and dining rooms, bedrooms, corridors and general purpose rooms, such as family rooms and dens.

Other materials suitable for finish flooring include resilient flooring (in tile or sheet form) and ceramic tile. These materials are water resistant and are used in bathrooms, kitchens, public entrance halls and general storage areas. Carpets may be acceptable as finish flooring in areas where there is no need for water resistance.

WOOD STRIP FLOORING

Wood-strip flooring is manufactured in various widths and thicknesses and is available in several grades. The strips come in random lengths in separate bundles. The thickness of wood-strip flooring required for various support conditions is shown in Table 37, p. 393.

To link the wood strips together, one edge of each strip has a tongue and the other a groove. Wood flooring is generally hollow-backed, and the top face is slightly wider than the bottom so that when the strips are driven together the upper edges touch, but the lower edges are slightly apart. The tongue must fit snugly, because a loose fit may cause the floor to squeak.

The flooring should not be laid until gypsum board taping and other interior wall and ceiling finishes are completed. All windows and exterior doors should also be in place. This precaution prevents damage to the wood flooring either due to wetting or other construction activities.

Strip flooring looks better when laid lengthwise in a rectangular room. When lumber subflooring is used, it is usually laid diagonally under wood strip flooring so that the strips can be laid either parallel or at right angles to the joists. Where it is necessary to place the wood strips parallel to the lumber subflooring, an underlay (described in a following section, Underlay for Resilient Flooring) should be used to provide a level base for the narrow strips.

Hardwood flooring should not be brought into the house until the basement floor slab has been placed and gypsum board taping is completed. Moisture given off during these operations can be absorbed by the flooring and make the wood swell; then, after being put into place, the wood strips will shrink and open the joints. The flooring should be stored in the warmest and driest place available in the house until it is installed.

Various types of nails, including annular and spiral-grooved types, are used for attaching the flooring. Minimum nail lengths and nail spacing are listed in Table 38, p. 393. Various types of staples applied with manual and pneumatic tools are also available.

To nail the wood strips in place, many installers use a mallet-driven nailing tool that drives the nail in the proper location, at the correct angle, and sets the head to the proper depth. Others drive the nails using a carpenter's hammer.

Figure 142B shows the method of nailing the first strip of flooring with the nail driven down through the board at the grooved edge. The nails should be driven into the subfloor or joist and near enough to the edge so that the base or shoe moulding will cover the nail heads. The first strip of flooring should also be nailed through the tongue.

Succeeding strips of flooring can be fastened (using a carpenters' hammer) by driving nails into each strip at a 45˙ angle at the spot where the tongue adjoins the shoulder (Figure 142C). Nails should not be driven home with the hammer as the wood may be struck and easily damaged. Instead, to finish the driving, a nail set is used. To avoid splitting, it is sometimes necessary to pre-drill the nail holes through the tongue. For all courses of flooring after the first, the pieces should be selected by length so that the butt joints are well separated from those in the previous course (Figure 142A). By using a piece of scrap flooring as a driving block, each board can be driven up tightly against the previous course with no danger of damaging the wood with the hammer.

WOOD-TILE FLOORING

Flooring manufacturers have developed a wide variety of special patterns of flooring that are sometimes called floor tile and sometimes referred to as parquet flooring. One type is a block available in various thicknesses and made up of several individual strips of flooring, with two edges tongued and the opposing edges grooved. In laying, the direction of the strips is alternated to create a checkerboard effect. Manufacturers provide specific directions for laying their own type of tile. These directions should be followed carefully.

UNDERLAY FOR RESILIENT FLOORING

When the subfloor is not constructed as a combination subfloor and underlay as described in the "Floor Framing" chapter, an underlay should be installed under resilient flooring or carpets.

Plywood sheets 1/4 in. (6 mm) thick are commonly used, though particleboard in the same thickness is also used. Ensure that the particleboard is approved for use with the finished flooring material by checking the manufacturer's installation instructions. The underlay is attached to the subfloor with annular grooved nails spaced 6 in. (150 mm) apart along the edges and at 8 in. (200 mm) on centre

Application of strip flooring

(A) general application

(B) laying first strip

(C) nailing method

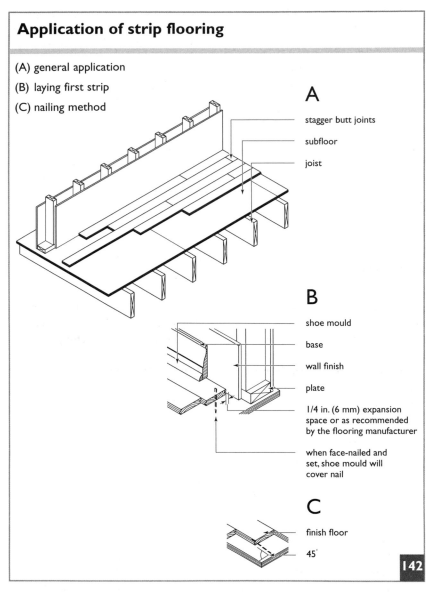

A

stagger butt joints

subfloor

joist

B

shoe mould

base

wall finish

plate

1/4 in. (6 mm) expansion
space or as recommended
by the flooring manufacturer

when face-nailed and
set, shoe mould will
cover nail

C

finish floor

45°

142

in both directions over the rest of the panel. Nails should be at least 3/4 in. (19 mm) long for 1/4 in. (6 mm) sheets and 7/8 in. (22 mm) long for 5/16 in. (7.9 mm) sheets. Staples or screws may also be used. Joints between the underlay and any defects in their surface should be filled with non-shrinking filler compound that will bond to the underlay. The filler should be sanded smooth after it has set.

Installation of Resilient Floor Covering

Resilient flooring is usually installed after other trades have finished their work. The more common types of resilient floor covering are vinyl and rubber. Both types are available in tile and sheet form.

Resilient flooring is usually cemented to the underlay with an adhesive recommended by the manufacturer for its compatibility with the flooring product. Waterproof adhesives are preferable to the non-waterproof types, especially in kitchens, bathrooms, entranceways and laundry rooms. Both tile and sheet material should be installed according to the manufacturer's recommendations. Immediately after the flooring is laid, it should be rolled in both directions, the surface cleaned and then, if necessary, sealed with the type of floor wax recommended for the material used.

Resilient flooring applied over concrete slabs must be a type recommended by the manufacturer for this use. A waterproof adhesive recommended by the manufacturer should be used for this application.

Seamless, Resin-constituent, Resilient Flooring

Resilient flooring can also be applied as a fluid, containing plastic chips or other decorative particles and fillers, that forms a resilient, seamless, wearing surface. Such flooring must be quality controlled as to components, application conditions and finished thickness in conformity with the manufacturer's specifications and procedures.

CARPETING

Carpeting is commonly used in living rooms, bedrooms, family rooms and dining rooms. In rooms such as kitchens, bathrooms, laundry rooms or other areas where water damage or staining is likely to occur, carpeting should be avoided. When carpet is desired in such areas, a synthetic-fibre type should be used. For hygienic reasons, carpet is not recommended for use in rooms containing a toilet.

Carpeting should be installed over a sheet-type subfloor or an underlay. Except for cushion-backed carpeting, felt or polymeric carpet underlay should be used.

CERAMIC TILE

Ceramic tile is available in different colours either with a glazed or unglazed surface. Since this tile has a hard impervious surface, it is often used as a floor covering in bathrooms and vestibules as well as for fireplace hearths.

Ceramic tile may be installed on a concrete subfloor, applied to a mortar base supported on the subfloor, or attached by a special adhesive to sheet-type underlay such as plywood or hardboard. When applied over a flexible floor like a wood joist floor, the joists and subflooring must be rigid enough to prevent the tiles from cracking. This may involve additional strengthening of the floor system.

When a mortar base is used, an asphalt-impregnated paper is placed over the subfloor to prevent moisture swelling of the subfloor. The base should be at least 1 1/4 in. (30 mm) thick and reinforced with wire mesh.

The mortar may consist of 1 part Portland cement, 1/4 part lime and 3 to 5 parts coarse sand. The tiles are pressed into the fresh mortar. To ensure a good bond between the joint material and base, the joints between the tiles should be filled the same day the tile is installed. To provide sufficient depth for the mortar bed, it is often desirable to drop the wood subfloor between the joists so that the finish floor will be level with floors in adjoining rooms (Figure 143). Where the tops of the joists have to be cut out for this purpose, the span of the joists should be calculated on the basis of the reduced depth.

When an adhesive is used to fasten the tiles to an underlay or concrete floor, the base must be smooth and free from surface irregularities. The adhesive is applied to both the tile and the base, and each tile is then pressed firmly in place. After the adhesive is well set, the joints between the tiles are filled with grout recommended by the tile manufacturer for this purpose.

Ceramic tiles in shower bases may be laid on a plastic liner that is connected to the shower drain. This will prevent water damage to the ceiling below should the tile and its cement base develop a crack.

Installation of ceramic tile floor

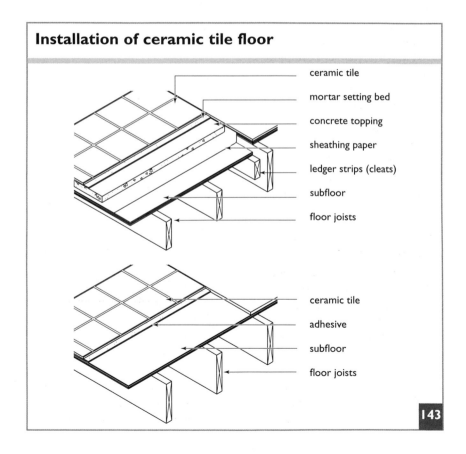

- ceramic tile
- mortar setting bed
- concrete topping
- sheathing paper
- ledger strips (cleats)
- subfloor
- floor joists

- ceramic tile
- adhesive
- subfloor
- floor joists

143

HEALTHY HOUSING INSIGHT

Floor Covering Selection

The selection of finish-flooring materials, adhesives and finishes has many implications for Healthy Housing in terms of occupant health and resource efficiency. Toxic substances should be avoided as well as materials or products that are non-renewable, non-reusable or non-recyclable. Products that are obtained from fragile ecosystems or produced using methods that are not environmentally responsible should not be selected. A large number of appropriate finish flooring options are still available after these Healthy Housing criteria are applied.

Appropriate Covering Choices

→ Stone and ceramic tile represent traditional floor coverings that are durable, easy to clean and maintain, and non-toxic provided appropriate adhesives and grouts are used.

→ Hardwood strip flooring is a product with proven performance. Hardwood trees can be found that have been sustainably harvested and processed. An appropriate finish must be selected to promote acceptable indoor air quality. Laminated (composite wood) flooring, bamboo flooring and cork tiles are suitable alternatives to hardwood strip flooring.

→ Natural or "battleship" linoleum is a highly durable floor finish made from completely renewable ingredients. Available in a wide variety of colours, it is regaining popularity over synthetic sheet and roll flooring.

→ Synthetic carpeting should be avoided since it is made from non-renewable materials and cannot be recycled. Appropriate alternatives include wool carpeting and area rugs, sisal and coir stair and hallway runners, and cotton area rugs.

Adhesives and Finishes

Many solvent-based adhesives and finishes contain toxic substances such as volatile organic compounds (VOCs). Their use may be avoided by selecting more appropriate types of products.

→ Use water-based adhesives and finishes wherever possible, since these contain fewer toxins than similar solvent-based products.

→ Look for the EcoLogo™ on products, indicating a reduced level of toxic contaminants.

Interior Doors, Frames and Trim

INTERIOR DOORS, FRAMES AND TRIM

Interior doors, door frames and interior trim are usually installed after hardwood flooring is in place, but before it is sanded and before the resilient flooring is laid. Kitchen cabinets and other millwork are also usually installed at this stage. The decorative treatment for interior doors and trim may be paint or natural finish using stain, filler and varnish, or other selected materials. The finish selected for woodwork in various rooms may determine the type or species of wood to be used.

Wood trim should be milled from smooth, clean, and sound stock suitable for finishing. Some of the commonly used species are oak, pine, fir, basswood and poplar. Finger-joined wood trim is acceptable for painted applications but solid wood is recommended for stains and clear finish applications. The moisture content of the wood trim at the time of installation should not be more than 12 per cent.

Door frames are made up of two jambs and a head, together with separate mouldings called doorstops. Stock jambs are made of ¾ in. nominal (19 mm) lumber and in widths to suit the thickness of the finished wall. Jambs are often dadoed at the mill, with doorstops and head cut to size (Figure 144). Frames may also be rabbetted to form the stop, in which case the thickness of the frame is usually increased to 1¼ in. (32 mm). If frames are unassembled when delivered, they should be securely nailed together at each corner.

Casing is the framing or edging trim used around door openings. Many standard patterns can be found in various widths and thicknesses. Those with moulded forms usually require mitre joints.

There are two general types of interior doors: flush and panel. The standard thickness of interior doors is 1⅜ in.

Interior door frame showing typical connection between jamb and head

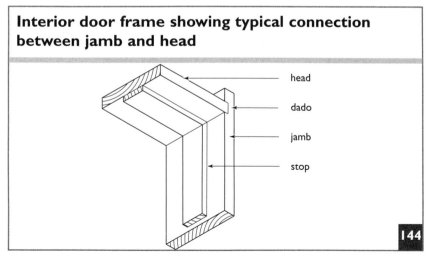

head

dado

jamb

stop

144

(35 mm). They may be obtained in various widths and heights.

The flush door is made up of facings of plywood or other sheet material glued to a light framework. For a natural or varnished finish, the face plies are selected for quality and colour. For a painted finish, the face plies may be less expensive or non-select grades.

The panel door consists of solid stiles and rails with panel fillers of various materials. These create relief panels in the door and are available in a number of designs.

Special doors are available with various kinds of hardware. Sliding doors and folding doors are popular for clothes closets.

Doors should be hinged so that they open in the direction of natural entry. Doors should also swing against a blank wall wherever possible and not be obstructed by other swinging doors.

Interior doors are usually 30 in. (760 mm) wide and 6 ft. 8 in. (1.98 m) high. Kitchen doors and doors providing access to laundry and utility rooms should be at least 32 in. (810 mm) wide. These sizes will generally allow easy passage of furniture. The National Building Code prescribes minimum sizes for interior doors.

Alignment of the interior door frame is done by means of shims between the jamb and rough-opening studs (Figure 145). Wood shingles may be used for this purpose. Frames are set plumb and

Door frame and trim showing frame blind-nailed under doorstop

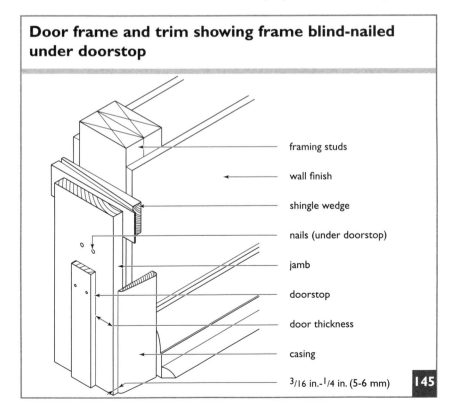

framing studs

wall finish

shingle wedge

nails (under doorstop)

jamb

doorstop

door thickness

casing

3/16 in.-1/4 in. (5-6 mm) **145**

square, wedges are fitted snugly, and the jambs are then securely nailed to the studs through the wedges. After nailing, the wedges are sawed flush with the face of the wall. Nails should be driven in pairs, as shown in Figure 145.

Casings are nailed to both the framing studs and the jambs with finish nails. Nails should be spaced about 16 in. (400 mm) apart and the heads countersunk and filled with wood putty. The casing is placed ⁵⁄₁₆ to ¼ in. (5 to 6 mm) from the inner edge of the jamb.

Stops are usually ⅜ x 1 ¼ in. (10 x 32 mm) and are nailed to the jamb with finishing nails after the door is hung.

Casing joints at the head of the frame are usually mitred. Careful cutting and fitting is required to ensure a tight joint. Mitred joints are sometimes glued because a glued joint is less likely to open if shrinkage occurs.

Standard clearances and the location of door hardware are shown in Figure 146. The clearances may vary slightly, but those shown are most commonly used. Hinges are placed approximately 7 in. (175 mm) from the top and 11 in. (275 mm) from the bottom of the door, but these distances may vary slightly, especially in panel doors. Where three hinges are used, the centre one is spaced midway between the top and bottom hinges. Standard knob height is 34 to 38 in. (860 to 960 mm) from the floor, and locks or latches should be installed accordingly. Lever-type handles permit easier operation by persons with limited dexterity.

Suggested door clearance and location of hardware

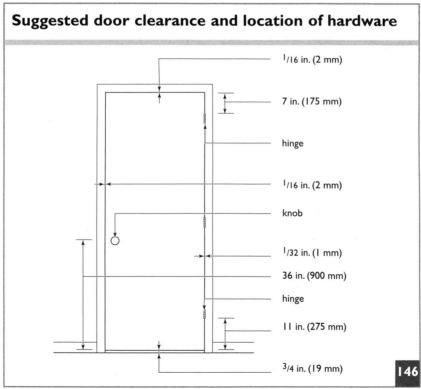

¹/16 in. (2 mm)	
7 in. (175 mm)	
hinge	
¹/16 in. (2 mm)	
knob	
¹/32 in. (1 mm)	
36 in. (900 mm)	
hinge	
11 in. (275 mm)	
³/4 in. (19 mm)	**146**

Clearance around the door should be ⅟₁₆ to ³⁄₃₂ in. (2 to 3 mm) on the latch side and ⅟₃₂ in. (1 mm) on the hinge side. A clearance of ⅟₁₆ in. (2 mm) at the top and ¾ in. (19 mm) at the bottom is usual, but if the door is to open over heavy carpeting, the bottom clearance should be greater. This permits air movement either into or out of the room.

Some manufacturers supply pre-fitted frames and doors, with the hinge slots already grooved for installation. Also available are sheet-metal door frames with formed stops and casings. Hinge slots and stops plates are integral to these units.

INSTALLATION OF DOOR HARDWARE

Hinges should be the proper size for the door they support. For 1⅜ in. (35 mm) thick interior doors, two 3 x 3 in. (76 x 76 mm) butt hinges are used. The door is first fitted to the jamb opening to ensure it has the proper clearances, then the door is removed, and the hinges are fitted to it. The door edge is mortised to take the two half hinges. The edge of each hinge should be at least ⅛ in. (3 mm) back from the face of the door. When the hinge halves are screwed in place, they must be flush with the surface and square.

The door is now placed in the opening and shimmed up at the bottom to provide the proper clearance. The jamb is marked at the hinge locations and mortised to take the other two hinge halves that are then fastened in place.

The door may now be placed in the opening, and the hinge pins inserted.

There are several types of door locks that vary both in cost and in method of installation. Lock sets are supplied with installation instructions. Passage locks may be used where privacy is a concern, such as in bathrooms.

The location of the latch is marked on the jamb, and the strike plate located to accommodate the latch. The marked outline is then mortised for the strike plate. The recess for the latch is also mortised (Figure 147A). The strike plate is then fixed in place and should be flush with or slightly below the face of the jamb. When the door is latched, the face of the door should be flush with the edge of the jamb.

Doorstops may have been set temporarily during the installation of the hardware, but now is the time to nail them permanently in place. The stop at the jamb on the latch side is nailed first (Figure 147B) and should be set against the door face when the door is latched. Allow space for movement and paint finishes. The stop on the hinge side is nailed next and should be given a ⅟₃₂ in. (1 mm) clearance from the door face to prevent scraping when opening the door. Finally, the head stop is nailed in place. Finishing nails should be used and the heads countersunk and filled. When door and trim are painted, some of the clearances allowed will be taken up.

Door installation

(A) typical strike plate

(B) stops

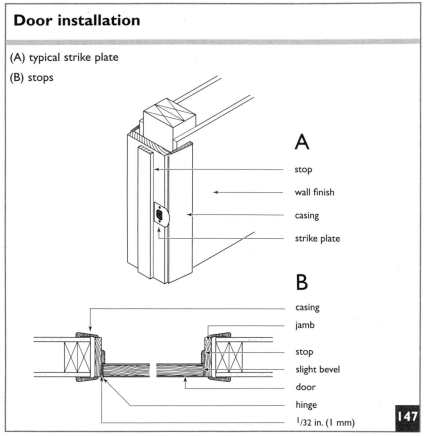

A

stop

wall finish

casing

strike plate

B

casing

jamb

stop

slight bevel

door

hinge

^{1}/32 in. (1 mm)

147

WINDOW TRIM INSTALLATION

Casing for window trim is usually the same pattern selected for the doors. Casing is applied with finishing nails on all four sides of the window, except where a sill is used. In this instance, the casing terminates on top of the sill, and an apron is added as a finish trim below the sill.

BASE MOULDINGS

Base moulding serves as a finish between the walls and floor. They may vary in size and form, but must be sufficiently thick at the bottom to cover the flooring joint. A two-piece base moulding consists of a baseboard fitted with a shoe mould at the bottom (Figure 148A). A one-piece base is milled with a thickened edge at the bottom to cover the flooring joint (Figure 148B).

When a two-piece base is used, the baseboard is nailed through to the wall plate and studs, high enough so that the lower edge clears the finish floor.

The shoe mould is later nailed to the floor using a long thin nail driven at an angle that holds the shoe mould tightly against both the baseboard and the finish floor. A one-piece base is fitted tightly to the finish floor and nailed to the wall plate or studs. The one-piece base or the shoe mould is installed after the resilient floor or carpet has been laid or after hardwood flooring has been sanded.

Joints at interior corners may either be mitred or butted and coped. Butted and coped corners are made by butting the first piece of trim against the corner. The second piece is then coped to match the profile of the first piece. Exterior corners are mitred. Fasten with finishing nails with heads countersunk and filled.

MILLWORK

Kitchen cabinets, shelving, mantels and other items of millwork are installed at the same time as the interior trim. This work is ordinarily carried out before the hardwood floors are sanded or the resilient flooring laid.

Cabinets may be either built in place or shop-built. The cabinets, shelving and other items can be made from a variety of wood products.

KITCHEN CABINETS

The kitchen deserves special attention, since it is a focal point of household activity and must accommodate several functions. An efficient arrangement

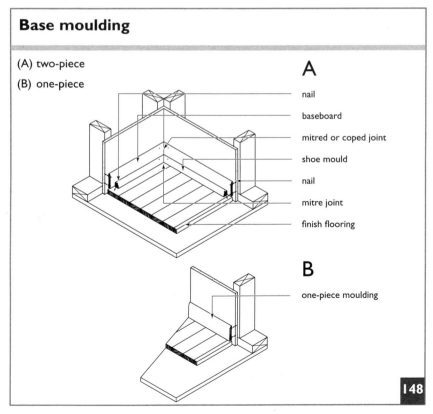

Base moulding

(A) two-piece
(B) one-piece

A

nail
baseboard
mitred or coped joint
shoe mould
nail
mitre joint
finish flooring

B

one-piece moulding

148

of kitchen cabinets, sink, refrigerator and appliances, such as microwave ovens and range, reduces work and saves steps.

Base units of kitchen cabinets are approximately 36 in. (900 mm) high, and the countertop is 25 in. (625 mm) deep (Figure 149). Various combinations of drawers and doors may be included in the base. Some cabinet arrangements include a corner cabinet equipped with revolving shelves. The countertop and backsplash (added along the wall above the countertop) are faced with plastic laminate or other impervious covering. Countertops are also manufactured with a number of finishes, such as laminates, and generally include the backsplash.

To provide workspace, wall units are set about 16 in. (400 mm) above the counter. The finishes and cabinetry installed directly above the location of the range or stove must be 30 in. (750 mm) away above the elements or burners. Where the cabinets are protected

---

An arrangement of kitchen cabinets

optional drop ceiling

wall cabinets

shelf

countertop splash back

drawer

shelf

base cabinets

toe space

space for refrigerator

149

CHECKING BACK

Advance Ordering of Cabinets

Items such as kitchen cabinets, bathroom vanities and any other custom built-in furnishings are not usually available on short notice. When planning the house, consult with suppliers to determine the lead time needed to ensure that the cabinets will be ready for delivery when the house is near completion. Allow for additional time during busy periods of construction when suppliers may be running behind schedule.

by non-combustible surfaces or are fitted with a metal hood projecting 5 in. (125 mm) beyond the edge of the cabinets, the distance between them and the burners can be reduced to 24 in. (600 mm). The shelves, which can be adjustable, are usually 11 to 12 in. (275 to 300 mm) deep. The ceiling may be dropped over the cabinets as shown in Figure 148.

CLOSETS

Although many variations are possible, coat and clothes closets are commonly provided with shelves and a closet rod or metal track. A standard interior door can be installed (Figure 150A);

however, sliding doors in pairs or other multiple combinations are often used. Sliding doors are hung on a track with rollers fastened to the doors (Figure 150C). Bifold doors, which resemble normal-size doors that have been divided in half and hinged in the middle, are also used.

Built-in cabinets may also be used in bedrooms. Although this type of unit costs more than a standard closet, built-in dressers and chests of drawers eliminate the need for much of the bedroom furniture (Figure 150B). Many modular arrangements of shelving and storage systems are available for use in closets.

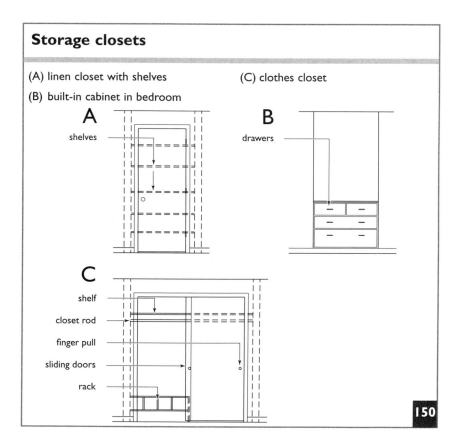

Storage closets

(A) linen closet with shelves

(C) clothes closet

(B) built-in cabinet in bedroom

A
shelves

B
drawers

C
shelf
closet rod
finger pull
sliding doors
rack

150

HEALTHY HOUSING INSIGHT

Interior Trim and Cabinet Selection

When selecting interior trim and cabinets, it is important to consider the source of materials, how they are obtained and processed, and their durability and reusability. Many of the hardwoods used for interior doors and trim are harvested from fragile ecosystems in a manner that is not environmentally responsible. In the case of kitchen cabinets, many products use particleboard bonded with urea-formaldehyde glues that off-gas formaldehyde—an irritant to the respiratory tract. The finishes on many cabinets employ synthetic veneers made from non-renewable and non-recyclable materials. When these become scratched or faded, the cabinets are often removed and end up in landfills. Inappropriate choices can become wasteful.

Viable Options

➜ Interior doors and trim are now available in local species, such as poplar, pine and spruce, or made using medium-density fibreboard (MDF). These products do not rely on exotic and endangered wood species and are easy to finish and maintain.

➜ Select kitchen cabinets that are modular and made from solid wood or particleboard bonded with low-toxicity glues. Standardized kitchen cabinet and drawer modules permit the easy replacing or refacing of door and drawer fronts. These cabinets may alternatively be sold for reuse to a growing number of used building supply stores, where their standard size keeps them in demand by homeowners with limited budgets.

➜ Select used interior doors, trims and cabinets over new products. In many cases, well-crafted products are available at a fraction of the cost for new products.

➜ Reduce the amount of built-in cabinetry and closets by opting for furniture intended to serve the same storage function. Furniture manufacturers have resumed production of more traditional items such as dry sinks, side tables, buffets and wardrobes. Consider investing in future heirlooms that can be used by subsequent generations.

Refer to the "Painting" chapter for more insights on appropriate finishes for interior doors, trim and cabinets.

Painting

EXTERIOR PAINTING AND STAINING

The primary purpose of exterior painting is to protect surfaces from the weather and to enhance appearance.

A wide variety of paints, stains and other coatings are available for exterior and interior use. Good quality materials should be selected and applied according to the manufacturer's recommendations. Since the cost of the materials is usually a small proportion of the total cost of painting, it is false economy to use poor quality materials. Good quality house paint, properly applied, will often last five years between paintings.

Surfaces to be painted should be clean and free from substances that will interfere with the adhesion of the paint. After the prime coat is applied, nail holes, cracks and other defects should be filled with putty or other suitable filler. Painting should not be carried out in temperatures below 50˚F (10˚C). The surface to be painted should be dry.

Clear coatings that provide a protective film over the surface of wood may be adversely affected by direct sunlight, and have a short life expectancy on surfaces exposed to the sun's rays unless they contain an ultraviolet inhibitor. Direct sunlight can cause the film to disintegrate and fall off in patches, leaving parts of the wood exposed. Since the parts of the film that remain are often hard and brittle, preparing the surface for re-coating becomes difficult. Coloured stains, either transparent or semi-transparent, soak into the wood

leaving no visible film on the surface and protect all sides of the house much longer than most clear finishes. Re-coating is also much easier as it can be done with a minor amount of surface preparation.

INTERIOR PAINTING

Interior surfaces are painted to provide a pleasing appearance, and to protect them from damage by moisture that is prevalent in the kitchen, bathroom and laundry room. Painted surfaces are also easier to clean.

Typically, walls and ceilings finished in drywall or plaster are painted, but doors, trim, and interior millwork may be painted, stained or varnished. The key to success for both types of finishes involves planning, preparation and proper application.

Interior painting should not proceed until practically all of the other work in the house is complete. Unless dust can be cleaned up beforehand, and controlled during the painting stage, it is unlikely that acceptable results will be achieved.

Surfaces must be smooth, clean, dry and free of greasy or oily films. Drywall should be dry-mopped or vacuumed before applying the primer coat. Any noticeable blemishes in the taping or filling of the drywall should be corrected, then cleaned up and re-primed before proceeding with the first coat of paint. Do not apply paints in temperatures below 50˚F (10˚C), and always allow the required amount of time between coats. Do not excessively thin paints as this greatly decreases their wear resistance and washability. Correct mixing will provide the required consistency for proper application.

When staining and varnishing wood doors, trim, interior millwork and floors, it is recommended to try the stain on a sample of the material before proceeding with a full application. Some wood species may require a sealant prior to staining to avoid uneven penetration of the stain. Wood-strip floors are usually sealed before applying any type of finish. When staining and sealing are completed, a light sanding is recommended before varnishing. Pre-finished wood flooring is available in several different wood species, colours and finishes. It offers the advantage of replacing a damaged piece without the need to match colour and gloss with adjoining areas.

Varnishes should not be applied in thick coats since they may run or sag. Two thin coats, with light sanding and sufficient drying time between, are adequate for most residential applications. Items such as stair treads and handrails may warrant a third coat.

When performing interior painting, it is important, in addition to maintaining the required indoor temperature, to provide sufficient ventilation and lighting. Store all solvent-based paints and cleaners outside the home. Dispose of all rags, paints, stains and thinners in an appropriate manner, usually at special depots for toxic wastes.

In all cases, follow the manufacturer's application instructions to attain proper finish appearance and performance.

HEALTHY HOUSING INSIGHT

Paint Finishes Selection

There is a wide variety of paint products available, and fortunately, the number of considerations involving the appropriate selection of painted finishes is far less numerous. These have been summarized below.

Environmental Concerns

➜ Indoor air quality can be jeopardized when painted finishes containing toxic chemicals are used in the house. This is due to the large surface area of the finish that is exposed and may continue to off-gas contaminants for a long period of time.

➜ Local air pollution is caused where paints containing volatile organic compounds (VOCs) are manufactured.

➜ Clean-up and disposal hazards associated with painted finishes that contain VOCs, or require cleaning solvents containing VOCs, may cause local pollution problems. The cost of properly disposing of solvent-based paints, thinners and cleaners is very high.

Environmental Choices

➜ Avoid solvent-based finishes and consider water-based (latex) alternatives instead.

➜ Look for finishes that bear the EcoLogo™, and use those where the levels of toxic substances in the paint product are minimal.

➜ Choose interior finishes that do not require a painted finish, such as natural wood panelling, decorative stucco, ceramic tile, stone and masonry.

➜ Select paint products that are easy to clean and durable so that the time between painting is maximized.

➜ Store paints outside the house and properly dispose of all paints and solvents. Never pour these down the drain or over the ground.

➜ Painted finishes that have minimal health and environmental impacts. are available for walls, ceilings, floors, and trim and should be considered as appropriate alternatives in Healthy Housing.

Eavestroughs
and Downspouts

EAVESTROUGHS AND DOWNSPOUTS

The use of eavestroughs and downspouts in Canadian housing has become so common that many people regard them as mandatory. They are not required, however, by most building codes. Eavestroughs and downspouts reduce groundwater adjacent to the foundation and thus provide extra insurance against foundation leakage. They may, however, contribute to ice-damming problems. (See Figure 75, p. 160, in the chapter on "Roof Sheathing and Coverings.")

Formed metal eavestroughs are available in continuous, one-piece lengths or in several different lengths. Fittings such as inside and outside corners, downspout connectors and elbows are available in sizes and angles to suit installation requirements. Plastic materials are also used for eavestroughs and downspouts.

Eavestroughs are installed after the exterior finish is complete. They are mounted on the fascia board as close as possible to the shingle overhang, with a slight slope toward the downspouts. Eavestroughs are fastened with 6 in. (150 mm) corrosion-resistant spikes spaced about 30 in. (750 mm) apart. A sheet-metal spacer tube or ferrule is placed between the interior surfaces of the eavestrough, and the spike is driven through the eavestrough and the ferrule into the fascia board and sub-fascia. Another method is to mount the eavestrough on metal brackets fitted inside the trough. Joints in the eavestrough are soldered or otherwise sealed.

Downspouts may be rectangular or round. Those made from metal are usually corrugated for added strength. The corrugated patterns are also less likely to burst when plugged with ice.

CHECKING BACK

Foundation and Site Drainage

When planning and before installing eavestroughs and downspouts, check back for any impacts on the foundation and site drainage that may be caused by the shedding of rainwater and snow melt from the roof of the house. Considerations involving foundation drainage may be found under the Foundation Drainage section of

"Footings, Foundations and Slabs." Factors to consider regarding site drainage may be found in the **Healthy Housing Insight** titled Siting for Sun, Wind and Water in the "Location and Excavation" chapter.

Goosenecks, composed of elbows and short sections of downspout piping, are used to bring the downspout in line with the wall.

Downspouts are fastened to the wall by means of straps and hooks. At least two hooks or straps should be used with each 10 ft. (3 m) length of downspout.

Where the downspouts are not connected to a storm sewer, an elbow with an extension, or a splash block, is used to direct the water away from the foundation wall and to avoid erosion. The final grading of the lot should ensure positive drainage away from the building and off the lot.

Decks, Porches
and Balconies

DECKS, PORCHES AND BALCONIES

Decks, porches and balconies must be designed to carry snow and occupant loads, be braced to ensure lateral stability, and be supported by a solid foundation. They must also be equipped with adequate guards when more than 2 ft (600 mm) above grade, and be constructed to resist exposure to water. They may be free-standing or attached to the building. When attached to the building, care is required to ensure the attachment does not create a path for water entry into the building envelope.

A 40 psf (1.9 kPa) live load and 10 psf (0.5 kPa) dead load are the design loads frequently used to size wood members for outdoor decks in Canada. If specified snow loads in a given area exceed 40 psf (1.9 kPa), the snow load should be used in the deck design. For the sizing of deck joists and beams refer to Tables 39 and 40, p. 394 and 396. Posts should be a minimum of 4x4 in. (89 x 89 mm) for lengths of up to 6 ft. (1.8 m) and wide enough to fully support all beam plys.

Decks, porches and balconies over 2 ft. (600 mm) and less than 5 ft. 11 in. (1070 mm) above the finished ground level are required to have guards at least 3 ft. (900 mm) high. Guards for decks higher than 5' 11" (1,800 mm) must have guards at least 42 in. (1,070 mm) high. Figure 150 shows a common arrangement for deck foundations, framing and guards. Outdoor decks differ from standard floor construction in that individual deck planks can carry the entire load—there is no subfloor to distribute the load. For this reason it is important to ensure that the decking is thick enough and adequately supported to withstand the anticipated loads. Deck planks should be at least 1 in. (25 mm) thick and common widths are 4 and 6 in. (89 and 140 mm).

Low-level decks should be built so that the bottoms of the deck joists are at least 6 in. (150 mm) above the ground to prevent moisture being transferred to the decking from grass or ground cover. Wood materials should be pressure treated or made from durable species like eastern or western cedar. All deck planks should be oriented so that the ends of the annual rings on the ends of the planks point down. In this way, any cupping that takes place will drain rather than puddle. In addition, a 1/8 in. (3 mm) space should be provided between the decking to allow drainage and drying.

Special attention is required when decks are bolted to the building envelope. Usually the surface of the deck should be located at least 3/4 in. (19 mm) below the floor level of the building and should slope a minimum of 1 per cent away from the building to remove rain and snowmelt. Decks attached to buildings with siding should have flashing installed behind the siding and lapped over the header joist or ledger (Figure 152).

Wood deck detail

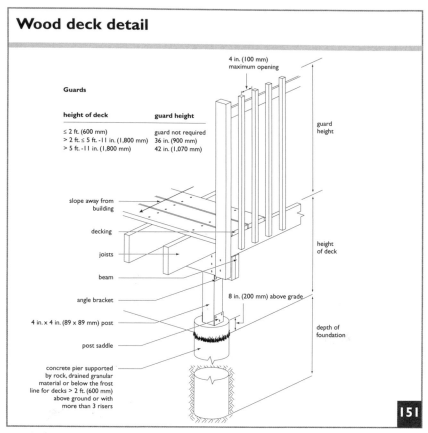

4 in. (100 mm)
maximum opening

guard
height

Guards

height of deck	guard height
≤ 2 ft. (600 mm)	guard not required
> 2 ft. ≤ 5 ft. -11 in. (1,800 mm)	36 in. (900 mm)
> 5 ft. -11 in. (1,800 mm)	42 in. (1,070 mm)

slope away from building

decking

joists

beam

angle bracket

4 in. x 4 in. (89 x 89 mm) post

post saddle

concrete pier supported by rock, drained granular material or below the frost line for decks > 2 ft. (600 mm) above ground or with more than 3 risers

8 in. (200 mm) above grade

height of deck

depth of foundation

151

Deck connection to house

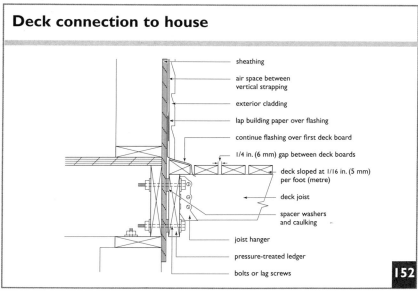

sheathing

air space between vertical strapping

exterior cladding

lap building paper over flashing

continue flashing over first deck board

1/4 in. (6 mm) gap between deck boards

deck sloped at 1/16 in. (5 mm) per foot (metre)

deck joist

spacer washers and caulking

joist hanger

pressure-treated ledger

bolts or lag screws

152

Garages and Carports

GARAGES AND CARPORTS

Garages can be classified as attached, detached or built-in. The type used is sometimes determined by the nature and size of the lot. Where it is feasible, the attached garage has many points in its favour. It is warmer during cold weather and, when equipped with a connecting door to the house, provides covered protection between car and house.

Built-in garages with living accommodation over the garage area are sometimes used in two-storey houses. A built-in garage may also be incorporated into the basement where reasonable access from the street can be provided. However, considering the snow and ice conditions in some regions, the slope of the driveway to the garage door should be gentle. A grated trough and drain should be installed in front of the garage door.

It is a mistake to make the garage too small for convenient use. Motor vehicles vary in size. The garage should be long and wide enough for most models and still leave space to walk around the vehicle. This requires a minimum of 20 ft. (6.1 m) between the inside face of the front and rear walls. If a workbench or storage space will be located on the rear wall, the length of the garage must be increased accordingly. A width of 10 ft. (3.05 m) clear should be a minimum, but 11 ft. 6 in. (3.5 m) or more is better so that doors on either side of the vehicle can be opened freely. A two-car garage should be at least 18 ft. 3 in. (5.55 m) wide. Since garage space is valuable for storage of

garden tools and equipment, bicycles, and other articles, additional space should be considered for this purpose.

Footings and foundations for garages are discussed in the chapter on "Footings, Foundations and Slabs."

The framing and exterior finish of the garage's sidewalls and roof are similar to that of the house. Interior finish is largely a matter of choice. For single dwellings, a fire separation is not required between the garage and the house, but there must be an air barrier in the separating walls to ensure fumes do not enter the living area. Any door between the garage and house must be fitted with weatherstripping and a self-closing device to prevent gas and exhaust fumes from entering the house. The operation of motor vehicles in garages is a potential source of carbon monoxide (CO), a colourless, odourless gas that can accumulate in lethal concentrations in enclosed spaces without occupants being aware of it. Even though an air barrier system is required between garages and living areas, there have been cases of CO from garages entering houses. Every bedroom that shares a wall with a garage, or shares a wall with an attic space that abuts a garage needs to be protected by a CO alarm located either in the bedroom, or not more than 16 ft. (5 m) (measured along hallways) from the bedroom door. Electrical and mechanical systems that run between a garage and a living area must be designed to keep fumes and exhausts from entering the house.

Common walls between the house and the garage should be insulated and fitted with air barriers and vapour retarders. If the garage is to be heated, insulation and an air barrier should be included and covered with a wall finish to protect them from damage.

There are many types of doors for garages, each with different advantages. The two most commonly used are the swing-up door (Figure 153) and the sectional overhead door (Figure 153B). The one-piece, swing-up door operates on a pivot principle with the track mounted on the ceiling and rollers located at the centre and top of the door. Counterbalance springs are mounted on the door, one at each side to make operation easier.

The sectional overhead door has rollers at each section fitted into a track up each side of the door and along the ceiling. It also has a counterbalance spring to ease the operation of the door. These doors are often fitted with automatic openers.

Carports are usually attached to the house with all or most of the other three sides open. Carport roofs are usually supported by posts located on top of concrete piers. Piers should be at least 8 x 8 in. (190 x 190 mm). Round piers formed in paper cylinders, called "sono tubes," are often used for this purpose. The base of the pier should be sufficiently large to ensure that the safe bearing pressure for the soil is not exceeded and far enough below grade to prevent frost heaving. Where wood posts are used, piers should extend at least 6 in. (150 mm) above the ground to protect the posts from ground moisture. Posts must be securely anchored to both piers and roof framing to resist wind uplift.

Types of garage doors

(A) overhead swing

(B) overhead sectional

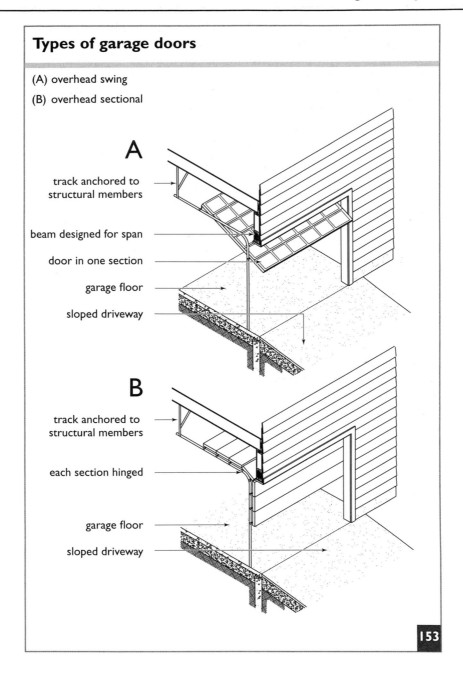

A

track anchored to structural members

beam designed for span

door in one section

garage floor

sloped driveway

B

track anchored to structural members

each section hinged

garage floor

sloped driveway

153

Surface Drainage, Driveways and Walkways

SURFACE DRAINAGE, DRIVEWAYS AND WALKWAYS

Site planning and grading needs to be considered at the initial planning stage (refer to "Typical House Construction Process," p. 19). To create a successful landscape plan, it is necessary to assess the needs for surface drainage, driveways and walkways. Driveways and walkways should be made of materials in character with the house and yard.

SURFACE DRAINAGE

Drainage must be considered in the initial planning stage to locate the house on a property and to plan the elevation of the house relative to the site and utilities. Drainage must also be considered for effective removal of rain and snowmelt from the site, and for the connection of the house to water and waste water services. A surface drainage pattern should be established which will drain the entire lot and direct water away from the house (Figure 3). Driveways and walkways should be set low enough to avoid interfering with the drainage pattern. If a well is used to supply water for the house, all surface drainage must be directed away from the well to avoid contaminating the water supply.

The finished grade should be sloped away from the foundation wall of the house, and provision made to carry the surface water off the property. A swale (a gently sloping ditch) is used for this purpose where the drainage slope around the house meets a reverse slope.

For example, if a lot slopes up from the front to rear, the swale should be located at the rear of the house so that the surface water flows along the swale, around the house, and out toward the street or roadside ditch. While a 5 per cent slope is acceptable, a 10 per cent slope for the first 6 ft. 6 in. (2 m) is preferred to ensure the correct slope after the soil settles and compacts. Use at least a 2 per cent slope for impermeable surfaces adjacent to the house, such as a driveway.

DRIVEWAYS

A safe driveway should not slope too steeply to the street due to winter's slippery conditions and should be graded so that the water will not accumulate on the surface. The suggested maximum gradient along the length is 5 per cent and for the cross slope it is 2 per cent. Whether concrete, asphalt or paving stone is used to surface the driveway, at least 6 in. (150 mm) of compacted granular sub-base should be provided.

The commonly used materials for driveways are concrete, asphalt, interlocking pavers and crushed stone. A full-width driveway is preferable, although a satisfactory driveway may be made of two ribbons at least 24 in. (600 mm) wide, spaced about 5 ft. (1.5 m) apart centre-to-centre. The ribbon type is more economical than full-width pavement. It is not, however, suitable for use where curves and turnout areas are required.

The full-width driveway is easier to drive over. In addition, by increasing its width, the full-width driveway may also serve as a walkway. A driveway should be at least 8 ft. (2.4 m) wide, and increased to 10 ft. (3 m) when it serves as a walkway.

In the construction of driveways, the area to be paved should be graded to a uniform smooth surface and be well compacted. All soft material, loose rocks and boulders must be removed to a depth of approximately 4 in. (100 mm) and the holes filled with granular material and well tamped. If the ground has recently been filled, it should be well compacted because any settlement in the subsoil is likely to cause cracking in the finished driveway. A well-compacted base of gravel or crushed stone, at least 4 in. (100 mm) thick, is necessary if the driveway is to be surfaced with asphalt. Asphalt is usually about 1 1/2 in. (40 mm) thick. Concrete 5 in. (125 mm) thick may be used without a base, but this thickness can be reduced to 3 in. (75 mm) when put down over a 5 in. (125 mm) granular base.

Concrete placing, finishing and curing should be carried out as described under Basement Floor Slabs in the chapter on "Footings, Foundations and Slabs." Overworking the surface during bull floating operations, that is, bringing up too much paste and bleed water, will result in a less durable finish. Control joints in concrete driveways should be placed from 10 to 12 ft. (3 to 3.5 m) apart. The resulting panels should be nearly square. Isolation joints, consisting of premoulded joint filler or sheathing paper, should be used to isolate the driveway from the curb, garage slab and house foundation wall. Control joints should be made as described under Basement Floor Slabs. Premoulded joint filler in isolating joints should extend to the full depth of the driveway slab and be 1/4 to 1/2 in. (6 to 12 mm) thick.

WALKWAYS

Cast-in-place concrete, precast slabs and flagstones are commonly used for walkways. Other types of material such as asphalt, or concrete pavers, fine gravel or crushed stone may also be used.

Walkways should be built on a well-compacted base, with a slight slope to drain the water off the surface. The recommended maximum gradient for a walkway along its length is 5 per cent with a maximum cross-slope of 2 per cent. A base course is not normally used under concrete walks but must be used under asphalt surfaces. Concrete walks should be at least 4 in. (100 mm) thick and asphalt at least 1 1/2 in. (40 mm) thick. Control joints are included in concrete walks for the same reason as described for driveways. These joints are usually spaced apart about one-and-a-half times the walkway width. Precast slabs are generally laid in a levelling bed of sand or stone dust.

RELATED PUBLICATION

Landscape Guide for Canadian Homes
Canada Mortgage and Housing Corporation

HEALTHY HOUSING INSIGHT

Environmental Control of Stormwater

There are a number of cases where the placing of a house on a site has had negative effects on the natural flow patterns of runoff. This may occur if the home is built in a rural area with a fragile ecosystem, but is more common in areas where a large number of homes is being constructed, and the entire site is being graded into a new topography. Some important considerations have been summarized below.

➜ Site the building so that natural drainage patterns are not interrupted; when this is not possible, grade the site so that these drainage patterns are maintained.

➜ Where possible avoid the drainage of roof runoff to the municipal sewer system or the foundation drainage system. In both cases, this increases the potential for basement flooding.

➜ Connect the downspouts of eavestroughs to a storage container, such as a rain barrel or cistern, and use this water for lawn watering and car washing.

➜ Plan landscaping that will capture and retain runoff in cases where a large roof area is drained to a single point. The retention of water in areas where it will slowly percolate back into the soil is an effective alternative.

Impacts of house construction can be minimized through careful planning and design. Consult environmental authorities for further assistance in the responsible management of stormwater.

Protection Against Decay
and Termites

PROTECTION AGAINST DECAY AND TERMITES

Wood will not decay when used in conditions where it is kept dry or even where it is subject to short periods of intermittent wetting followed by rapid drying. However, all wood and wood products used in construction are subject to decay if allowed to remain wet for long periods. Most of the wood used in a house is not subject to this condition, provided suitable precautions are taken. Protection is afforded by methods of design and construction, by use of suitable materials, and in some cases by treating the materials.

The building site should be well drained, and untreated wood should not come in contact with the soil. Foundation walls should extend at least 6 in. (150 mm) above the ground and where wood siding or wood-base sidings are used, they should be kept at least 8 in. (200 mm) from the ground. The ground level in a crawl space should be at least 12 in. (300 mm) below joists and beams, increased to 18 in. (450 mm) where termites are a problem.

Steps, porches, doorsills and windowsills should be sloped to ensure water run-off. A waterproof sill flashing should be installed at the bottom of the door and window rough openings and extend at least 6 in. (150 mm) up the sides of the opening, before the doors and windows are installed. Flashing should be used over doors and windows and other projections where water is likely to seep into the structure. (See the chapter on "Flashing.") Roofs with considerable overhang give added protection to the siding and other parts of the house. Similarly, covered entranceways protect doors.

Exterior wood steps, rails and porch floors exposed to rain and snow have a high decay potential. Unless they are pressure-treated wood members, such applications should not be in direct contact with the ground. It is important to protect the end grain of wood at the joints since end grain absorbs water easily. If pressure-treated lumber must be cut on the job site, the cut ends should be soaked in preservative until they have absorbed as much preservative as possible. The ends and joints in siding may be treated during installation or filled later to prevent the entry of water. A good quality caulking compound should be used around the window frames, door frames, siding that comes in contact with masonry, under doorsills that are not fully protected from rain, and at other similar locations to prevent the entry of water into the structure.

For many years, CCA (chromated copper arsenate) has been the principal treatment for residential applications. This product is being phased out and will be replaced by wood products treated with ACQ (alkaline copper quaternary) and CA (copper azole). Wood products treated with these new preservatives are similar in appearance to the characteristic green colour of CCA. Recommendations for the safe use and handling of wood treated with the new preservatives are similar to those first recommended for CCA. Treated wood contains chemicals and care is required in the handling of treated wood. Gloves should be worn when handling treated wood, a mask should be worn for cutting (as for the cutting of many materials), and treated wood should be discarded in accordance with local regulations and should never be burned. Regular nails or screws should not be used with CCA or ACQ pressure-treated wood, due to the risk of corrosion. Instead, it is recommended to use corrosion-resistant fasteners such as hot dipped galvanized or stainless steel fasteners. Electric galvanized fasteners should also be avoided when using pressure-treated wood as the thin coating on the nail may chip and leave the nail exposed.

Borate is another chemical used to treat wood against termites and decay. Borate treatment is usually colourless and results in a much deeper penetration of the chemical into the wood than other treatment methods. Borates tend to leach out of wood that is exposed to rain. For this reason, borate treated wood is approved only for uses where the wood is protected from direct exposure to moisture.

If a moisture barrier is not used on the ground surface, crawl spaces are apt to become very humid and expose the framing members to conditions conducive to decay. The ground cover, which prevents moisture in the ground from entering the space, should be installed as described in the Crawl Space Ventilation and Ground Cover section of the chapter on "Footings, Foundations and Slabs." An unheated crawl space should also be ventilated in the summer.

In some areas, wood is subject to attack by termites, carpenter ants and powder post beetles. The cold climate of Canada means that termites are present only in a few localized areas in the southernmost parts of British Columbia, Alberta, Manitoba and Ontario. Where termites are known to occur, the clearance between structural wood elements and the ground must be at least 18 in. (450 mm) unless the wood is treated with a chemical that is toxic to termites (for example, ACQ and CA). It is important that structural supports be visible for inspection and the detection of mud tubes that termites build to travel to a food source. Where the foundations are insulated or otherwise constructed in a way that could conceal termite activity, a metal or plastic barrier must be installed through the insulation above finished ground level to control termite passage.

Maintenance

MAINTENANCE

A house that is well built using suitable materials, with adequate attention to construction details as described in this publication, will require far less maintenance than a house that is not well constructed and built of poor quality materials. Yet, while sound construction methods and suitable materials in the initial construction will greatly reduce the cost of maintenance, they will not result in a "maintenance-free" house. Some maintenance can be expected even during the first year of occupancy.

In a newly built house, it is quite common, for example, for the interior wall finish to develop some minor cracks and for some of the doors to stick. These flaws usually show up during or after the first heating season when the wood-frame members may shrink slightly due to changes in moisture content or after the bearing members have settled to their final position under loading.

Quite frequently, the backfill material around the house foundation will settle, which can cause the surface water to pond against the basement or foundation wall. This should be corrected by filling up any settled areas to their proper level as soon as settling has taken place.

Prudent homeowners develop a well-planned program of care and maintenance which they continue throughout the years. Just as maintenance costs are greatly reduced by adequate attention to the methods and materials used in construction, it is equally true that a continuing program of maintenance will further reduce the cost of upkeep, enhance the value of the property, and greatly increase the useful life of the wood-frame house.

RELATED PUBLICATIONS

Home Care: A Guide to Repair and Maintenance
Canada Mortgage and Housing Corporation

Homeowner's Inspection Checklist
Canada Mortgage and Housing Corporation

Homeowner's Manual
Canada Mortgage and Housing Corporation

Appendix A - Tables

Table 1
Conversion factors

Framing terms

	Imperial - nominal (unplaned) dimensions	Metric - dimensions
Lumber	2 in. x 2 in.	38x38 mm
	2 in. x 4 in.	38x89 mm
	2 in. x 6 in.	38x140 mm
	2 in. x 8 in.	38x184 mm
	2 in. x 10 in.	38x235 mm
	2 in. x 12 in.	38x286 mm
Panels	2 ft. x 8 ft.	600 x 2,400 mm
	4 ft. x 8 ft.	1,200 x 2,400 mm
Spacings	12 in. O.C.	300 mm
	16 in. O.C.	400 mm
	24 in. O.C.	600 mm

Units of Measure

°C	x 1.8 + 32 =	°F
kg	x 2.205 =	lb
kPa	x 0.1450 =	lbf/in^2 (psi)
kPa	x 20.88 =	lbf/ft^2
L	x 0.2200 =	gal (imp.)
L/s	x 13.20 =	gal/min (gmp)
lx	x 0.09290 =	ft-candle
m	x 3.281 =	ft
m^2	x 10.76 =	ft^2
m^3	x 35.31 =	ft^3
mm	x 0.03937 =	in.
m^3/h	x 0.5886	ft^3/min (cfm)
m/s	x 196.8 =	ft/min
MJ	x 947.8 =	Btu
N	x 0.2248	lbf
Watts	x 3.412 =	Btu/h
ng/(Pa.s.m^2)	x 0.0174	Perms
Pa	x 0.004014 =	in. of water

Table 2
Concrete mixes (by volume)

Concrete Strength	Cement (part)	Water (not more than)	Sand (parts)	Coarse Aggregate
2,200 psi (15 MPa)	1	4.4 imp. gal. (20 l) per 88 lb. (40 kg.) bag of cement	2	4 parts up to 2 in. (50 mm) in size
	1	4.4 imp. gal. (20 l) per 88 lb. (40 kg.) bag of cement	-	6 parts pit run gravel
3,000 psi (20 MPa)	1	4.0 imp. gal. (18 l) per 88 lb. (40 kg.) bag of cement	1$\frac{3}{4}$	3 parts up to 1$\frac{1}{2}$ in. (40 mm) in size
	1	4.0 imp. gal. (18 l) per 88 lb. (40 kg.) bag of cement	-	4$\frac{3}{4}$ parts pit run gravel

Note to Table 2
1. For higher strength concretes, use commercial suppliers to ensure strength and air entrainement requirements are met.

Table 3
Minimum depths of foundations

Type of Soil	Foundations Containing Heated Basement or Crawl Space		Foundations Containing No Heated Space	
	Good Soil Drainage to at Least the DEPTH of Frost Penetration	Poor Soil Drainage	Good Soil Drainage to at Least the DEPTH of Frost Penetration	Poor Soil Drainage
Clay or soils not clearly defined	4 ft. (1.2 m)	4 ft. (1.2 m)	4 ft. (1.2 m) but not less than the depth of frost penetration	4 ft. (1.2 m) but not less than the depth of frost penetration
Silt	No limit	No limit	Below the depth of frost penetration	Below the depth of frost penetration
Coarse grained soils	No limit	No limit	No limit	Below the depth of frost penetration
Rock	No limit	No limit	No limit	No limit

Table 4
Minimum footing sizes
(Length of supported joists 16 ft. [4.9 m] or less)
(Design floor load 50 lb./sq. ft. [2.4 kN/m²] maximum)

No. of Floors Supported	Minimum Widths of Strip Footings, in. (mm)		Minimum Area of Column Footings[1], sq. ft. (m²)
	Supporting Exterior Walls	Supporting Interior Walls	
1	10 (250)[2]	8 (200)[3]	4.3 (0.4)
2	14 (350)[2]	14 (350)[3]	8 (0.75)
3	18 (450)[2]	20 (500)[3]	11 (1.0)

Notes to Table 4

1. Sizes are based on columns spaced 9 ft., 10 in. (3 m) (on centre). For other column spacings, footing areas must be adjusted in proportion to the distance between columns.

2. For each storey of masonry veneer over wood-frame construction, footing widths must be increased by 2 1/2 in. (65 mm). For each storey of masonry construction other than foundation walls, the footing width must be increased by 5 1/8 in. (130 mm).

3. For each storey of masonry supported by the footing, the footing width must be increased by 4 in. (100 mm).

Table 5
Minimum thickness of foundation walls

Type of Foundation Wall	Minimum Wall Thickness, in. (mm)	Maximum Height of Exterior Finish Grade Above Basement Floor or Inside Grade, ft.–in. (m)	
		Foundation Wall Laterally Unsupported at the Top[1 to 4]	Foundation Wall Laterally Supported at the Top[1 to 4]
Solid concrete, 2,200 psi (15 MPa) minimum strength	6 (150)	2–7 (0.80)	4–11 (1.50)
	8 (200)	3–11 (1.20)	7–0 (2.15)
	10 (250)	4–7 (1.40)	7–6 (2.30)
	12 (300)	4–11 (1.50)	7–6 (2.30)
Solid concrete, 2,900 psi (20 MPa) minimum strength	6 (150)	2–7 (0.80)	5–10 (1.80)
	8 (200)	3–11 (1.20)	7–6 (2.30)
	10 (250)	4–7 (1.40)	7–6 (2.30)
	12 (300)	4–11 (1.50)	7–6 (2.30)
Unit masonry	5 1/2 (140)	1–11 (0.60)	2–7 (0.80)
	9 7/16 (240)	3–11 (1.20)	5–10 (1.80)
	11 7/16 (290)	4–7 (1.40)	7–2 (2.20)

Notes to Table 5

1. Foundation walls are considered laterally supported at the top if the floor joists are embedded in the top of the foundation walls, or if the floor system is anchored to the top of the foundation walls with anchor bolts, in which case the joists may run either parallel or perpendicular to the foundation wall.

2. When a foundation wall contains an opening of more than 3 ft., 11 in. (1.2 m) in length or openings in more than 25 per cent of its length, the portion of the wall beneath such openings is considered laterally unsupported unless the wall around the opening is reinforced to withstand the earth pressure.

3. When the length of solid wall between windows is less than the average length of the windows, the combined length of such windows is considered a single opening.

4. When foundation walls support solid masonry walls, the foundation wall is considered laterally supported by the first floor.

Table 6
Mortar mix proportions (by volume)

Permissible Use of Mortar	Portland Cement	Masonry Cement (Type H)	Lime	Aggregate
All locations[1]	$1/2$ to 1	1	—	
	1	—	$1/4$ to $1/2$	
All locations[1], except foundation walls and piers	—	1	—	Not less than $2 1/4$ and not more than 3 times the sum of the volumes of the cement and lime
	1	—	$1/2$ to $1 1/4$	
All locations, except loadbearing walls of hollow units	1	—	$1 1/4$ to $2 1/2$	
All non-loadbearing partitions and all loadbearing walls of solid units except foundation walls	1	—	$2 1/4$ to 4	
	—	—	1	

Note to Table 6
1. Must not be used for sand-lime brick or concrete brick.

Table 7
Dimension lumber – grades and uses

Sizes, in. (mm)	Grades	Common Grade Mix[1]	Principal Uses	Grade Category
2 to 4 in. (38 to 89 mm) thick; 2 to 4 in (38 to 89 mm) wide	Select structural No. 1 and No. 2	No. 2 and better (No. 2 & Btr.)	Most common; used in most construction. Shows high strength, stiffness and good appearance. Preferred for trusses, rafters and roof joists.	Structural light framing
	No. 3[3]	—	Used in construction where high strength and appearance are not important, such as studs in non-loadbearing walls.	
	Construction[3] Standard[3]	Standard and better (Std. & Btr.)	Most common, used in general framing work. Has less strength than No. 2 and better structural light framing, but is stronger and allows longer spans than No. 3.	Light framing
	Utility[2]	—	Used most economically where high strength is not important, such as studs and plates in partition walls, blocking, and bracing.	
	Economy[2]	—	Used in temporary or low-cost construction where strength and appearance are not important.	

Continued on p. 359

Table 7 (continued)
Dimension lumber – grades and uses

Sizes, in. (mm)	Grades	Common Grade Mix[1]	Principal Uses	Grade Category
2 to 4 in. (38 to 89 mm) thick; 5 in. (114 mm) and wider	Select Structural No. 1 and No. 2	No. 2 & Btr.	Most common; used in most construction where high strength and stiffness are desired, such as floor joists, roof joists and rafters.	Structural joists and planks
	No. 3[3]	—	Used in general construction where strength is not important.	
	Economy[2]	—	Used in temporary or low-cost construction where strength and appearance are not important.	
2 to 4 in. (38 to 89 mm) thick; 2 in. (38 mm) and wider	Stud[3]	—	Most common; special purpose grade intended for all stud uses, including bearing walls	Stud
	Economy stud[2]	—	Used in temporary or low-cost construction where strength and appearance are not important.	

Notes to Table 7

1. For ease in grade sorting at the mill, the higher grades are combined and sold as a grade mix. Pieces of lumber in the grade mix are still individually grade stamped.

2. Except for the utility and economy grades, all grades are stress graded, which means specified strengths have been assigned and span tables calculated.

3. Construction, Standard, Stud and No. 3 Grades are typically used in designs that are not composed of 3 or more essentially parallel members spaced on 24-in. (600 mm) centres or less, so arranged or connected to mutually support loading.

Table 8
Facsimiles of lumber grade marks approved for use in Canada

* Approved to stamp machine-stress rated (MSR) lumber

Facsimile or Grade Mark	Association or organization
A.F.P.A® 00 S-P-F NLGA KD-HT 1	***Alberta Forest Products Association** #200-11738 Kingsway Ave. Edmonton, Alberta T5G 0X5 **Tel:** (780) 452-2841 **Website:** www.abforest.org
CLA 100 SPRUCE PINE FIR No.1 S-DRY	***Canadian Lumbermen's Association** 27 Goulburn Avenue Ottawa, Ontario K1N 8C7 **Tel:** (613) 233-6205 **Website:** cla-ca.ca

COFI   No 1
        S-DRY
        NLGA
100 HEM-FIR(N)
 	
CMSA.   No 1
        KD-HT
        NLGA
100   S-P-F
	*Canadian Mill Services Association
	#200 601 – 6th Street
	New Westminster, British Columbia.
	V3L 3C1
	Tel: (604) 523-1288
	Website: www.canserve.org

CFPA® 00 S-P-F S-DRY CONST	***Central Forest Products Association Inc.** Box 1169, Hudson Bay, Saskatchewan S0E 0Y0 **Tel:** (306) 865-2595
CSI® No 1 S-DRY 000 HEM - FIR (N)	***Canadian Softwood Inspection Agency Inc.** 22089 - 28 Avenue Langley, British Columbia V2Z 1P1 **Tel:** (604) 532-7624

Continued on p. 361

Table 8 (continued)
Facsimiles of lumber grade marks approved for use in Canada

*Approved to stamp machine-stress rated (MSR) lumber

Facsimile or Grade Mark	Association or organization
	***Council of Forest Industries** 360 - 1855 Kirschner Road Kelowna, British Columbia V1Y 4N7 **Tel:** (250) 860-9663 **Website:** www.cofi.org
	**Gateway Lumber Inspection Bureau Limited** 992 Burns Street North Bay, Ontario, P1B 3V4 **Tel:** (705) 474-9148
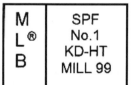	***Interior Lumber Manufacturers' Association** 360 - 1855 Kirschner Road Kelowna, British Columbia V1Y 4N7 **Tel:** (250) 860-9663 **Website:** www.ilma.com
	***Macdonald Inspection Service Ltd.** Suite #110 - 1720 14th Ave. Campbell River, British Columbia V9W 8B9 **Tel:** (250) 287-4422 **Website:** www.gradestamp.com
	**Maritime Lumber Bureau** P.O. Box 459 Amherst, Nova Scotia B4H 4A1 **Tel:** (902) 667-3889 **Website:** www.mlb.ca
(NLGA box mark)	**Newfoundland & Labrador Lumber Producers Association** P.O. Box 8 Glovertown, Newfoundland A0G 2L0 **Tel:** (709) 533-2206 **Website:** www3.nf.sympatico.ca/nllpa

N L P A — N L G A / S-P-F / NO.1 / 000 / KD HT

Continued on p. 362

Table 8 (continued)
Facsimiles of lumber grade marks approved for use in Canada

* Approved to stamp machine-stress rated (MSR) lumber

Facsimile or Grade Mark	Association or organization
10 CONST S-P-F S-GRN	**Northwest Territories Forest Industries Association** P.O. Box 220 Fort Smith, N.W.T. X0E 0P0 **Tel:** (867) 872-2155
O.L.M.A.® 01-1 CONST.　S-DRY SPRUCE - PINE - FIR	*Ontario Lumber Manufacturers' Association** 65 Queen Street West, Suite 210 Toronto, Ontario M5H 2M5 **Tel:** (416) 367-9717 **Website:** www.olma.ca
 NLGA RULE No 1 S-DRY 00　S—P—F	*Pacific Lumber Inspection Bureau** P.B. Box 19118 Fourth Avenue Postal Outlet Vancouver, British Columbia V6K 4R8 **Tel:** (604) 732-1782 **Website:** www.plib.org
ⓡ S-P-F 1 000 S-DRY	*Québec Forest Industry Council** **Conseil de l'industrie forestière du Québec** 1175, avenue Lavigerie, bureau 200 Sainte-Foy, Québec G1V 4P1 **Tel:** (418) 657-7916 **Website:** www.qfic.qc.ca

Table 9
Commercial species of lumber

Commercial Species Group Designation	Grade Stamp Identification	Species in Combination	Wood Characteristics
Spruce – Pine – Fir	S – P – F	Spruce (all species except coast sitka spruce), lodgepole pine, jack pine, alpine fir, balsam fir	Woods of similar characteristics. They work easily, take paint easily and hold nails well. Generally white to pale yellow in colour.
Douglas Fir – Larch	D. Fir – L	Douglas fir, western larch	High degree of hardness and good resistance to decay. Good nail holding, gluing and painting qualities. Colour ranges from reddish-brown to yellowish white.
Hem – Fir	Hem – Fir	Pacific coast hemlock, amabilis fir	They work easily, take paint well and hold nails well. Good gluing characteristics. Colour range pale yellow-brown to white.
Northern Species	North	Western red cedar	Wood with exceptional resistance to decay. Moderate in strength. High in appearance qualities, it works easily and takes fine finishes. Colour varies from reddish-brown heart wood to light sapwood.
	North	Red pine, ponderosa pine	Fairly strong and easy to work woods that take a good finish and hold nails and screws well. Moderately durable; they season with little checking or cupping. Sapwood is a pale yellow colour; heartwood pale brown to reddish tinge.
		Western white pine, eastern white pine	Softest of the Canadian pines, they work and finish exceptionally well. Not as strong as most pines but do not tend to split or splinter. Good nail holding properties. Low shrinkage, better than all other Canadian species except the cedars. Take stains, paints and varnishes well. Colour of sapwood almost white; heartwood creamy white to light straw brown.
		Trembling aspen, largetooth aspen, balsam poplar	Light woods of moderate strength, they work easily, finish well and hold nails well. Generally light in colour, varying from almost white to greyish-white.

ble 10
zes for dimension lumber and boards

	Nominal Sizes, in.	Actual Sizes, in.		Metric Equivalents, mm		Metric Nomen-clature, mm
		Dry	Green	Dry	Green	
Dimension Lumber	2 x 2	1½ x 1½	1⁹⁄₁₆ x 1⁹⁄₁₆	38 x 38	40 x 40	38 x 38
	3	2½	2⁹⁄₁₆	64	65	64
	4	3½	3⁹⁄₁₆	89	90	89
	6	5½	5 ⅝	140	143	140
	8	7¼	7½	184	190	184
	10	9¼	9½	235	241	235
	12	11¼	11½	286	292	286
	3 x 3, etc.	2½ x 2½	2⁹⁄₁₆ x 2⁹⁄₁₆	64 x 64	65 x 65	64 x 64
	4 x 4, etc.	3½ x 3½	3⁹⁄₁₆ x 3⁹⁄₁₆	89 x 89	90 x 90	89 x 89
Boards	1 x 2	¾ x 1½	¹³⁄₁₆ x 1⁹⁄₁₆	19 x 38	21 x 40	19 x 38
	3	2½	2⁹⁄₁₆	64	65	64
	4	3½	3⁹⁄₁₆	89	90	89
	5	4½	4⅝	114	117	114
	6	5½	5⅝	140	143	140
	8	7¼	7½	184	190	184
	10	9¼	9½	235	241	235
	12	11¼	11½	286	292	286
	1¼ x 2, etc.	1 x 1½	1¹⁄₃₂ x 1⁹⁄₁₆	25 x 38	26 x 40	25 x 38
	1½ x2, etc.	1¼ x 1½	1⁹⁄₃₂ x 1⁹⁄₁₆	32 x 38	33 x 40	32 x 38

Table 11
Maximum spans for built-up floor beams supporting not more than one floor[1,2]

Commercial Designation	Grade	Supported Length,[5,6] ft. (m)	2 x 8 (38 x 184) 3-ply	4-ply	5-ply	2 x 10 (38 x 235) 3-ply	4-ply	5-ply	2 x 12 (38 x 286) 3-ply	4-ply	5-ply
D.Fir Larch	No. 1 and No. 2	8	9–8	11–2	12–6	11–10	13–8	15–3	13–8	15–10	17–8
		2.4	2.97	3.42	3.82	3.63	4.19	4.68	4.21	4.86	5.43
		10	8–8	10–0	11–2	10–7	12–2	13–8	12–3	14–2	15–10
		3.0	2.65	3.06	3.42	3.24	3.75	4.19	3.76	4.35	4.86
		12	7–11	9–1	10–2	9–8	11–2	12–5	11–2	12–11	14–5
		3.6	2.42	2.80	3.13	2.96	3.42	3.82	3.44	3.97	4.44
		14	7–4	8–5	9–5	8–11	10–4	11–6	10–4	11–11	13–4
		4.2	2.24	2.59	2.89	2.74	3.17	3.54	3.18	3.67	4.11
		16	6–10	7–11	8–10	8–4	9–8	10–9	9–8	11–2	12–6
		4.8	2.10	2.42	2.71	2.56	2.96	3.31	2.98	3.44	3.84
		18	6–5	7–5	8–4	7–10	9–1	10–2	9–2	10–7	11–9
		5.4	1.98	2.28	2.55	2.42	2.79	3.12	2.81	3.24	3.62
		20	6–1	7–1	7–11	7–6	8–7	9–8	8–8	10–0	11–2
		6.0	1.88	2.17	2.42	2.29	2.65	2.96	2.66	3.07	3.44
Hem-Fir	No. 1 and No. 2	8	10–1	11–7	12–6	12–5	14–4	15–11	14–4	16–07	18–7
		2.4	3.11	3.55	3.82	3.80	4.39	4.88	4.41	5.10	5.70
		10	9–1	10–5	11–7	11–1	12–9	14–4	12–10	14–10	16–7
		3.0	2.78	3.21	3.55	3.40	3.93	4.39	3.95	4.56	5.10
		12	8–3	9–7	10–8	10–1	11–8	13–1	11–9	13–7	15–2
		3.6	2.54	2.93	3.28	3.11	3.59	4.01	3.60	4.16	4.65
		14	7–8	8–10	9–11	9–4	10–10	12–1	10–10	12–6	14–0
		4.2	2.35	2.72	3.04	2.88	3.32	3.71	3.34	3.85	4.31
		16	7–2	8–3	9–3	8–9	10–1	11–4	10–2	11–9	13–1
		4.8	2.20	2.54	2.84	2.69	3.11	3.47	3.12	3.60	4.03
		18	6–9	7–10	8–9	8–3	9–6	10–8	9–7	11–1	12–4
		5.4	2.07	2.39	2.68	2.54	2.93	3.27	2.94	3.40	3.80
		20	6–5	7–5	8–3	7–10	9–0	10–1	9–1	10–6	11–9
		6.0	1.97	2.27	2.54	2.41	2.78	3.11	2.79	3.22	3.60
S-P-F	No. 1 and No. 2	8	10–0	11–0	11–11	12–10	14–1	15–2	14–11	17–2	18–3
		2.4	3.07	3.38	3.64	3.92	4.32	4.65	4.57	5.25	5.59
		10	9–4	10–3	11–0	11–6	13–1	14–1	13–4	15–4	17–2
		3.0	2.85	3.14	3.38	3.52	4.01	4.32	4.09	4.72	5.25
		12	8–7	9–8	10–5	10–6	12–1	13–3	12–2	14–0	15–8
		3.6	2.63	2.95	3.18	3.22	3.71	4.06	3.73	4.31	4.82
		14	7–11	9–2	9–10	9–8	11–2	12–6	11–3	13–0	14–6
		4.2	2.44	2.80	3.02	2.98	3.44	3.84	3.46	3.99	4.46
		16	7–5	8–7	9–5	9–1	10–6	11–8	10–6	12–2	13–7
		4.8	2.28	2.63	2.89	2.79	3.22	3.60	3.23	3.73	4.17
		18	7–0	8–1	9–0	8–7	9–10	11–0	9–11	11–5	12–10
		5.4	2.15	2.48	2.77	2.63	3.03	3.39	3.05	3.52	3.93
		20	6–8	7–8	8–7	8–1	9–4	10–6	9–5	10–10	12–2
		6.0	2.04	2.35	2.63	2.49	2.88	3.22	2.89	3.34	3.73

Maximum Span, ft.–in. (m)[3,4]

Size of Built-up Beam, in. (mm)

Continued on p. 366

able 11 (continued)
Maximum spans for built-up floorbeams supporting not more than one floor[1,2]

Commercial Designation	Grade	Supported Length,[5,6] ft. (m)	2 x 8 (38 x 184)			2 x 10 (38 x 235)			2 x 12 (38 x 286)		
			3-ply	4-ply	5-ply	3-ply	4-ply	5-ply	3-ply	4-ply	5-ply
Northern	No. 1	8	8–5	9–9	10–9	10–3	11–11	13–3	11–11	13–9	15–5
Species	and	2.4	2.59	2.99	3.29	3.16	3.65	4.08	3.67	4.24	4.74
	No. 2	10	7–6	8–8	9–9	9–2	10–8	11–11	10–8	12–4	13–9
		3.0	2.31	2.67	2.99	2.83	3.27	3.65	3.28	3.79	4.24
		12	6–10	7–11	8–10	8–5	9–8	10–10	9–9	11–3	12–7
		3.6	2.11	2.44	2.73	2.58	2.98	3.33	3.00	3.46	3.87
		14	6–4	7–4	8–3	7–9	9–0	10–1	9–0	10–5	11–8
		4.2	1.95	2.26	2.52	2.39	2.76	3.09	2.77	3.20	3.58
		16	5–11	6–10	7–8	7–3	8–5	9–5	8–5	9–9	10–11
		4.8	1.83	2.11	2.36	2.24	2.58	2.89	2.59	3.00	3.35
		18	5–7	6–6	7–3	6–10	7–11	8–10	8–0	9–2	10–3
		5.4	1.72	1.99	2.23	2.11	2.43	2.72	2.45	2.82	3.16
		20	5–4	6–2	6–10	6–6	7–6	8–5	7–7	8–9	9–9
		6.0	1.64	1.89	2.11	2.00	2.31	2.58	2.32	2.68	3.00

Maximum Span, ft.–in. (m)[3,4]

Size of Built-up Beam, in. (mm)

Notes to Table 11
1. Spans apply only where the floors serve residential areas.
2. When the floors have a concrete topping of not more than 2 in. (51 mm), the spans must be multiplied by 0.8.
3. Spans are clear spans between supports. For total span, add two bearing lengths.
4. 3-ply beams with supported lengths greater than 13 ft. 8 in. (4.2 m) require 4 1/2 in. (114 mm) of bearing. All other beams require 3 in. (76 mm) bearing.
5. Supported length means half the sum of the joist spans on both sides of the beam. SJL
6. Straight interpolation may be used for other supported lengths.

Table 12
Maximum spans for built-up floor beams supporting not more than two floors[1,2]

			Maximum Span, ft.–in. (m)[3,4]								
			Size of Built-up Beam, in. (mm)								
		Supported Length, ft.	2 x 8 (38 x 184)			2 x 10 (38 x 235)			2 x 12 (38 x 286)		
Commercial Designation	Grade	(m)[5,6]	3-ply	4-ply	5-ply	3-ply	4-ply	5-ply	3-ply	4-ply	5-ply
D.Fir	No. 1	8	7–3	8–4	9–4	8–10	10–2	11–5	10–3	11–10	13–3
Larch	and	2.4	2.22	2.56	2.87	2.72	3.14	3.51	3.15	3.64	4.07
	No. 2	10	6–6	7–6	8–4	7–11	9–2	10–2	9–2	10–7	11–10
		3.0	1.99	2.29	2.56	2.43	2.80	3.14	2.82	3.25	3.64
		12	5–11	6–10	7–7	7–3	8–4	9–4	8–4	9–8	10–10
		3.6	1.81	2.09	2.34	2.22	2.56	2.86	2.57	2.97	3.32
		14	5–6	6–4	7–1	6–8	7–9	8–7	7–9	8–11	10–0
		4.2	1.68	1.94	2.17	2.05	2.37	2.65	2.38	2.75	3.07
		16	5–1	5–11	6–7	6–3	7–3	8–1	7–3	8–4	9–4
		4.8	1.57	1.81	2.03	1.92	2.22	2.48	2.23	2.57	2.88
		18	4–10	5–7	6–3	5–11	6–10	7–7	6–10	7–11	8–10
		5.4	1.48	1.71	1.91	1.81	2.09	2.34	2.10	2.43	2.71
		20	4–7	5–3	5–11	5–7	6–5	7–3	6–6	7–6	8–4
		6.0	1.40	1.62	1.81	1.72	1.98	2.22	1.99	2.30	2.57
Hem-Fir	No. 1	8	7–7	8–9	9–9	9–3	10–8	12–0	10–9	12–5	13–11
	and	2.4	2.33	2.69	3.01	2.85	3.29	3.68	3.30	3.82	4.27
	No. 2	10	6–9	7–10	8–9	8–3	9–7	10–8	9–7	11–1	12–5
		3.0	2.08	2.41	2.69	2.55	2.94	3.29	2.96	3.41	3.82
		12	6–2	7–2	8–0	7–7	8–9	9–9	8–9	10–2	11–4
		3.6	1.90	2.20	2.45	2.33	2.68	3.00	2.70	3.12	3.48
		14	5–9	6–7	7–5	7–0	8–1	9–1	8–2	9–5	10–6
		4.2	1.76	2.03	2.27	2.15	2.49	2.78	2.50	2.88	3.22
		16	5–4	6–2	6–11	6–7	7–7	8–6	7–6	8–9	9–10
		4.8	1.65	1.90	2.13	2.01	2.33	2.60	2.30	2.70	3.02
		18	5–1	5–10	6–6	6–0	7–2	8–0	6–10	8–3	9–3
		5.4	1.55	1.79	2.00	1.86	2.19	2.45	2.11	2.54	2.84
		20	4–8	5–6	6–2	5–7	6–9	7–7	6–4	7–10	8–9
		6.0	1.44	1.70	1.90	1.72	2.08	2.33	1.96	2.41	2.70
S-P-F	No. 1	8	7–10	9–1	9–11	9–7	11–1	12–5	11–2	12–10	14–5
	and	2.4	2.41	2.79	3.03	2.95	3.41	3.81	3.42	3.95	4.42
	No. 2	10	7–0	8–1	9–1	8–7	9–11	11–1	10–0	11–6	12–10
		3.0	2.16	2.49	2.79	2.64	3.05	3.41	3.06	3.53	3.95
		12	6–5	7–5	8–3	7–10	9–1	10–1	9–1	10–6	10–9
		3.6	1.97	2.27	2.54	2.41	2.78	3.11	2.79	3.23	3.61
		14	5–11	6–10	7–8	7–3	8–5	9–4	8–5	9–9	10–10
		4.2	1.82	2.11	2.35	2.23	2.57	2.88	2.59	2.99	3.34
		16	5–7	6–5	7–2	6–9	7–10	8–9	7–11	9–1	10–2
		4.8	1.71	1.97	2.20	2.09	2.41	2.69	2.42	2.79	3.12
		18	5–3	6–1	6–9	6–5	7–5	8–3	7–5	8–7	9–7
		5.4	1.61	1.86	2.08	1.97	2.27	2.54	2.28	2.63	2.95
		20	5–0	5–9	6–5	6–0	7–0	7–10	6–10	8–2	9–1
		6.0	1.53	1.76	1.97	1.86	2.15	2.41	2.11	2.50	2.79

Continued on p. 368

Table 12 (continued)
Maximum spans for built-up floor beams supporting not more than two floors[1,2]

Commercial Designation	Grade	Supported Length, ft. (m)[5,6]	2 x 8 (38 x 184)			2 x 10 (38 x 235)			2 x 12 (38 x 286)		
			3-ply	4-ply	5-ply	3-ply	4-ply	5-ply	3-ply	4-ply	5-ply
Northern	No. 1	8	6–4	7–3	8–2	7–8	8–11	9–11	8–11	10–4	11–6
Species	and	2.4	1.94	2.24	2.50	2.37	2.73	3.06	2.75	3.17	3.55
	No. 2	10	5–8	6–6	7–3	6–11	7–11	8–11	8–0	9–3	10–4
		3.0	1.73	2.00	2.24	2.12	2.44	2.73	2.46	2.84	3.17
		12	5–2	5–11	6–8	6–3	7–3	8–1	7–4	8–5	9–5
		3.6	1.58	1.83	2.04	1.93	2.23	2.50	2.24	2.59	2.90
		14	4–9	5–6	6–2	5–10	6–9	7–6	6–9	7–10	8–9
		4.2	1.46	1.69	1.89	1.79	2.07	2.31	2.08	2.40	2.68
		16	4–5	5–2	5–9	5–5	6–3	7–0	6–4	7–4	8–2
		4.8	1.37	1.58	1.77	1.67	1.93	2.16	1.94	2.24	2.51
		18	4–2	4–10	5–5	5–2	5–11	6–8	6–0	6–11	7–8
		5.4	1.29	1.49	1.67	1.58	1.82	2.04	1.83	2.11	2.36
		20	4–0	4–7	5–2	4–10	5–8	6–3	5–8	6–6	7–4
		6.0	1.22	1.41	1.58	1.50	1.73	1.93	1.74	2.01	2.24

Maximum Span, ft.–in. (m)[3,4]

Size of Built-up Beam, in. (mm)

Notes to Table 12

1. Spans apply only where the floors serve residential areas.
2. When the floors have a concrete topping of not more than 2 in. (51 mm), the spans must be multiplied by 0.8.
3. Spans are clear spans between supports. For total span, add two bearing lengths.
4. 3-ply beams with supported lengths greater than 13 ft. 8 in. (4.2 m) require 4 1/2 in. (114 mm) of bearing. All other beams require 3 in. (76 mm) bearing.
5. Supported length means half the sum of the joist spans on both sides of the beam.
6. Straight interpolation may be used for other supported lengths.

Table 13
Maximum spans for built-up floor beams supporting not more than three floors[1,2]

			2 x 8 (38 x 184)			2 x 10 (38 x 235)			2 x 12 (38 x 286)		
			Maximum Span, ft.–in. (m)[3,4]								
			Size of Built-up Beam, in. (mm)								
Commercial Designation	Grade	Supported Length, ft. (m)[5,6]	3-ply	4-ply	5-ply	3-ply	4-ply	5-ply	3-ply	4-ply	5-ply
D.Fir Larch	No. 1 and No. 2	8	6–0	6–11	7–9	7–4	8–6	9–6	8–7	9–10	11–0
		2.4	1.85	2.14	2.39	2.26	2.61	2.92	2.63	3.03	3.39
		10	5–5	6–3	6–11	6–7	7–7	8–6	7–8	8–10	9–10
		3.0	1.66	1.91	2.14	2.02	2.34	2.61	2.35	2.71	3.03
		12	4–11	5–8	6–4	6–0	6–11	7–9	7–0	8–1	9–0
		3.6	1.51	1.74	1.95	1.85	2.13	2.39	2.14	2.48	2.77
		14	4–7	5–3	5–11	5–7	6–5	7–2	6–6	7–6	8–4
		4.2	1.40	1.62	1.81	1.71	1.98	2.21	1.99	2.29	2.56
		16	4–3	4–11	5–6	5–3	6–0	6–9	6–1	7–0	7–10
		4.8	1.31	1.51	1.69	1.60	1.85	2.07	1.86	2.14	2.40
		18	4–0	4–8	5–2	4–11	5–8	6–4	5–8	6–7	7–4
		5.4	1.23	1.42	1.59	1.51	1.74	1.95	1.75	2.02	2.26
		20	3–10	4–5	4–11	4–8	5–5	6–0	5–5	6–3	7–0
		6.0	1.17	1.35	1.51	1.43	1.65	1.85	1.66	1.92	2.14
Hem-Fir	No. 1 and No. 2	8	6–4	7–4	8–2	7–9	8–11	10–0	9–0	10–4	11–7
		2.4	1.94	2.24	2.51	2.37	2.74	3.06	2.75	3.18	3.56
		10	5–8	6–6	7–4	6–11	8–0	8–11	8–0	9–3	10–4
		3.0	1.74	2.00	2.24	2.12	2.45	2.74	2.46	2.84	3.18
		12	5–2	5–11	6–8	6–3	7–3	8–2	7–1	8–5	9–5
		3.6	1.58	1.83	2.05	1.92	2.24	2.50	2.18	2.60	2.90
		14	4–8	5–6	6–2	5–7	6–9	7–6	6–4	7–10	8–9
		4.2	1.43	1.69	1.89	1.71	2.07	2.32	1.95	2.40	2.69
		16	4–2	5–2	5–9	5–1	6–3	7–1	5–9	7–1	8–2
		4.8	1.30	1.58	1.77	1.56	1.92	2.17	1.77	2.18	2.51
		18	3–10	4–9	5–5	4–8	5–8	6–8	5–4	6–6	7–8
		5.4	1.19	1.47	1.67	1.44	1.76	2.04	1.64	2.00	2.35
		20	3–7	4–5	5–2	4–4	5–3	6–3	5–0	6–0	7–1
		6.0	1.11	1.36	1.58	1.34	1.63	1.92	1.53	1.85	2.18
S-P-F	No. 1 and No. 2	8	6–7	7–7	8–5	8–0	9–3	10–4	9–3	10–9	12–0
		2.4	2.01	2.32	2.60	2.46	2.84	3.17	2.85	3.29	3.68
		10	5–10	6–9	7–7	7–2	8–3	9–3	8–4	9–7	10–9
		3.0	1.80	2.08	2.32	2.20	2.54	2.84	2.55	2.95	3.29
		12	5–4	6–2	6–11	6–6	7–7	8–5	7–7	8–9	9–9
		3.6	1.64	1.90	2.12	2.01	2.32	2.59	2.33	2.69	3.01
		14	4–11	5–9	6–5	6–0	7–0	7–10	6–10	8–1	9–1
		4.2	1.52	1.75	1.96	1.85	2.15	2.40	2.10	2.49	2.78
		16	4–6	5–4	6–0	5–5	6–6	7–4	6–2	7–7	8–6
		4.8	1.40	1.64	1.84	1.68	2.01	2.24	1.91	2.33	2.60
		18	4–2	5–0	5–8	5–0	6–2	6–11	5–9	7–0	8–0
		5.4	1.28	1.55	1.73	1.54	1.89	2.12	1.76	2.16	2.46
		20	3–10	4–9	5–4	4–8	5–8	6–6	5–4	6–6	7–7
		6.0	1.19	1.47	1.64	1.44	1.76	2.01	1.64	2.00	2.33

Continued on p. 370

Table 13 (continued)
Maximum spans for built-up floor beams supporting not more than three floors[1,2]

Commercial Designation	Grade	Supported Length, ft. (m)[5,6]	2 x 8 (38 x 184)			2 x 10 (38 x 235)			2 x 12 (38 x 286)		
			3-ply	4-ply	5-ply	3-ply	4-ply	5-ply	3-ply	4-ply	5-ply
Northern	No. 1	8	5–3	6–1	6–9	6–5	7–5	8–3	7–5	8–7	9–7
Species	and	2.4	1.61	1.86	2.08	1.97	2.28	2.55	2.29	2.64	2.96
	No. 2	10	4–8	5–5	6–1	5–9	6–8	7–5	6–8	7–8	8–7
		3.0	1.44	1.67	1.86	1.76	2.04	2.28	2.05	2.36	2.64
		12	4–3	4–11	5–6	5–3	6–1	6–9	6–1	7–0	7–10
		3.6	1.32	1.52	1.70	1.61	1.86	2.08	1.87	2.16	2.41
		14	4–0	4–7	5–1	4–10	5–7	6–3	5–8	6–6	7–3
		4.2	1.22	1.41	1.57	1.49	1.72	1.93	1.73	2.00	2.23
		16	3–9	4–3	4–10	4–6	5–3	5–10	5–3	6–1	6–10
		4.8	1.14	1.32	1.47	1.40	1.61	1.80	1.62	1.87	2.09
		18	3–6	4–1	4–6	4–3	4–11	5–6	5–0	5–9	6–5
		5.4	1.08	1.24	1.39	1.32	1.52	1.70	1.53	1.76	1.97
		20	3–4	3–10	4–3	4–1	4–8	5–3	4–9	5–5	6–1
		6.0	1.02	1.18	1.32	1.25	1.44	1.61	1.45	1.67	1.87

Maximum Span, ft.–in. (m)[3,4]

Size of Built-up Beam, in. (mm)

Notes to Table 13

1. Spans apply only where the floors serve residential areas.
2. When the floors have a concrete topping of not more than 2 in. (51 mm), the spans must be multiplied by 0.8.
3. Spans are clear spans between supports. For total span, add two bearing lengths.
4. 3-ply beams with supported lengths greater than 13 ft. 8 in. (4.2 m) require 4 1/2 in. (114 mm) of bearing. All other beams require 3 in. (76 mm) bearing.
5. Supported length means half the sum of the joist spans on both sides of the beam.
6. Straight interpolation may be used for other supported lengths.

Table 14
Spans for steel floor beams

Section	Supported Joist Length, ft. (m), (half the sum of joist spans for both sides of the beam)											
	7ft. 10 in.	2.4 m	9 ft. 9 in.	3 m	11 ft. 9 in.	3.6 m	13 ft. 9 in.	4.2 m	15 ft. 8 in.	4.8 m	17 ft. 8 in.	5.4 m	19 ft. 11 in. 6.0 m

One storey supported

Section													
W150x22	18-0	5.5	17-1	5.2	16-1	4.9	15-8	4.8	15-1	4.6	14-9	4.5	14-1	4.3
W200x21	21-3	6.5	20-3	6.2	19-5	5.9	18-8	5.7	17-8	5.4	16-8	5.1	16-1	4.9
W200x27	23-10	7.3	22-7	6.9	21-7	6.6	20-8	6.3	20-0	6.1	19-4	5.9	19-0	5.8
W200x31	25-7	7.8	24-3	7.4	23-3	7.1	22-3	6.8	21-7	6.6	21-0	6.4	20-3	6.2
W250x24	26-7	8.1	24-10	7.6	23-10	7.3	23-0	7.0	21-7	6.6	20-3	6.2	19-4	5.9
W250x33	30-2	9.2	28-6	8.7	27-2	8.3	26-2	8.0	25-3	7.7	24-7	7.5	23-10	7.3
W250x39	32-9	10.0	30-9	9.4	29-6	9.0	28-2	8.6	27-7	8.4	26-7	8.1	25-10	7.9
W310x31	34-1	10.4	32-1	9.8	30-9	9.4	29-2	8.9	27-7	8.4	26-2	8.0	24-10	7.6
W310x39	37-4	11.4	35-1	10.7	32-9	10.0	32-1	9.8	31-2	9.5	30-2	9.2	29-6	9.0

Two storeys supported

Section													
W150x22	16-1	4.9	14-3	4.4	13-3	4.1	12-6	3.8	12-6	3.5	11-2	3.4	10-6	3.2
W200x21	18-4	5.6	16-8	5.1	15-1	4.6	14-1	4.3	13-4	4.1	12-6	3.8	12-1	3.7
W200x27	21-0	6.4	20-0	6.1	18-4	5.6	17-4	5.3	16-1	4.9	15-4	4.7	14-4	4.4
W200x31	22-7	6.9	21-3	6.5	20-3	6.2	19-0	5.8	17-8	5.4	16-8	5.1	16-1	4.9
W250x24	22-3	6.8	20-0	6.1	18-4	5.6	17-1	5.2	16-1	4.9	15-1	4.6	14-4	4.4
W250x33	26-10	8.2	25-3	7.7	23-0	7.0	21-3	6.5	20-0	6.1	19-0	5.8	18-0	5.5
W250X39	28-10	8.8	27-2	8.3	25-7	7.8	23-7	7.2	22-3	6.8	21-0	6.4	20-0	6.1
W310x31	28-6	8.7	25-7	7.8	23-7	7.2	22-0	6.7	20-3	6.2	19-4	5.9	18-4	5.6
W310x39	32-9	10.0	30-6	9.3	27-10	8.5	25-10	7.9	24-3	7.4	23-0	7.0	22-0	6.7

Note to Table 14

1. The section information provides the beam depth and weight in metric units. For example,
   a W150 X 22 beam is 6" (150 mm) deep and weighs 14.8 lbs. per foot (22 kg. per metre).

Table 15
Maximum spans for glue-laminated floor beams – 20f-E grade[1]

			Maximum Span, ft.-in. (m)[2 to 5]						
			Beam Depth, in. (mm)						
Number of Floors Supported	Beam Width, in. (mm)	Supported Length, ft. (m)[6, 7]	9 (228)	10½ (266)	12 (304)	13½ (342)	15 (380)	16½ (418)	18 (456)
1	3 (80)	8 (2.4)	14–1 (4.32)	16–5 (5.04)	18–9 (5.76)	21–1 (6.48)	23–5 (7.20)	25–9 (7.92)	28–2 (8.64)
		10 (3.0)	12–7 (3.87)	14–8 (4.51)	16–9 (5.15)	18–10 (5.80)	21–0 (6.44)	23–1 (7.09)	25–2 (7.73)
		12 (3.6)	11–6 (3.53)	13–5 (4.12)	15–4 (4.70)	17–3 (5.29)	19–2 (5.88)	21–1 (6.47)	23–0 (7.06)
		14 (4.2)	10–8 (3.27)	12–5 (3.81)	14–2 (4.36)	15–11 (4.90)	17–9 (5.44)	19–6 (5.99)	21–3 (6.53)
		16 (4.8)	9–11 (3.06)	11–7 (3.57)	13–3 (4.07)	14–11 (4.58)	16–7 (5.09)	18–3 (5.60)	19–11 (6.11)
		18 (5.4)	9–5 (2.88)	10–11 (3.36)	12–6 (3.84)	14–1 (4.32)	15–8 (4.80)	17–2 (5.28)	18–9 (5.76)
		20 (6.0)	8–11 (2.73)	10–5 (3.19)	11–10 (3.64)	13–4 (4.10)	14–10 (4.56)	16–4 (5.01)	17–10 (5.47)
1	5 (130)	8 (2.4)	17–11 (5.51)	20–11 (6.43)	23–11 (7.35)	26–11 (8.26)	29–11 (9.18)	32–11 (10.10)	35–10 (11.02)
		10 (3.0)	16–0 (4.93)	18–9 (5.75)	21–5 (6.57)	24–1 (7.39)	26–9 (8.21)	29–5 (9.03)	32–1 (9.86)
		12 (3.6)	14–8 (4.50)	17–1 (5.25)	19–6 (6.00)	22–0 (6.75)	24–5 (7.50)	26–10 (8.25)	29–3 (9.00)
		14 (4.2)	13–7 (4.16)	15–10 (4.86)	18–1 (5.55)	20–4 (6.25)	22–7 (6.94)	24–10 (7.64)	27–1 (8.33)
		16 (4.8)	12–8 (3.90)	14–10 (4.54)	16–11 (5.19)	19–0 (5.84)	21–2 (6.49)	23–3 (7.14)	25–4 (7.79)
		18 (5.4)	11–11 (3.67)	13–11 (4.28)	15–11 (4.90)	17–11 (5.51)	19–11 (6.12)	21–11 (6.73)	23–11 (7.35)
		20 (6.0)	11–4 (3.48)	13–3 (4.07)	15–1 (4.65)	17–0 (5.23)	18–11 (5.81)	20–10 (6.39)	22–8 (6.97)
2	3 (80)	8 (2.4)	10–8 (3.28)	12–5 (3.83)	14–3 (4.37)	16–0 (4.92)	17–9 (5.47)	19–7 (6.01)	21–4 (6.56)
		10 (3.0)	9–7 (2.93)	11–2 (3.42)	12–9 (3.91)	14–4 (4.40)	15–11 (4.89)	17–6 (5.38)	19–1 (5.87)
		12 (3.6)	8–9 (2.68)	10–2 (3.12)	11–7 (3.57)	13–1 (4.02)	14–6 (4.46)	16–0 (4.91)	17–5 (5.36)
		14 (4.2)	8–1 (2.48)	9–5 (2.89)	10–9 (3.31)	12–1 (3.72)	13–5 (4.13)	14–10 (4.54)	16–2 (4.96)
		16 (4.8)	7–7 (2.32)	8–10 (2.71)	10–1 (3.09)	11–4 (3.48)	12–7 (3.86)	13–10 (4.25)	15–1 (4.64)
		18 (5.4)	7–1 (2.19)	8–4 (2.55)	9–6 (2.91)	10–8 (3.28)	11–10 (3.64)	13–1 (4.01)	14–3 (4.37)
		20 (6.0)	6–9 (2.07)	7–11 (2.42)	9–0 (2.77)	10–2 (3.11)	11–3 (3.46)	12–5 (3.80)	13–6 (4.15)

Continued on p. 373

Table 15 (continued)
Maximum spans for glue-laminated floor beams – 20f-E grade[1]

			Maximum Span, ft.-in. (m)[2 to 5]						
			Beam Depth, in. (mm)						
Number of Floors Supported	Beam Width, in. (mm)	Supported Length, ft. (m)[6, 7]	9 (228)	10½ (266)	12 (304)	13½ (342)	15 (380)	16½ (418)	18 (456)
2	5 (130)	8 (2.4)	13–7 (4.18)	15–10 (4.88)	18–2 (5.57)	20–5 (6.27)	22–8 (6.97)	24–11 (7.66)	27–3 (8.36)
		10 (3.0)	12–2 (3.74)	14–2 (4.36)	16–3 (4.99)	18–3 (5.61)	20–3 (6.23)	22–4 (6.85)	24–4 (7.48)
		12 (3.6)	11–1 (3.41)	13–0 (3.98)	14–10 (4.55)	16–8 (5.12)	18–6 (5.69)	20–4 (6.26)	22–3 (6.83)
		14 (4.2)	10–3 (3.16)	12–0 (3.69)	13–9 (4.21)	15–5 (4.74)	17–2 (5.27)	18–10 (5.79)	20–7 (6.32)
		16 (4.8)	9–7 (2.96)	11–3 (3.45)	12–10 (3.94)	14–5 (4.43)	16–0 (4.93)	17–8 (5.42)	19–3 (5.91)
		18 (5.4)	9–1 (2.79)	10–7 (3.25)	12–1 (3.72)	13–7 (4.18)	15–1 (4.64)	16–8 (5.11)	18–2 (5.57)
		20 (6.0)	8–7 (2.64)	10–0 (3.08)	11–6 (3.53)	12–11 (3.97)	14–4 (4.41)	15–9 (4.85)	17–3 (5.29)
3	3 (80)	8 (2.4)	8–11 (2.75)	10–5 (3.21)	11–11 (3.66)	13–5 (4.12)	14–11 (4.58)	16–5 (5.04)	17–11 (5.50)
		10 (3.0)	8–0 (2.46)	9–4 (2.87)	10–8 (3.28)	12–0 (3.69)	13–4 (4.10)	14–8 (4.51)	16–0 (4.92)
		12 (3.6)	7–4 (2.24)	8–6 (2.62)	9–9 (2.99)	10–11 (3.37)	12–2 (3.74)	13–5 (4.11)	14–7 (4.49)
		14 (4.2)	6–9 (2.08)	7–11 (2.42)	9–0 (2.77)	10–2 (3.12)	11–3 (3.46)	12–5 (3.81)	13–6 (4.15)
		16 (4.8)	6–4 (1.94)	7–5 (2.27)	8–5 (2.59)	9–6 (2.91)	10–6 (3.24)	11–7 (3.56)	12–8 (3.89)
		18 (5.4)	6–0 (1.83)	6–11 (2.14)	7–11 (2.44)	8–11 (2.75)	9–11 (3.05)	10–11 (3.36)	11–11 (3.66)
		20 (6.0)	5–8 (1.74)	6–7 (2.03)	7–7 (2.32)	8–6 (2.61)	9–5 (2.90)	10–4 (3.19)	11–4 (3.48)
3	5 (130)	8 (2.4)	11–5 (3.50)	13–4 (4.09)	15–2 (4.67)	17–1 (5.25)	19–0 (5.84)	20–11 (6.42)	22–10 (7.01)
		10 (3.0)	10–2 (3.13)	11–11 (3.66)	13–7 (4.18)	15–4 (4.70)	17–0 (5.22)	18–8 (5.74)	20–5 (6.27)
		12 (3.6)	9–4 (2.86)	10–10 (3.34)	12–5 (3.81)	14–0 (4.29)	15–6 (4.77)	17–1 (5.24)	18–7 (5.72)
		14 (4.2)	8–7 (2.65)	10–1 (3.09)	11–6 (3.53)	12–11 (3.97)	14–4 (4.41)	15–10 (4.85)	17–3 (5.30)
		16 (4.8)	8–1 (2.48)	9–5 (2.89)	10–9 (3.30)	12–1 (3.72)	13–5 (4.13)	14–9 (4.54)	16–1 (4.95)
		18 (5.4)	7–7 (2.34)	8–10 (2.72)	10–2 (3.11)	11–5 (3.50)	12–8 (3.89)	13–11 (4.28)	15–2 (4.67)
		20 (6.0)	7–3 (2.22)	8–5 (2.58)	9–7 (2.95)	10–10 (3.32)	12–0 (3.69)	13–3 (4.06)	14–5 (4.43)

Notes to Table 15
1. Spans apply only where the floors serve residential areas.
2. Spans are valid for glue-laminated timber conforming to CAN/CSA-O122-M and CAN/CSA-O177-M.
3. Spans are clear spans between supports. For total span, add two bearing lengths.
4. Provide a minimum bearing length of 3½ in. (89 mm).
5. Top edge of beam assumed to be fully laterally supported by joists.
6. Supported length means half the sum of the joist spans on both sides of the beam.
7. Straight interpolation may be used for other supported lengths.

Table 16
Maximum spans for floor joists – general cases[1,2]

Maximum Span, ft.-in. (m)

Joist Spacing, in. (mm)

Commercial Designation	Grade	Joist Size, in. (mm)	With Strapping 12 (300)	16 (400)	24 (600)	With Bridging 12 (300)	16 (400)	24 (600)	With Strapping and Bridging 12 (300)	16 (400)	24 (600)
Douglas fir – larch (includes Douglas fir and western larch)	No. 1 and No. 2	2x6 (38x140)	10–2 (3.09)	9–7 (2.91)	8–7 (2.62)	10–10 (3.29)	9–10 (2.99)	8–7 (2.62)	10–10 (3.29)	9–10 (2.99)	8–7 (2.62)
		2x8 (38x184)	12–2 (3.71)	11–7 (3.53)	11–0 (3.36)	13–1 (4.00)	12–4 (3.76)	11–3 (3.44)	13–9 (4.19)	12–10 (3.90)	11–3 (3.44)
		2x10 (38x235)	14–4 (4.38)	13–8 (4.16)	13–0 (3.96)	15–3 (4.66)	14–4 (4.38)	13–6 (4.11)	15–10 (4.84)	14–10 (4.51)	(4.20)
		2x12 (38x286)	16–5 (4.99)	15–7 (4.75)	14–10 (4.52)	17–2 (5.26)	16–2 (4.94)	15–3 (4.65)	17–10 (5.43)	16–7 (5.06)	15–6 (4.72)
Hem – fir (includes western hemlock and amabilis fir)	No. 1 and No. 2	2x6 (38x140)	10–2 (3.09)	9–7 (2.91)	8–7 (2.62)	10–10 (3.29)	9–10 (2.99)	8–7 (2.62)	10–10 (3.29)	9–10 (2.99)	8–7 (2.62)
		2x8 (38x184)	12–2 (3.71)	11–7 (3.53)	11–0 (3.36)	13–1 (4.00)	12–4 (3.76)	11–3 (3.44)	13–9 (4.19)	12–10 (3.90)	11–3 (3.44)
		2x10 (38x235)	14–4 (4.38)	13–8 (4.16)	13–0 (3.96)	15–3 (4.66)	14–4 (4.38)	13–6 (4.11)	15–10 (4.84)	14–10 (4.51)	(4.20)
		2x12 (38x286)	16–5 (4.99)	15–7 (4.75)	14–10 (4.52)	17–2 (5.26)	16–2 (4.94)	15–3 (4.65)	17–10 (5.43)	16–7 (5.06)	15–6 (4.72)
Spruce – pine – fir (includes spruce [all species except coast sitka spruce], jack pine, lodgepole pine, balsam fir and alpine fir)	No. 1 and No. 2	2x6 (38x140)	9–7 (2.92)	8–11 (2.71)	8–2 (2.49)	10–4 (3.14)	9–4 (2.85)	8–2 (2.49)	10–4 (3.14)	9–4 (2.85)	8–2 (2.49)
		2x8 (38x184)	11–7 (3.54)	11–0 (3.36)	10–6 (3.20)	12–5 (3.81)	11–9 (3.58)	10–9 (3.27)	13–1 (3.99)	12–2 (3.72)	10–9 (3.27)
		2x10 (38x235)	13–8 (4.17)	13–0 (3.96)	12–4 (3.77)	14–6 (4.44)	13–8 (4.17)	12–10 (3.92)	15–1 (4.60)	14–1 (4.29)	13–2 (4.00)
		2x12 (38x286)	15–7 (4.75)	14–10 (4.52)	14–1 (4.30)	16–4 (5.01)	15–5 (4.71)	14–6 (4.42)	17–0 (5.17)	15–10 (4.82)	14–9 (4.49)
Northern species (includes any Canadian species covered by the NLGA Standard Grading Rules)	No. 1 and No. 2	2x6 (38x140)	8–3 (2.51)	7–8 (2.33)	7–1 (2.16)	9–3 (2.83)	8–5 (2.57)	7–5 (2.25)	9–4 (2.83)	8–5 (2.57)	7–5 (2.25)
		2x8 (38x184)	10–6 (3.19)	10–0 (3.04)	9–4 (2.84)	11–3 (3.44)	10–7 (3.23)	9–8 (2.96)	11–10 (3.60)	11–0 (3.36)	9–8 (2.96)
		2x10 (38x235)	12–4 (3.76)	11–9 (3.58)	11–2 (3.41)	13–1 (4.01)	12–4 (3.77)	11–7 (3.54)	13–8 (4.16)	12–9 (3.88)	(3.62)
		2x12 (38x286)	14–1 (4.29)	13–5 (4.08)	12–9 (3.88)	14–9 (4.53)	13–11 (4.25)	13–1 (4.00)	15–4 (4.67)	14–4 (4.35)	13–4 (4.06)

Note to Table 16

1. Spans apply only where the floors serve residential areas.

2. Subfloor must comply with minimum requirements from tables 18 and 19.

Table 17
Maximum spans for floor joists – special cases[1, 2]

			Maximum Span, ft.–in. (m)								
			Joists with Ceilings Attached to Wood Furring						Joists with Concrete Topping		
			Joist Spacing, in. (mm)						Joist Spacing, in (mm)		
		Joist Size, in. (mm)	Without Bridging			With Bridging			With or Without Bridging[3]		
Commercial Designation	Grade		12 (300)	16 (400)	24 (600)	12 (300)	16 (400)	24 (600)	12 (300)	16 (400)	24 (600)
Douglas fir – larch (includes Douglas fir and western larch)	No. 1 and No. 2	2x6 (38x140)	10-10 (3.29)	9-10 (2.99)	8-7 (2.62)	10-10 (3.29)	9-10 (2.99)	8-7 (2.62)	10-10 (3.29)	9-10 (2.99)	8-5 (2.55)
		2x8 (38x184)	13-4 (4.06)	12-7 (3.83)	11-3 (3.44)	14-2 (4.33)	12-11 (3.93)	11-3 (3.44)	14-2 (4.33)	12-6 (3.81)	10-2 (3.11)
		2x10 (38x235)	15-8 (4.78)	14-9 (4.50)	13-6 (4.11)	17-2 (5.24)	16-4 (4.98)	14-2 (4.31)	17-8 (5.37)	15-3 (4.65)	12-6 (3.80)
		2x12 (38x286)	17-10 (5.44)	16-10 (5.12)	15-4 (4.68)	19-5 (5.93)	18-6 (5.64)	16-5 (5.00)	20-6 (6.24)	17-9 (5.40)	14-6 (4.41)
Hem – fir (includes western hemlock and amabilis fir)	No. 1 and No. 2	2x6 (38x140)	10-10 (3.29)	9-10 (2.99)	8-7 (2.62)	10-10 (3.29)	9-10 (2.99)	8-7 (2.62)	10-10 (3.29)	9-10 (2.99)	8-7 (2.62)
		2x8 (38x184)	13-4 (4.06)	12-7 (3.83)	11-3 (3.44)	14-2 (4.33)	12-11 (3.93)	11-3 (3.44)	14-2 (4.33)	12-11 (3.93)	10-8 (3.26)
		2x10 (38x235)	15-8 (4.78)	14-9 (4.50)	13-6 (4.11)	17-2 (5.24)	16-4 (4.98)	14-5 (4.39)	18-2 (5.53)	16-0 (4.88)	13-1 (3.99)
		2x12 (38x286)	17-10 (5.44)	16-10 (5.12)	15-4 (4.68)	19-5 (5.93)	18-6 (5.64)	17-3 (5.25)	21-6 (6.54)	18-7 (5.66)	15-2 (4.63)
Spruce – pine – fir (includes spruce [all species except coast sitka spruce], jack pine, lodgepole pine, balsam fir and alpine fir)	No. 1 and No. 2	2x6 (38x140)	10-4 (3.14)	9-4 (2.85)	8-2 (2.49)	10-4 (3.14)	9-4 (2.85)	8-2 (2.49)	10-4 (3.14)	9-4 (2.85)	8-2 (2.49)
		2x8 (38x184)	12-8 (3.87)	11-11 (3.64)	10-9 (3.27)	13-6 (4.12)	12-4 (3.75)	10-9 (3.27)	13-6 (4.12)	12-4 (3.75)	10-9 (3.27)
		2x10 (38x235)	14-11 (4.55)	14-1 (4.28)	12-10 (3.91)	16-4 (4.99)	15-7 (4.75)	13-9 (4.18)	17-3 (5.27)	15-8 (4.79)	13-7 (4.13)
		2x12 (38x286)	17-0 (5.18)	16-0 (4.88)	14-7 (4.46)	18-6 (5.65)	17-7 (5.37)	16-7 (5.06)	20-5 (6.23)	19-1 (5.81)	15-9 (4.79)
Northern species (includes any Canadian species covered by the NLGA Standard Grading Rules)	No. 1 and No. 2	2x6 (38x140)	9-4 (2.83)	8-5 (2.57)	7-5 (2.25)	9-4 (2.83)	8-5 (2.57)	7-5 (2.25)	9-4 (2.83)	8-5 (2.57)	7-4 (2.23)
		2x8 (38x184)	11-6 (3.50)	10-10 (3.29)	9-8 (2.96)	12-3 (3.72)	11-1 (3.38)	9-8 (2.96)	12-3 (3.72)	10-11 (3.32)	8-11 (2.71)
		2x10 (38x235)	13-6 (4.11)	12-8 (3.87)	11-7 (3.54)	14-9 (4.51)	14-1 (4.29)	12-4 (3.76)	15-4 (4.69)	13-4 (4.06)	10-10 (3.31)
		2x12 (38x286)	15-4 (4.68)	14-5 (4.40)	13-2 (4.03)	16-9 (5.10)	15-11 (4.85)	14-4 (4.36)	17-10 (5.44)	15-5 (4.71)	12-7 (3.84)

Notes to Table 17
1. Spans apply only where the floors serve residential areas.
2. Subfloor must comply with minimum requirements from tables 18 and 19.
3. No bridging is assumed for spans for floor joists with concrete topping.

Table 18
Minimum thickness of subflooring

	Minimum Subflooring Thickness, in. (mm), for Maximum Joist Spacing at		
	16 (400)	20 (500)	24 (600)
Plywood and OSB, O-2 grade	$5/8$ (15.5)	$5/8$ (15.5)	$23/32$ (18.5)
OSB, O-1 grade, and waferboard, R-1 Grade	$5/8$ (15.9)	$5/8$ (15.9)	$3/4$ (19.0)
Particleboard	$5/8$ (15.9)	$3/4$ (19.0)	1 (25.4)
Panel mark (performance-rated panels) sub-floor only	1F16	1F20	1F24
Panel mark (performance-rated panels) sub-floor and underlay	2F16	2F20	2F24
Lumber	$11/16$ (17.0)	$3/4$ (19.0)	$3/4$ (19.0)

Table 19
Sheathing and subfloor attachment

	Minimum Length of Fasteners for Sheathing and Subfloor Attachment, in. (mm)				
Element	Common or Spiral Nails	Ring Thread Nails or Screws	Roofing Nails	Staples	Minimum No. or Maximum Spacing of Fasteners
Plywood, OSB or waferboard up to $3/8$ in. (10 mm) thick	2 (51)	$13/4$ (45)	N/A	$11/2$ (38)	
Plywood, OSB or waferboard $3/8$ in. (10 mm) to $13/16$ in. (20 mm) thick	2 (51)	$13/4$ (45)	N/A	2 (51)	
Plywood, OSB or waferboard over $13/16$ in. (20 mm) thick	$21/4$ (57)	2 (51)	N/A	N/A	6 in. (150 mm) o.c. along edges and 12 in. (300 mm) o.c. along intermediate supports
Fibreboard sheathing up to $1/2$ in. (13 mm) thick	N/A	N/A	$13/4$ (44)	$11/8$ (28)	
Gypsum sheathing up to $1/2$ in. (13mm) thick	N/A	N/A	$13/4$ (44)	N/A	
Board lumber 8 in. (184 mm) or less wide	2 (51)	$13/4$ (45)	N/A	2 (51)	2 per support
Board lumber more than 8 in. (184 mm) wide	2 (51)	$13/4$ (45)	N/A	2 (51)	3 per support

Table 20
Nailing for framing[1]

Construction Detail	Minimum Length of Nails, in. (mm)		Minimum Number or Maximum Spacing of Nails
Floor joist to plate – toe nail	3¼	(82)	2
Wood or metal strapping to underside of floor joists	2¼	(57)	2
Cross bridging to joists	2¼	(57)	2 at each end
Double header or trimmer joists	3	(76)	12 in. (300 mm) (o.c.)
Floor joist to stud (balloon construction)	3	(76)	2
Ledger strip to wood beam	3¼	(82)	2 per joist
Joist to joist splice (See Table 29)	3	(76)	2 at each end
Tail joist to adjacent header joist (end nailed) around openings	3¼ 4	(82) (101)	5 3
Each header joist to adjacent trimmer joist (end nailed) around openings	3¼ 4	(82) (101)	5 3
Stud to wall plate (each end) toe nail or end nail	2½ 3¼	(63) (82)	4 2
Doubled studs at openings, or studs at walls or wall intersections and corners	3	(76)	30 in. (750 mm) (o.c.)
Doubled top wall plates	3	(76)	24 in. (600 mm) (o.c.)
Bottom wall plate or sole plate to joists or blocking (exterior walls)[1]	3¼	(82)	16 in. (400 mm) (o.c)
Interior walls to framing or subflooring	3¼	(82)	24 in. (600 mm) (o.c.)
Horizontal members over openings in non-loadbearing walls – each end	3¼	(82)	2
Lintels to studs	3¼	(82)	2 at each end
Ceiling joist to plate – toe nail each end	3¼	(82)	2
Roof rafter, roof truss or roof joist to plate – toe nail	3¼	(82)	3
Rafter plate to each ceiling joist	4	(101)	2
Rafter to joist (with ridge supported)	3	(76)	3
Rafter to joist (with ridge unsupported)	3	(76)	See Table 30
Gusset plate to each rafter at peak	2¼	(57)	4

Continued on p. 378

Table 20 (continued)
Nailing for framing[1]

Construction Detail	Minimum Length of Nails, in. (mm)		Minimum Number or Maximum Spacing of Nails
Rafter to ridge board – toe nail – end nail	3 1/4	(82)	3
Collar tie to rafter – each end	3	(76)	3
Collar tie lateral support to each collar tie	2 1/4	(57)	2
Jack rafter to hip or valley rafter	3 1/4	(82)	2
Roof strut to rafter	3	(76)	3
Roof strut to loadbearing wall – toe nail	3 1/4	(82)	2
2 in.x6 in. (38 mmx140 mm) or less plank decking to support	3 1/4	(82)	2
Plank decking wider than 2 in.x6 in. (38 mmx140 mm) to support	3 1/4	(82)	3
2 in. (38 mm) edge laid plank decking to support (toe nail)	3	(76)	1
2 in. (38 mm) edge laid plank to each other	3	(76)	18 in. (450 mm) (o.c.)

Note to Table 20

1. Where the bottom wall plate or sole plate of an exterior wall is not nailed to joists or blocking, the exterior wall is permitted to be fastened to the floor framing by plywood, OSB, or waferboard sheathing that extends down over the floor framing and is fastened to that framing by nails or staples. The wall can also be fastened by tying the wall framing to the floor framing with galvanized strips that are 2 in. (50 mm) wide, 0.016 in. (0.41 mm) in thickness or more, spaced not more than 48 in. (1.2 m) apart and fastened at each end with at least two 2 1/2-in. (63 mm) nails.

Table 21
Size and spacing of studs

Type of Wall	Supported Loads (including dead loads)	Minimum Stud Size in. (mm)	Maximum Stud Spacing, in. (mm)	Maximum Unsupported Height ft.–in. (m),
Interior	No load	2 x 2 (38 x 38)	16 (400)	8–0 (2.4)
		2 x 4 (38 x 89) flat[1]	16 (400)	11–10 (3.6)
	Attic not accessible by a stairway	2 x 3 (38 x 64)	24 (600)	9–10 (3.0)
		2 x 3 (38 x 64) flat[1]	16 (400)	8–0 (2.4)
		2 x 4 (38 x 89)	24 (600)	11–10 (3.6)
		2 x 4 (38 x 89) flat[1]	16 (400)	8–0 (2.4)
	Attic accessible by a stairway plus one floor Roof load plus one floor Attic not accessible by a stairway plus two floors	2 x 4 (38 x 89	16 (400)	11–10 (3.6)
	Roof load Attic accessible by a stairway Attic not accessible by a stairway plus one floor	2 x 3 (38 x 64)	16 (400)	8–0 (2.4)
		2 x 4 (38 x 89)	24 (600)	11–10 (3.6)
	Attic accessible by a stairway plus two floors Roof load plus two floors	2 x 4 (38 x 89)	12 (300)	11–10 (3.6)
		2 x 6 (38 x 140)	16 (400)	13–9 (4.2)
	Attic accessible by a stairway plus three floors	2 x 6 (38 x 140)	12 (300)	13–9 (4.2)
Exterior	Roof with or without attic storage	2 x 3 (38 x 64)	16 (400)	8–0 (2.4)
		2 x 4 (38 x 89)	24 (600)	9–10 (3.0)
	Roof with or without attic storage plus one floor	2 x 4 (38 x 89)	16 (400)	9–10 (3.0)
		2 x 6 (38 x 140)	24 (600)	9–10 (3.0)
	Roof with or without attic storage plus two floors	2 x 4 (38 x 89)	12 (300)	9–10 (3.0)
		2 x 6 (38 x 140)	16 (400)	11–10 (3.6)
	Roof with or without attic storage plus three floors	2 x 6 (38 x 140)	12 (300)	6–0 (1.8)

Note to Table 21

1. Studs on the flat are permitted to be used in gable ends of roofs that contain only unfinished space or in non-loadbearing interior walls within the limits described in the National Building Code of Canada. Studs supporting only a load from an attic not accessible from a stairway are permitted to be placed on the flat, in accordance with this table, if they are clad on not less than one side with plywood, OSB, or waferboard sheathing fastened to the face of the studs with a structural adhesive, and if the portion of the roof supported by the studs does not exceed 6 ft., 10 in. (2.1 m) in width.

Table 22
Maximum spans for spruce – pine – fir lintels – No. 1 or No. 2 grade – non-structural sheathing[7]

		Maximum Span, ft.–in. (m)[2,3]					
		Exterior Walls					
		Specified Snow Load, psf (kPa)[6]					
Lintel Supporting	Lintel Size, in. (mm)[4], 2-ply	20.9 1.0	31.3 1.5	41.8 2.0	52.2 2.5	62.7 3.0	Interior Walls
Limited attic storage and ceiling	2–2 x 4 2–38 x 89						4–2 1.27
	2–2 x 6 2–38 x 140						6–4 1.93
	2–2 x 8 2–38 x 184		This area intentionally left blank				7–9 2.35
	2–2 x 10 2–38 x 235)						9–5 2.88
	2–2 x 12 2–38 x 286						11–0 3.34
Lintel Supporting Roof and ceiling only (tributary width 2 ft. (0.6 m))[6]	2-2x4 2-38x89	8-4 2.55	7-4 2.23	6-8 2.02	6-2 1.88	5-10 1.77	6-2 1.88
	2-2x6 2-38x140	13-2 4.01	11-6 3.50	10-5 3.18	9-8 2.96	9-2 2.78	9-8 2.96
	2-2x8 2-38x184	17-4 5.27	15-1 4.61	13-9 4.18	12-9 3.88	12-0 3.66	12-9 3.88
	2-2x10 2-38x235	20-11 6.37	18-11 5.76	17-6 5.34	16-3 4.96	15-4 4.67	16-3 4.96
	2-2x12 2-38x286	24-3 7.38	21-11 6.67	20-4 6.21	19-3 5.87	18-5 5.61	19-3 5.87
Lintel Supporting Roof and ceiling only (tributary width 16 ft. 0 in. (4.9 m))[1]	2-2x4 2-38x89	4-2 1.27	3-8 1.11	3-4 1.01	3-1 0.93	2-10 0.87	3-1 0.93
	2-2x6 2-38x140	6-4 1.93	5-5 1.66	4-10 1.48	4-5 1.35	4-1 1.25	4-5 1.35
	2-2x8 2-38x184	7-9 2.35	6-8 2.02	5-11 1.80	5-5 1.64	5-0 1.52	5-5 1.64
	2-2x10 2-38x235	9-5 2.88	8-1 2.47	7-3 2.20	6-7 2.01	6-1 1.84	6-7 2.01
	2-2x12 2-38x286	11-0 3.34	9-5 2.87	8-5 2.56	7-8 2.33	6-10 2.09	7-8 2.33
Lintel Supporting Roof ceiling and 1 storey[1,2,5]	2-2x4 2-38x89	3-5 1.05	3-2 0.96	2-11 0.89	2-9 0.84	2-7 0.79	2-5 0.74
	2-2x6 2-38x140	4-11 1.49	4-6 1.37	4-2 1.27	3-11 1.19	3-8 1.13	3-4 1.02
	2-2x8 2-38x184	6-0 1.82	5-6 1.67	5-1 1.55	4-9 1.44	4-4 1.33	3-11 1.20
	2-2x10 2-38x235	7-3 2.22	6-8 2.04	6-2 1.89	5-8 1.73	5-3 1.59	4-9 1.45
	2-2x12 2-38x286	8-5 2.58	7-9 2.36	7-1 2.15	6-5 1.96	5-11 1.81	5-5 1.66

Continued on p. 381

Table 22 (continued)
Maximum spans for spruce – pine – fir lintels – No. 1 or No. 2 grade – non-structural sheathing[7]

		Maximum Span, ft.–in. (m)[2,3]					
		Exterior Walls					
	Lintel Size,	Specified Snow Load, psf (kPa)[6]					
Lintel Supporting	in. (mm)[4], 2-ply	20.9 1.0	31.3 1.5	41.8 2.0	52.2 2.5	62.7 3.0	Interior Walls
Lintel Supporting	2-2x4	3-1	2-11	2-9	2-7	2-6	2-1
Roof ceiling and	2-38x89	0.94	0.88	0.83	0.79	0.76	0.64
2 storeys[1,2,5]	2-2x6	4-5	4-2	3-11	3-8	3-6	2-11
	2-38x140	1.34	1.26	1.19	1.13	1.06	0.88
	2-2x8	5-4	5-0	4-9	4-4	4-1	3-5
	2-38x184	1.63	1.53	1.44	1.33	1.25	1.05
	2-2x10	6-6	6-2	5-8	5-3	4-11	4-2
	2-38x235	1.99	1.87	1.72	1.60	1.50	1.27
	2-2x12	7-7	6-11	6-5	6-0	5-7	4-9
	2-38x286	2.31	2.12	1.96	1.82	1.71	1.45
Lintel Supporting	2-2x4	2-11	2-9	2-7	2-6	2-5	1-11
Roof ceiling and	2-38x89	0.88	0.83	0.80	0.77	0.74	0.59
3 storeys[1,2,5]	2-2x6	4-1	3-11	3-9	3-7	3-4	2-8
	2-38x140	1.25	1.19	1.14	1.08	1.02	0.81
	2-2x8	5-0	4-9	4-5	4-2	3-11	3-2
	2-38x184	1.52	1.44	1.35	1.27	1.21	0.97
	2-2x10	6-1	5-8	5-4	5-0	4-9	3-10
	2-38x235	1.86	1.73	1.62	1.53	1.45	1.17
	2-2x12	6-11	6-5	6-1	5-9	5-5	4-5
	2-38x286	2.11	1.96	1.84	1.74	1.66	1.35

Notes to Table 22

1. Lintel spans are calculated based on a maximum floor joist, roof joist or rafter span of 16 ft., 0 in. (4.9) m and a maximum roof truss span of 32 ft., 0 in. (9.8 m). Lintel spans may be increased by 5% if rafter and joist spans are no greater than 14 ft., 1 in. (4.3 m), and roof truss spans are no greater than 28 ft., 3 in. (8.6 m). Spans may be increased by 10% if rafter and joist spans are no greater than 12 ft., 2 in. (3.7 m), and roof truss spans are no greater than 24 ft., 3 in. (7.4 m).

2. If floor joists span the full width of the building without support, lintel spans shall be reduced by 15% for "Roof, ceiling and 1 storey", by 20% for "Roof, ceiling and 2 storeys" and by 25% for "Roof, ceiling and 3 storeys".

3. For ends of lintels fully supported by walls, provide minimum 1 1/2 in. (38 mm) of bearing for lintel spans up to 10 ft. (3 m), or minimum 3 in. (76 mm) of bearing for lintelspans greater than 10 ft. (3 m).

4. A single piece of 3 1/2 in. (89 mm) thick lumber may be used in lieu of 2 pieces of 1 1/2 in. (38 mm) thick lumber on edge.

5. Spans apply only where the floors serve residential areas.

6. Spans for 2 ft. (0.6 m) tributary width are calculated for lintels in end walls that support only a 2 ft. (0.6 m) width of roof and ceiling, but do not support roof joists, roof rafters or roof trusses.

7. When structural sheathing is used, lintel spans may be increased by 15%. Structural sheathing consists of a minimum 3/8 in. (9.5 mm) thick structural panel conforming to CSA O121, CSA O151, CSA O437 or CSA O325 fastened with at least two rows of fasteners conforming to Table 20 to the exterior face of the lintel, and a single row to the top plates and studs.

Table 23
Maximum spans for built-up ridge beams and lintels supporting roof and ceiling only, No. 1 or No. 2 grade

Commercial Designation	Lintel Size, in. (mm)		Maximum Span, ft.–in. (m) [1, 2, 3]				
			Specified Snow Load, psf (kPa)				
			20.9 1.0	31.3 1.5	41.8 2.0	52.2 2.5	62.7 3.0
Spruce – pine – fir (includes Spruce (all species except Coast Sitka Spruce), Jack Pine, Lodgepole Pine, Balsam Fir and Alpine Fir)	2 x 8 38 x 184	3-ply	9–6 2.88	8–2 2.48	7–3 2.21	6–7 2.01	6–1 1.86
		4-ply	10–10 3.30	9–5 2.86	8–4 2.55	7–7 2.32	7–0 2.14
		5-ply	11–8 3.55	10–2 3.10	9–3 2.82	8–6 2.59	7–10 2.40
	2 x 10 38 x 235	3-ply	11–7 3.53	9–11 3.03	8–10 2.70	8–1 2.46	7–5 2.27
		4-ply	13–4 4.07	11–6 3.50	10–3 3.12	9–4 2.84	8–7 2.62
		5-ply	14–11 4.54	12–10 3.91	11–5 3.43	10–5 3.17	9–7 2.93
	2 x 12 38 x 286	3-ply	13–9 4.09	11–6 3.52	10–3 3.13	9–4 2.85	8–8 2.63
		4-ply	15–6 4.72	13–4 4.06	11–10 3.62	10–10 3.29	10–0 3.04
		5-ply	17–4 5.28	14–11 4.54	13–3 4.04	12–1 3.68	11–2 3.40

Notes to Table 23

1. Beam and lintel spans are calculated based on a maximum supported length of 16 ft., 0 in. (4.9 m). Spans may be increased by 5% for supported lengths not more than 14 ft., 1 in. (4.3 m), by 10% for supported lengths not more than 12 ft., 2 in. (3.7 m) and by 25% for supported lengths not more than 7 ft., 10 in. (2.4 m).

 DOESN'T APPLY

2. For ridge beams, supported length means half the sum of the rafter, joist or truss span on both sides of the beam. For lintels, supported length means half the sum of truss, roof joist or rafter spans supported by the lintel plus the length of the overhang beyond the lintel.

3. Provide minimum 3 in. (76 mm) bearing.

Table 24
Minimum thickness of wall sheathing

Minimum Thickness, in. (mm)

Type of Sheathing	With Supports 16 (400) o.c.	With Supports 20 (500) o.c.	With Supports 24 (600) o.c.	Material Standards
Structural				
Fibreboard (insulating)	3/8 (9.5)	-	7/16 (11.1)	CAN/CSA-A247
Gypsum sheathing	3/8 (9.5)	-	1/2 (12.7)	CAN/CSA-A82.27-M
Plywood (exterior type)	1/4 (6.0)	-	5/16 (7.5)	CSA O121-M
				CSA O151-M
				CSA O153-M
OSB, O-1 grade, and waferboard, R-1 grade	1/4 (6.35)	-	5/16 (7.9)	CSA O437.0
Panel mark (performance-rated panels)	W16	W20	W24	CSA O325.0
Lumber	11/16 (17.0)	-	11/16 (17.0)	See Table 7
Mineral fibre, rigid board, type 2	1 (25)	-	1 (25)	CSA A101-M
OSB, O-2 grade	1/4 (6.0)	-	5/16 (7.5)	CSA O437.0
Phenolic, faced	1 (25)	-	1 (25)	CAN/CGSB-51.25-M
Non-Structural				
Expanded Polystyrene (Types 1 and 2)	1-1/2 (38)		1-1/2 (38)	CAN/CGSB-51.20-M
Expanded Polystyrene (Types 3 and 4)	1 (25)		1 (25)	CAN/CGSB-51.20-M
Urethane and isocyanurate (Types 1, 2 and 4)	1-1/2 (38)		1-1/2 (38)	CGSB 51-GP-21M
Urethane and isocyanurate (Type 3)	1 (25)		1 (25)	CGSB 51-GP-21M
Urethane and isocyanurate (Types 1 and 2), faced	1 (25)		1 (25)	CAN/CGSB-51.26-M

Table 25
Maximum spans for roof joists – specified roof snow loads 20.9 to 41.8 psf (1.0 to 2.0 kPa)

			Maximum Span, ft.–in. (m)								
			Specified Snow Load, psf (kPa)[1]								
			20.9 (1.0)			31.3 (1.5)			41.8 (2.0)		
			Joist Spacing, in. (mm)			Joist Spacing, in. (mm)			Joist Spacing, in. (mm)		
Commercial Designation	Grade	Joist Size, in. (mm)	12 (300)	16 (400)	24 (600)	12 (300)	16 (400)	24 (600)	12 (300)	16 (400)	24 (600)
Douglas fir – larch (includes Douglas fir and western larch)	No. 1 and No. 2	2x4 (38x89)	8–6 (2.59)	7–9 (2.36)	6–9 (2.06)	7–5 (2.27)	6–9 (2.06)	5–11 (1.80)	6–9 (2.06)	6–2 (1.87)	5–4 (1.63)
		2x6 (38x140)	13–5 (4.08)	12–2 (3.71)	10–8 (3.24)	11–8 (3.57)	10–8 (3.24)	9–3 (2.83)	10–8 (3.24)	9–8 (2.94)	8–5 (2.57)
		2x8 (38x184)	17–7 (5.36)	16–0 (4.87)	14–0 (4.26)	15–4 (4.69)	14–0 (4.26)	12–2 (3.72)	14–0 (4.26)	12–8 (3.87)	11–1 (3.38)
		2x10 (38x235)	22–6 (6.85)	20–5 (6.22)	17–10 (5.44)	19–8 (5.98)	17–10 (5.44)	15–7 (4.74)	17–10 (5.44)	16–2 (4.94)	13–10 (4.22)
		2x12 (38x286)	27–4 (8.34)	24–10 (7.57)	21–0 (6.40)	23–11 (7.28)	21–9 (6.62)	18–1 (5.50)	21–9 (6.62)	19–8 (6.00)	16–1 (4.90)
Hem – fir (includes western hemlock and amabilis fir)	No. 1 and No. 2	2x4 (38x89)	8–6 (2.59)	7–9 (2.36)	6–9 (2.06)	7–5 (2.27)	6–9 (2.06)	5–11 (1.80)	6–9 (2.06)	6–2 (1.87)	5–4 (1.63)
		2x6 (38x140)	13–5 (4.08)	12–2 (3.71)	10–8 (3.24)	11–8 (3.57)	10–8 (3.24)	9–3 (2.83)	10–8 (3.24)	9–8 (2.94)	8–5 (2.57)
		2x8 (38x184)	17–7 (5.36)	16–0 (4.87)	14–0 (4.26)	15–4 (4.69)	14–0 (4.26)	12–2 (3.72)	14–0 (4.26)	12–8 (3.87)	11–1 (3.38)
		2x10 (38x235)	22–6 (6.85)	20–5 (6.22)	17–10 (5.44)	19–8 (5.98)	17–10 (5.44)	15–7 (4.75)	17–10 (5.44)	16–2 (4.94)	14–2 (4.32)
		2x12 (38x286)	27–4 (8.34)	24–10 (7.57)	21–9 (6.62)	23–11 (7.28)	21–9 (6.62)	18–11 (5.77)	21–9 (6.62)	19–9 (6.01)	16–10 (5.25)
Spruce – pine – fir (includes spruce [all species except coast sitka spruce], jack pine, lodgepole pine, balsam fir and alpine fir)	No. 1 and No. 2	2x4 (38x89)	8–1 (2.47)	7–4 (2.24)	6–5 (1.96)	7–1 (2.16)	6–5 (1.96)	5–7 (1.71)	6–5 (1.96)	5–10 (1.78)	5–1 (1.56)
		2x6 (38x140)	12–9 (3.89)	11–7 (3.53)	10–1 (3.08)	11–2 (3.40)	10–1 (3.08)	8–10 (2.69)	10–1 (3.08)	9–2 (2.80)	8–0 (2.45)
		2x8 (38x184)	16–9 (5.11)	15–3 (4.64)	13–4 (4.05)	14–8 (4.46)	13–4 (4.05)	11–7 (3.54)	13–4 (4.05)	12–1 (3.68)	10–7 (3.22)
		2x10 (38x35)	21–5 (6.52)	19–5 (5.93)	17–0 (5.18)	18–8 (5.70)	17–0 (5.18)	14–10 (4.52)	17–0 (5.18)	15–5 (4.70)	13–6 (4.11)
		2x12 (38x286)	26–1 (7.94)	23–8 (7.21)	20–8 (6.30)	22–9 (6.94)	20–8 (6.30)	18–1 (5.50)	20–8 (6.30)	18–9 (5.73)	16–5 (5.00)
Northern species (includes any Canadian species covered by the NLGA Standard Grading Rules)	No. 1 and No. 2	2x4 (38x89)	7–4 (2.23)	6–8 (2.03)	5–10 (1.77)	6–5 (1.95)	5–10 (1.77)	5–1 (1.55)	5–10 (1.77)	5–3 (1.61)	4–7 (1.41)
		2x6 (38x140)	11–6 (3.51)	10–6 (3.19)	9–2 (2.79)	10–1 (3.07)	9–2 (2.79)	8–0 (2.43)	9–2 (2.79)	8–4 (2.53)	7–3 (2.21)
		2x8 (38x184)	15–2 (4.61)	13–9 (4.19)	12–0 (3.66)	13–3 (4.03)	12–0 (3.66)	10–6 (3.20)	12–0 (3.66)	10–11 (3.33)	9–6 (2.91)
		2x10 (38x235)	19–4 (5.89)	17–7 (5.35)	15–4 (4.68)	16–11 (5.15)	15–4 (4.68)	13–5 (4.09)	15–4 (4.68)	13–11 (4.25)	12–1 (3.68)
		2x12 (38x286)	23–6 (7.17)	21–5 (6.52)	18–4 (5.58)	20–7 (6.26)	18–8 (5.69)	15–9 (4.80)	18–8 (5.69)	17–0 (5.17)	14–0 (4.27)

Note to Table 25

1. To determine the specified snow load in your location, contact your municipal building department.

Table 26
Maximum spans for roof joists – specified roof snow loads 52.2 and 62.7 psf (2.5 and 3.0 kPa)

			Maximum Span, ft.–in. (m)					
			Specified Snow Load, psf (kPa)[1]					
			52.2 (2.5)			62.7 (3.0)		
		Joist Size, in. (mm)	Joist Spacing, in. (mm)			Joist Spacing, in. (mm)		
Commercial Designation	Grade		12 (300)	16 (400)	24 (600)	12 (300)	16 (400)	24 (600)
Douglas fir – larch (includes Douglas fir and western larch)	No. 1 and No. 2	2x4 (38x89)	6–3 (1.91)	5–8 (1.74)	5–0 (1.52)	5–11 (1.80)	5–4 (1.63)	4–8 (1.43)
		2x6 (38x140)	9–10 (3.01)	9–0 (2.73)	7–10 (2.39)	9–3 (2.83)	8–5 (2.57)	7–4 (2.25)
		2x8 (38x184)	13–0 (3.95)	11–9 (3.59)	10–3 (3.14)	12–2 (3.72)	11–1 (3.38)	9–6 (2.90)
		2x10 (38x235)	16–7 (5.05)	15–1 (4.59)	12–7 (3.84)	15–7 (4.75)	14–2 (4.32)	11–8 (3.55)
		2x12 (38x286)	20–2 (6.14)	17–11 (5.46)	14–8 (4.46)	19–0 (5.78)	16–7 (5.05)	13–6 (4.12)
Hem – fir (includes western hemlock and amabilis fir)	No. 1 and No. 2	2x4 (38x89)	6–3 (1.91)	5–8 (1.74)	5–0 (1.52)	5–11 (1.80)	5–4 (1.63)	4–8 (1.43)
		2x6 (38x140)	9–10 (3.01)	9–0 (2.73)	7–10 (2.39)	9–3 (2.83)	8–5 (2.57)	7–4 (2.25)
		2x8 (38x184)	13–0 (3.95)	11–9 (3.59)	10–3 (3.14)	12–2 (3.72)	11–1 (3.38)	9–8 (2.95)
		2x10 (38x235)	16–7 (5.05)	15–1 (4.59)	13–2 (4.01)	15–7 (4.75)	14–2 (4.32)	12–3 (3.72)
		2x12 (38x286)	20–2 (6.14)	18–4 (5.58)	15–4 (4.68)	19–0 (5.78)	17–3 (5.25)	14–2 (4.32)
Spruce – pine – fir (includes spruce [all species except coast sitka spruce], jack pine, lodgepole pine, balsam fir and alpine fir)	No. 1 and No. 2	2x4 (38x89)	6–0 (1.82)	5–5 (1.65)	4–9 (1.44)	5–7 (1.71)	5–1 (1.56)	4–6 (1.36)
		2x6 (38x140)	9–5 (2.86)	8–6 (2.60)	7–5 (2.27)	8–10 (2.69)	8–0 (2.45)	7–0 (2.14)
		2x8 (38x184)	12–4 (3.76)	11–3 (3.42)	9–10 (2.99)	11–7 (3.54)	10–7 (3.22)	9–3 (2.81)
		2x10 (38x235)	15–9 (4.81)	14–4 (4.37)	12–6 (3.82)	14–10 (4.52)	13–6 (4.11)	11–9 (3.59)
		2x12 (38x286)	19–2 (5.85)	17–5 (5.31)	15–3 (4.64)	18–1 (5.50)	16–5 (5.00)	14–4 (4.37)
Northern species (includes any Canadian species covered by the NLGA Standard Grading Rules)	No. 1 and No. 2	2x4 (38x89)	5–5 (1.64)	4–11 (1.49)	4–3 (1.31)	5–1 (1.55)	4–7 (1.41)	4–0 (1.23)
		2x6 (38x140)	8–6 (2.59)	7–9 (2.35)	6–9 (2.05)	8–0 (2.43)	7–3 (2.21)	6–4 (1.93)
		2x8 (38x184)	11–2 (3.40)	10–2 (3.09)	8–10 (2.70)	10–6 (3.20)	9–6 (2.91)	8–4 (2.53)
		2x10 (38x235)	14–3 (4.34)	12–11 (3.94)	11–0 (3.35)	13–5 (4.09)	12–2 (3.71)	10–2 (3.10)
		2x12 (38x286)	17–4 (5.28)	15–7 (4.76)	12–9 (3.89)	16–4 (4.97)	14–5 (4.40)	11–9 (3.59)

Note to Table 26
1. To determine the specified snow load in your location, contact your municipal building department.

Table 27
Maximum spans for roof rafters – specified roof snow loads 20.9 to 41.8 psf (1.0 to 2.0 kPa)

			Maximum Span, ft.–in. (m)								
			Specified Snow Load, psf (kPa)[1]								
			20.9 (1.0)			31.3 (1.5)			41.8 (2.0)		
			Rafter Spacing, in. (mm)			Rafter Spacing, in. (mm)			Rafter Spacing, in. (mm)		
Commercial Designation	Grade	Rafter Size, in. (mm)	12 (300)	16 (400)	24 (600)	12 (300)	16 (400)	24 (600)	12 (300)	16 (400)	24 (600)
Douglas fir – larch (includes Douglas fir and western larch)	No. 1 and No. 2	2x4 (38x89)	10–9 (3.27)	9–9 (2.97)	8–6 (2.59)	9–4 (2.86)	8–6 (2.59)	7–5 (2.27)	8–6 (2.59)	7–9 (2.36)	6–9 (2.06)
		2x6 (38x140)	16–10 (5.14)	15–4 (4.67)	12–11 (3.95)	14–9 (4.49)	13–5 (4.08)	10–11 (3.34)	13–5 (4.08)	11–10 (3.60)	9–8 (2.94)
		2x8 (38x184)	22–2 (6.76)	19–4 (5.88)	15–9 (4.80)	18–10 (5.74)	16–4 (4.97)	13–4 (4.06)	16–7 (5.06)	14–5 (4.38)	11–9 (3.58)
		2x10 (38x235)	27–3 (8.30)	23–7 (7.19)	19–3 (5.87)	23–0 (7.02)	19–11 (6.08)	16–3 (4.96)	20–4 (6.19)	17–7 (5.36)	14–4 (4.38)
		2x12 (38x286)	31–7 (9.63)	27–5 (8.34)	22–4 (6.81)	26–9 (8.14)	23–2 (7.05)	18–11 (5.76)	23–7 (7.18)	20–5 (6.22)	16–8 (5.08)
Hem – fir (includes western hemlock and amabilis fir)	No. 1 and No. 2	2x4 (38x89)	10–9 (3.27)	9–9 (2.97)	8–6 (2.59)	9–4 (2.86)	8–6 (2.59)	7–5 (2.27)	8–6 (2.59)	7–9 (2.36)	6–9 (2.06)
		2x6 (38x140)	16–10 (5.14)	15–4 (4.67)	13–5 (4.08)	14–9 (4.49)	13–5 (4.08)	11–6 (3.50)	13–5 (4.08)	12–2 (3.71)	10–1 (3.08)
		2x8 (38x184)	22–2 (6.76)	20–2 (6.14)	16–6 (5.04)	19–4 (5.90)	17–1 (5.21)	14–0 (4.26)	17–5 (5.31)	15–1 (4.60)	12–4 (3.75)
		2x10 (38x235)	28–4 (8.63)	24–9 (7.54)	20–2 (6.16)	24–2 (7.36)	20–11 (6.37)	17–1 (5.20)	21–4 (6.49)	18–5 (5.62)	15–1 (4.59)
		2x12 (38x286)	33–2 (10.11)	28–9 (8.75)	23–5 (7.15)	28–0 (8.54)	24–3 (7.40)	19–10 (6.04)	24–9 (7.53)	21–5 (6.52)	17–6 (5.33)
Spruce – pine – fir (includes spruce [all species except coast sitka spruce], jack pine, lodgepole pine, balsam fir and alpine fir)	No. 1 and No. 2	2x4 (38x89)	10–3 (3.11)	9–3 (2.83)	8–1 (2.47)	8–11 (2.72)	8–1 (2.47)	7–1 (2.16)	8–1 (2.47)	7–4 (2.24)	6–5 (1.96)
		2x6 (38x140)	16–1 (4.90)	14–7 (4.45)	12–9 (3.89)	14–0 (4.28)	12–9 (3.89)	11–2 (3.40)	12–9 (3.89)	11–7 (3.53)	10–1 (3.08)
		2x8 (38x184)	21–1 (6.44)	19–2 (5.85)	16–9 (5.11)	18–5 (5.62)	16–9 (5.11)	14–6 (4.41)	16–9 (5.11)	15–3 (4.64)	12–9 (3.89)
		2x10 (38x235)	27–0 (8.22)	24–6 (7.47)	20–11 (6.38)	23–7 (7.18)	21–5 (6.52)	17–8 (5.39)	21–5 (6.52)	19–1 (5.82)	15–7 (4.75)
		2x12 (38x286)	32–10 (10.00)	29–9 (9.06)	24–3 (7.40)	28–8 (8.74)	25–2 (7.66)	20–6 (6.25)	25–7 (7.80)	22–2 (6.76)	18–1 (5.52)
Northern species (includes any Canadian species covered by the NLGA Standard Grading Rules)	No. 1 and No. 2	2x4 (38x89)	9–3 (2.81)	8–5 (2.55)	7–4 (2.23)	8–1 (2.46)	7–4 (2.23)	6–5 (1.95)	7–4 (2.23)	6–8 (2.03)	5–10 (1.77)
		2x6 (38x140)	14–6 (4.42)	13–2 (4.02)	11–3 (3.44)	12–8 (3.86)	11–6 (3.51)	9–6 (2.91)	11–6 (3.51)	10–4 (3.14)	8–5 (2.56)
		2x8 (38x184)	19–1 (5.81)	16–10 (5.13)	13–9 (4.19)	16–5 (5.00)	14–3 (4.33)	11–7 (3.54)	14–6 (4.41)	12–6 (3.82)	10–3 (3.12)
		2x10 (38x235)	23–9 (7.24)	20–7 (6.27)	16–10 (5.12)	20–1 (6.12)	17–5 (5.30)	14–2 (4.33)	17–8 (5.40)	15–4 (4.67)	12–6 (3.82)
		2x12 (38x286)	27–7 (8.40)	23–10 (7.27)	19–6 (5.94)	23–3 (7.10)	20–2 (6.15)	16–6 (5.02)	20–6 (6.26)	17–9 (5.42)	14–6 (4.43)

Note to Table 27

1. To determine the specified snow load in your location, contact your municipal building department.

Table 28
Maximum spans for roof rafters – specified roof snow loads
52.2 and 62.7 psf (2.5 and 3.0 kPa)

Commercial Designation	Grade	Rafter Size, in. (mm)	Maximum Span, ft.–in. (m)					
			Specified Snow Load, psf (kPa)[1]					
			52.2 (2.5)			62.7 (3.0)		
			Rafter Spacing, in. (mm)			Rafter Spacing, in. (mm)		
			12 (300)	16 (400)	24 (600)	12 (300)	16 (400)	24 (600)
Douglas fir – larch (includes Douglas fir and western larch)	No. 1 and No. 2	2x4 (38x89)	7–11 (2.41)	7–2 (2.19)	6–1 (1.86)	7–5 (2.27)	6–9 (2.06)	5–7 (1.71)
		2x6 (38x140)	12–4 (3.76)	10–8 (3.26)	8–9 (2.66)	11–4 (3.46)	9–10 (3.00)	8–0 (2.45)
		2x8 (38x184)	15–0 (4.58)	13–0 (3.96)	10–7 (3.24)	13–10 (4.21)	12–0 (3.65)	9–9 (2.98)
		2x10 (38x235)	18–4 (5.60)	15–11 (4.85)	13–0 (3.96)	16–11 (5.15)	14–8 (4.46)	11–11 (3.64)
		2x12 (38x286)	21–4 (6.50)	18–5 (5.63)	15–1 (4.59)	19–7 (5.98)	17–0 (5.17)	13–10 (4.23)
Hem – fir (includes western hemlock and amabilis fir)	No. 1 and No. 2	2x4 (38x89)	7–11 (2.41)	7–2 (2.19)	6–3 (1.91)	7–5 (2.27)	6–9 (2.06)	5–11 (1.80)
		2x6 (38x140)	12–5 (3.79)	11–3 (3.42)	9–2 (2.79)	11–8 (3.57)	10–4 (3.14)	8–5 (2.57)
		2x8 (38x184)	15–9 (4.80)	13–8 (4.16)	11–2 (3.40)	14–6 (4.42)	12–7 (3.83)	10–3 (3.12)
		2x10 (38x235)	19–3 (5.87)	16–8 (5.08)	13–7 (4.15)	17–9 (5.40)	15–4 (4.68)	12–6 (3.82)
		2x12 (38x286)	22–4 (6.81)	19–4 (5.90)	15–10 (4.82)	20–7 (6.27)	17–10 (5.43)	14–6 (4.43)
Spruce – pine – fir (includes spruce [all species except coast sitka spruce], jack pine, lodgepole pine, balsam fir and alpine fir)	No. 1 and No. 2	2x4 (38x89)	7–6 (2.29)	6–10 (2.08)	6–0 (1.82)	7–1 (2.16)	6–5 (1.96)	5–7 (1.71)
		2x6 (38x140)	11–10 (3.61)	10–9 (3.28)	9–5 (2.86)	11–2 (3.40)	10–1 (3.08)	8–9 (2.66)
		2x8 (38x184)	15–7 (4.74)	14–2 (4.31)	11–6 (3.52)	14–8 (4.46)	13–0 (3.96)	10–7 (3.23)
		2x10 (38x235)	19–10 (6.06)	17–3 (5.27)	14–1 (4.30)	18–4 (5.59)	15–11 (4.84)	13–0 (3.96)
		2x12 (38x286)	23–2 (7.06)	20–1 (6.11)	16–4 (4.99)	21–4 (6.49)	18–5 (5.62)	15–1 (4.59)
Northern species (includes any Canadian species covered by the NLGA Standard Grading Rules)	No. 1 and No. 2	2x4 (38x89)	6–10 (2.07)	6–2 (1.88)	5–4 (1.62)	6–5 (1.95)	5–10 (1.77)	4–11 (1.49)
		2x6 (38x140)	10–8 (3.26)	9–4 (2.84)	7–7 (2.32)	9–11 (3.02)	8–7 (2.61)	7–0 (2.13)
		2x8 (38x184)	13–1 (3.99)	11–4 (3.46)	9–3 (2.82)	12–1 (3.67)	10–5 (3.18)	8–6 (2.60)
		2x10 (38x235)	16–0 (4.88)	13–10 (4.23)	11–4 (3.45)	14–9 (4.49)	12–9 (3.89)	10–5 (3.17)
		2x12 (38x286)	18–7 (5.66)	16–1 (4.90)	13–2 (4.00)	17–1 (5.21)	14–10 (4.51)	12–1 (3.68)

Note to Table 28
1. To determine the specified snow load in your location, contact your municipal building department.

Table 29
Maximum spans for ceiling joists – attic not accessible by a stairway

			Maximum Span, ft.–in. (m)		
		Joist	Joist Spacing, in. (mm)		
Commercial Designation	Grade	Size, in. (mm)	12 (300) o/c	16 (400) o/c	24 (600) o/c
Douglas fir – larch (includes Douglas fir and western larch)	No. 1 and No. 2	2x4 (38x89) 2x6 (38x140) 2x8 (38x184) 2x10 (38x235) 2x12 (38x286)	10–9 (3.27) 16–10 (5.14) 22–2 (6.76) 28–4 (8.63) 34–5 (10.50)	9–9 (2.97) 15–4 (4.67) 20–2 (6.14) 25–9 (7.84) 31–3 (9.54)	8–6 (2.59) 13–5 (4.08) 17–7 (5.36) 22–6 (6.85) 27–4 (8.34)
Hem – fir (includes western hemlock and amabilis fir)	No. 1 and No. 2	2x4 (38x89) 2x6 (38x140) 2x8 (38x184) 2x10 (38x235) 2x12 (38x286)	10–9 (3.27) 16–10 (5.14) 22–2 (6.76) 28–4 (8.63) 34–5 (10.50)	9–9 (2.97) 15–4 (4.67) 20–2 (6.14) 25–9 (7.84) 31–3 (9.54)	8–6 (2.59) 13–5 (4.08) 17–7 (5.36) 22–6 (6.85) 27–4 (8.34)
Spruce – pine – fir (includes spruce [all species except coast sitka spruce], jack pine, lodgepole pine, balsam fir and alpine fir)	No. 1 and No. 2	2x4 (38x89) 2x6 (38x140) 2x8 (38x184) 2x10 (38x235) 2x12 (38x286)	10–3 (3.11) 16–1 (4.90) 21–1 (6.44) 27–0 (8.22) 32–10 (10.00)	9–3 (2.83) 14–7 (4.45) 19–2 (5.85) 24–6 (7.47) 29–10 (9.09)	8–1 (2.47) 12–9 (3.89) 16–9 (5.11) 21–5 (6.52) 26–1 (7.94)
Northern species (includes any Canadian species covered by the NLGA Standard Grading Rules)	No. 1 and No. 2	2x4 (38x89) 2x6 (38–140) 2x8 (38x184) 2x10 (38x235) 2x12 (38x286)	9–3 (2.81) 14–6 (4.42) 19–1 (5.81) 24–4 (7.42) 29–8 (9.03)	8–5 (2.55) 13–2 (4.02) 17–4 (5.28) 22–2 (6.74) 26–11 (8.21)	7–4 (2.23) 11–6 (3.51) 15–2 (4.61) 19–4 (5.89) 23–6 (7.17)

Table 30
Minimum rafter-to-joist nailing

		Rafter Tied to Every Joist						Rafter Tied to Joist Every 3 ft., 11 in. (1.2 m)					
		Building Width up to						Building Width up to					
		26 ft., 3 in. (8 m)			32 ft., 2 in. (9.8 m)			26 ft., 3 in. (8 m)			32 ft., 2 in. (9.8 m)		
		Roof Snow Load, psf (kPa)[3]											
Roof Slope	Rafter Spacing, in. (mm)	20 (1) or less	30 (1.5)	40 (2.0) or more	20 (1) or less	30 (1.5)	40 (2.0) or more	20 (1) or less	30 (1.5)	40 (2.0) or more	20 (1) or less	30 (1.5)	40 (2.0) or more
1:3	16 (400)	4	5	6	5	7	8	11	–	–	–	–	–
	24 (600)	6	8	9	8	–	–	11	–	–	–	–	–
1:2.4	16 (400)	4	4	5	5	6	7	7	10	–	9	–	–
	24 (600)	5	7	8	7	9	11	7	10	–	–	–	–
1:2	16 (400)	4	4	4	4	4	5	6	8	9	8	–	–
	24 (600)	4	5	6	5	7	8	6	8	9	8	–	–
1:1.71	16 (400)	4	4	4	4	4	4	5	7	8	7	9	11
	24 (600)	4	4	5	5	6	7	5	7	8	7	9	11
1:1.33	16 (400)	4	4	4	4	4	4	4	5	6	5	6	7
	24 (600)	4	4	4	4	4	5	4	5	6	5	6	7
1:1	16 (400)	4	4	4	4	4	4	4	4	4	4	4	5
	24 (600)	4	4	4	4	4	4	4	4	4	4	4	5

Notes to Table 30

1. Nails not less than 3 1/8 in. (79 mm).

2. Ceiling joists must be fastened together with at least one more nail per joist splice than required for the rafter-to-joist connection.

3. To determine the specified snow load in your location, contact your municipal building department.

Table 31
Minimum thickness of flashing materials

Material	Minimum Thickness, in. (mm)			
	Roof Flashing	Wall flashing		
		Cladding	Above Grade Masonry	
			Exposed	Concealed
Aluminum	0.019 (0.48)	0.019 (0.48)	0.019 (0.48)	–
Copper	0.018 (0.46)	0.018 (0.46)	0.014 (0.36)	0.014 (0.36)
Copper or aluminum laminated to felt or kraft paper	–	–	–	0.002 (0.05)
Galvanized steel	0.013 (0.33)	0.013 (0.33)	0.013 (0.33)	0.013 (0.33)
Lead sheet	0.068 (1.73)	0.068 (1.73)	0.068 (1.73)	0.068 (1.73)
Polyethylene	–	–	–	0.02 (0.50)
Roll roofing, types	–	–	–	Standard
Zinc	0.014 (0.35)	0.014 (0.35)	0.014 (0.35)	0.014 (0.35)
Vinyl	–	0.04 (1.02)	–	–

Table 32
Minimum thickness of roof sheathing for sloping roofs[1]

		Sheathing Thickness, in. (mm), for Truss or Rafter Spacing at			
		12 (300)	16 (400)	20 (500)	24 (600)
Plywood and OSB, O-2 grade	Supported[2] edges	5/16 (7.5)	5/16 (7.5)		3/8 (9.5)
	Unsupported edges	5/16 (7.5)	3/8 (9.5)		1/2 (12.7)
OSB, O-1 grade and waferboard R-1 grade	Supported edges	3/8 (9.5)	3/8 (9.5)		7/16 (11.1)
	Unsupported edges	3/8 (9.5)	7/16 (11.1)		1/2 (12.7)
Panel mark (performance-rated panels)	Supported[2] edges	-	1R16	1R20	1R24
Panel mark (performance-rated panels)	Unsupported edges	-	2R16	2R20	2R24
Lumber[3]		11/16 (17)	11/16 (17)		3/4 (19)

Notes for Table 32

1. The thickness of sheathing for flat roofs used as walking decks is the same as for subfloors (see Table 18).
2. Supported edges between panels by means of H clips or minimum 2 in.x2 in. (38mmx38 mm) blocking between trusses or rafters.
3. For eastern white pine and red pine, minimum lumber grade is No. 4 common. For all other species, the minimum grades shall be standard or No. 3 common.

Table 33
Roofing types and slope limits for roofs

Type of Roofing	Slope	
	Minimum	Maximum
Built-up roofing		
Asphalt base (graveled)	1 in 50	1 in 4
Asphalt base (without gravel)	1 in 25	1 in 2
Coal-tar base (graveled)	1 in 50	1 in 25
Cold process	1 in 25	1 in 1.33
Asphalt shingles		
Normal Application	1 in 3	No limit
Low slope application	1 in 6	No limit
Roll roofing		
Smooth and mineral surfaced	1 in 4	No limit
19 in. (480 mm) wide selvage asphalt roofing	1 in 6	No limit
Cold application felt	1 in 50	1 in 1.33
Wood shingles	1 in 4	No limit
Handsplit shakes	1 in 3	No limit
Asbestos-cement corrugated sheets	1 in 4	No limit
Corrugated metal roofing	1 in 4	No limit
Sheet metal shingles	1 in 4	No limit
Slate shingles	1 in 2	No limit
Clay tile	1 in 2	No limit
Glass fibre reinforced polyester roofing panels	1 in 4	No limit

Table 34
Exposure and thickness of wood shingles and machine-grooved shakes – walls

Shake or Shingle Length, in. (mm)	Maximum Exposure, in. (mm)		Minimum Butt Thickness, in. (mm)
	Single Coursing	Double Coursing	
16 (400)	7 1/2 (190)	12 (305)	3/8 (10)
18 (450)	8 1/2 (216)	14 (356)	7/16 (11)
24 (600)	11 1/2 (292)	16 (406)	1/2 (13)

Table 35
Stapling table, in. (mm)

A) Asphalt shingles to wood decks
  (1) 16 gauge (1.6 mm) thick, 7/8 (22.2) long, 7/16 (11.1) crown
      Corrosion resistant
      1/3 more staples than the number of nails required
  (2) 16 gauge (1.6 mm) thick, 3/4 (19) long, 1 (25.4) crown
      Corrosion resistant
      Equivalent to number of nails required

B) Cedar shingles to wood decks
  16 gauge (1.6 mm) thick, 1 1/8 (28.6) long, 3/8 (9.5) crown
  Corrosion resistant

C) Gypsum plaster lath, 3/8 (9.5) thick
  16 gauge (1.6 mm) thick, 1 (25.4) long, 3/4 (19) crown
  Gypsum plaster lath, 3/8 (9.5) thick
  16 gauge (1.6 mm) thick, 1 1/8 (28.6) long, 3/4 (19) crown

D) 5/16 and 3/8 (7.5 and 9.5) plywood wall sheathing
  16 gauge (1.6 mm) thick, 1 1/2 (38.1) long, 3/8 (9.5) crown

E) 3/8 (9.5) plywood roof sheathing
  16 gauge (1.6 mm) thick, 1 1/2 (38.1) long, 3/8 (9.5) crown

F) 7/16 and 1/2 (11.1 and 12.7) fibreboard wall sheathing
  16 gauge (1.6 mm) thick, 1 1/2 (38.1) long, 3/8 (9.5) crown

G) 1/4 (6.4) underlayment
  18 gauge (1.2 mm) thick, 1 1/8 (28.6) long, 3/8 (9.5) crown

H) 5/16 and 3/8 (7.9 and 9.5) hardboard underlayment
  18 gauge (1.2 mm) thick, 1 1/8 (28.6) long, 5/16 (7.9) crown

I) Metal plaster lath
  14 gauge (2mm) thick, 1 1/2 (38.1) long, 3/4 (19) crown

Table 36
Stucco mixes (by volume)

Portland Cement	Masonry Cement, Type H	Lime	Aggregate
I	–	1/4 to 1	31/4 to 4 parts per part of cementitious material
I	I	I	

Table 37
Dimensions for wood-strip flooring

Type of Flooring	Maximum Joist Spacing, in, (mm)	Minimum Thickness of Flooring, in, (mm)	
		With Subfloor	No Subfloor
Matched hardwood (interior use only)	16 (400) 24 (600)	5/16 (7.9) 5/16 (7.9)	3/4 (19.0) 15/16 (33.3)
Matched softwood (interior or exterior use)	16 (400) 24 (600)	3/4 (19.0) 3/4 (19.0)	3/4 (19.0) 11/4 (31.7)
Square edge softwood (exterior use only)	16 (400) 24 (600)	– –	1 (25.4) 11/2 (38.1)

Table 38
Nailing of wood-strip flooring

Finish Floor Thickness, in. (mm)	Minimum Length of Flooring Nails, in. (mm)	Maximum Spacing of Flooring Nails, in. (mm)
5/16 (7.9)	11/2 (38)	8 (200)
7/16 (11.1)	2 (51)	12 (300)
3/4 (19.0)	21/4 (57)	16 (400)
1 (25.4)	21/2 (63)	16 (400)
1 1/4 (31.7)	23/4 (70)	24 (600)
1 1/2 (38.1)	31/4 (83)	24 (600)

Note to Table 38
1. Staples are permitted to be used to fasten wood strip flooring not more than 5/16 in. (7.9 mm) in thickness provided the staples are not less than 13/16 in. (29 mm) long with a shank diameter of 0.047 in. (1.19 mm) and a width of 3/16 in. (4.7 mm) crowns.

Table 39
Built-up beams for exterior decks (lumber not incised)

Number and Size of Plys in. (mm)

	Post Spacing ft. (m)	Joist Span 8 ft. (2.4 m)	9 ft. (2.7 m)	10 ft. (3.0 m)	11 ft. (3.3 m)	12 ft. (3.7 m)	14 ft. (4.3 m)
D.Fir-L	4 ft. (1.2 m)	1- 2 x 6 (1-38 x 140)	1- 2 x 6 (1-38 x 140)	1- 2 x 6 (1-38 x 140)	1- 2 x 6 (1-38 x 140)	1- 2 x 6 (1-38 x 140)	1- 2 x 8 (1-38 x 184)
	6 ft. (1.8 m)	1- 2 x 8 (1-38 x 184)	1- 2 x 8 (1-38 x 184)	1 - 2 x 10 (1-38 x 235)	1 - 2 x 10 (1-38 x 235)	1 - 2 x 10 (1-38 x 235)	2- 2 x 8 (2-38 x 184)
	8 ft. (2.4 m)	2- 2 x 8 (2-38 x 184)	2- 2 x 8 (2-38 x 184)	2- 2 x 8 (2-38 x 184)	2- 2 x 8 (2-38 x 184)	2 - 2 x 10 (2-38 x 235)	2 - 2 x 10 (2-38 x 235)
Hem-Fir	4 ft. (1.2 m)	1- 2 x 6 (1-38 x 140)	1- 2 x 6 (1-38 x 140)	1- 2 x 6 (1-38 x 140)	1- 2 x 6 (1-38 x 140)	1- 2 x 6 (1-38 x 140)	1- 2 x 6 (1-38 x 140)
	6 ft. (1.8 m)	1- 2 x 8 (1-38 x 184)	1- 2 x 8 (1-38 x 184)	1- 2 x 8 (1-38 x 184)	1 - 2 x 10 (1-38 x 235)	1 - 2 x 10 (1-38 x 235)	1 - 2 x 10 (1-38 x 235)
	8 ft. (2.4 m)	1 - 2 x 10 (1-38 x 235)	2- 2 x 8 (2-38 x 184)	2- 2 x 8 (2-38 x 184)	2- 2 x 8 (2-38 x 184)	2- 2 x 8 (2-38 x 184)	2 - 2 x 10 (2-38 x 235)
S-P-F	4 ft. (1.2 m)	1- 2 x 6 (1-38 x 140)	1- 2 x 6 (1-38 x 140)	1- 2 x 6 (1-38 x 140)	1- 2 x 6 (1-38 x 140)	1- 2 x 6 (1-38 x 140)	1- 2 x 6 (1-38 x 140)
	6 ft. (1.8 m)	1- 2 x 8 (1-38 x 184)	1- 2 x 8 (1-38 x 184)	1- 2 x 8 (1-38 x 184)	1 - 2 x 10 (1-38 x 235)	1 - 2 x 10 (1-38 x 235)	1 - 2 x 10 (1-38 x 235)
	8 ft. (2.4 m)	1 - 2 x 10 (1-38 x 235)	2- 2 x 8 (2-38 x 184)	2- 2 x 8 (2-38 x 184)	2- 2 x 8 (2-38 x 184)	2- 2 x 8 (2-38 x 184)	2 - 2 x 10 (2-38 x 235)
Northern Species	4 ft. (1.2 m)	1- 2 x 6 (1-38 x 140)	1- 2 x 6 (1-38 x 140)	1- 2 x 6 (1-38 x 140)	1- 2 x 8 (1-38 x 184)	1- 2 x 8 (1-38 x 184)	1- 2 x 8 (1-38 x 184)
	6 ft. (1.8 m)	1 - 2 x 10 (1-38 x 235)	1 - 2 x 10 (1-38 x 235)	1 - 2 x 10 (1-38 x 235)	2- 2 x 8 (2-38 x 184)	2- 2 x 8 (2-38 x 184)	2- 2 x 8 (2-38 x 184)
	8 ft. (2.4 m)	2- 2 x 8 (2-38 x 184)	1 - 2 x 10 (2-38 x 235)	1 - 2 x 10 (2-38 x 235)	1 - 2 x 10 (2-38 x 235)	1 - 2 x 10 (2-38 x 235)	2 - 2 x 12 (2-38 x 286)

Continued on p. 395

Table 39 (continued)
Built-up beams for exterior decks (lumber incised)[1]

Number and Size of Plys in. (mm)

	Post Spacing ft. (m)	Joist Span					
		8 ft. (2.4 m)	9 ft. (2.7 m)	10 ft. (3.0 m)	11 ft. (3.3 m)	12 ft. (3.7 m)	14 ft. (4.3 m)
D.Fir-L	4 ft. (1.2 m)	1- 2 x 6 (1-38 x 140)	1- 2 x 6 (1-38 x 140)	1- 2 x 6 (1-38 x 140)	1- 2 x 6 (1-38 x 140)	1- 2 x 8 (1-38 x 184)	1- 2 x 8 (1-38 x 184)
	6 ft. (1.8 m)	1 - 2 x 10 (1-38 x 235)	1 - 2 x 10 (1-38 x 235)	1 - 2 x 10 (1-38 x 235)	1 - 2 x 10 (1-38 x 235)	2- 2 x 8 (2-38 x 184)	2- 2 x 8 (2-38 x 184)
	8 ft. (2.4 m)	2- 2 x 8 (2-38 x 184)	2- 2 x 8 (2-38 x 184)	2 - 2 x 10 (2-38 x 235)	2 - 2 x 10 (2-38 x 235)	2 - 2 x 10 (2-38 x 235)	2 - 2 x 10 (2-38 x 235)
Hem-Fir	4 ft. (1.2 m)	1- 2 x 6 (1-38 x 140)	1- 2 x 6 (1-38 x 140)	1- 2 x 6 (1-38 x 140)	1- 2 x 6 (1-38 x 140)	1- 2 x 6 (1-38 x 140)	1- 2 x 8 (1-38 x 184)
	6 ft. (1.8 m)	1- 2 x 8 (1-38 x 184)	1 - 2 x 10 (1-38 x 235)	1 - 2 x 10 (1-38 x 235)	1 - 2 x 10 (1-38 x 235)	1 - 2 x 10 (1-38 x 235)	2- 2 x 8 (2-38 x 184)
	8 ft. (2.4 m)	2- 2 x 8 (2-38 x 184)	2- 2 x 8 (2-38 x 184)	2- 2 x 8 (2-38 x 184)	2 - 2 x 10 (2-38 x 235)	2 - 2 x 10 (2-38 x 235)	2 - 2 x 10 (2-38 x 235)
S-P-F	4 ft. (1.2 m)	1- 2 x 6 (1-38 x 140)	1- 2 x 6 (1-38 x 140)	1- 2 x 6 (1-38 x 140)	1- 2 x 6 (1-38 x 140)	1- 2 x 6 (1-38 x 140)	1- 2 x 8 (1-38 x 184)
	6 ft. (1.8 m)	1- 2 x 8 (1-38 x 184)	1 - 2 x 8 (1-38 x 184)	1 - 2 x 10 (1-38 x 235)	1 - 2 x 10 (1-38 x 235)	1 - 2 x 10 (1-38 x 235)	2- 2 x 8 (2-38 x 184)
	8 ft. (2.4 m)	2- 2 x 8 (2-38 x 184)	2- 2 x 8 (2-38 x 184)	2- 2 x 8 (2-38 x 184)	2- 2 x 8 (2-38 x 184)	2 - 2 x 10 (2-38 x 235)	2 - 2 x 10 (2-38 x 235)
Northern Species	4 ft. (1.2 m)	1- 2 x 6 (1-38 x 140)	1 - 2 x 6 (1-38 x 140)	1- 2 x 8 (1-38 x 184)	1- 2 x 8 (1-38 x 184)	1- 2 x 8 (1-38 x 184)	1 - 2 x 10 (1-38 x 235)
	6 ft. (1.8 m)	1 - 2 x 10 (1-38 x 235)	2- 2 x 8 (2-38 x 184)	2- 2 x 8 (2-38 x 184)	2- 2 x 8 (2-38 x 184)	2- 2 x 8 (2-38 x 184)	2 - 2 x 10 (2-38 x 235)
	8 ft. (2.4 m)	2 - 2 x 10 (2-38 x 235)	2 - 2 x 10 (2-38 x 235)	2 - 2 x 10 (2-38 x 235)	2 - 2 x 10 (2-38 x 235)	2 - 2 x 12 (2-38 x 286)	2 - 2 x 12 (2-38 x 286)

Notes to Table 39
1. Incising is knife cutting the surface of wood to help perservatives penetrate the wood.
2. Design based on 2001 CAN/CSA O86.
3. Live load = 40 psf (1.9 kPa), Dead load = 10 psf (0.5 kPa).
4. Lumber No. 2 and Better grade, pressure treated, wet service.
5. Beam selection is for a beam on the edge of a deck. Double the number of plys for middle beams supporting joists on both sides.
6. Nail-laminate the beams to act as a single member (see Columns and Beams).

Table 40
Joists for exterior decks

Joist Size in. (mm)	Joist span, ft. - in. (m)			
	Joists not incised		Joists incised	
	Joist spacing, in. (mm)			
	16 in. (400 mm)	24 in. (600 mm)	16 in. (400 mm)	24 in. (600 mm)
Douglas fir - larch (includes Douglas fir and western larch				
2x6 (38x140)	9-6 (2.9)	7-6 (2.3)	8-6 (2.6)	7-2 (2.2)
2x8 (38x184)	11-6 (3.5)	9.2 (2.8)	10-6 (3.2)	8-6 (2.6)
2x10 (38x235)	14-1 (4.3)	11-6 (3.5)	12-9 (3.9)	10-6 (3.2)
Hem - fir (includes western hemlock and amabilis fir)				
2x6 (38x140)	9-6 (2.9)	8-2 (2.5)	9-2 (2.8)	7-6 (2.3)
2x8 (38x184)	12-1 (3.7)	9-9 (3.0)	11-2 (3.4)	8-10 (2.7)
2x10 (38x235)	14-1 (4.3)	11-9 (3.6)	13-4 (4.1)	11-2 (3.4)
Spruce - pine - fir (includes spruce [all species except coast sitka spruce], jack pine, lodgeploe pine, balsam fir and alpine fir)				
2x6 (38x140)	9-2 (2.8)	7-10 (2.4)	8-10 (2.7)	7-6 (2.3)
2x8 (38x184)	12-1 (3.7)	10-2 (3.1)	11-6 (3.5)	9-2 (2.8)
2x10 (38x235)	14-1 (4.3)	12-6 (3.8)	14-1 (4.3)	11-6 (3.5)
Northern species (includes any Canadian species covered by the NLGA Standard Grading Rules				
2x6 (38x140)	8-2 (2.5)	6-7 (2.0)	7-6 (2.3)	6-2 (1.9)
2x8 (38x184)	9-9 (3.0)	8-2 (2.5)	9-2 (2.8)	7-6 (2.3)
2x10 (38x235)	12-1 (3.7)	9-9 (3.0)	11-2 (3.4)	9-2 (2.8)

Notes to Table 40
1. Incising is knife cutting the surface of wood to help perservatives penetrate the wood.
2. Design based on 2001 CAN / CSA O86
3. Live load + 40 psf (1.9 kPa), Dead load = 10 psf (0.5 kPa).
4. Lumber No. 2 and Better grade, pressure treated, wet service conditions.

Appendix B - Site-built Trusses

APPENDIX B - SITE-BUILT TRUSSES

Light-frame wood trusses are economical, efficient and the most common method of framing roofs. The truss industry manufactures trusses under controlled conditions and each truss is specifically engineered using design procedures set out in the National Building Code. Trusses are manufactured to meet code requirements by qualified truss manufacturers. The following tables are provided as guidance in certain atypical circumstances, such as remote locations, where manufactured trusses are not available.

This appendix provides guidelines for standard designs of "W"(Fink) type trusses using plywood-nailed gusset plates, for use in residential construction. The plywood gusseted truss designs in this section are based on older test data and tables in earlier editions of the Building Code. These tables are no longer referenced in the current National Building Code due to refinements to truss analysis and design procedures and the numerous possibilities of truss design, shapes, combinations and variations in joint details.

The truss designs in Appendix B are applicable only for the limitations noted. Site-building of trusses is valid only when the design and fabrication instructions described here are strictly applied and the same care required for the storage, handling and bracing of factory-manufactured trusses is applied. Users are advised to check with the local authority having juris-diction to ensure that the use of site-built trusses is acceptable.

LIMITATIONS

There are an infinite number of spans and roof slopes that can be used in residential roof construction. The information on site-built trusses is applicable only when the following conditions are met:

Applicability: The designs are not intended for use in buildings with attics accessible by stairway or where the bottom chord may be subject to concentrated loads.

Roof slope: The roof slope is limited to 4 in 12 (1:3) or 3 in 12 (1:4). There is one table for each slope.

Roof span: The maximum roof span is 36.3 ft. (11,075 mm). The tables provide increments of 2 ft. (600 mm). Use the higher span for spans between two values. The span is the clear span measured between supports.

Truss Spacing: The trusses are designed for a spacing of 24 in. (600 mm). To accommodate higher Specified Snow Loads not covered by the tables, an additional table (Table B-1) is provided allowing for truss spacing as low as 12 in. (300 mm).

Specified Snow Load: The tables are developed for three specified snow loads, 22.6 psf (1.08 kPa), 30.1 psf (1.44 kPa, and 37.4 psf (1.79 kPa). For values between these values, use the higher specified snow loads. For higher values than those on the chart or to adjust the truss spacing, use Table B-1 to select the appropriate load.

LUMBER REQUIRE-MENTS

Lumber species and grades vary in strength. The tables in Appendix B are based on using the lumber species and grades indicated. It is not acceptable to make substitutions. The site-built truss designs are based on the use of lumber graded in accordance with 1970 NLGA Standard Grading Rules for Canadian Lumber as follows:

Chords (top and bottom members): No. 1 or No. 2 and Better S-P-F

Webs (interior members): . . . . . . No. 1 or No. 2 and Better S-P-F

Note: No. 1 and No. 2 grades have the same strength characteristics. No. 2 and Better is a grade that includes No. 2 and may include No. 1 and select pieces.

The S-P-F lumber designation includes the following species:

Balsam Fir

White Spruce

Lodgepole Pine

Engleman Spruce

Jack Pine

Black Spruce

Alpine Fir

Red Spruce

All gussets (plywood connector plates) shall be 1/2 in. (12.5 mm) thick Douglas Fir Plywood (DFP), sheathing grade (SHG), exterior bond type, conforming to CSA 0121. The grain of the plywood faces shall be parallel to the bottom chord except for the gussets joining the short web members to the top chord where the face grain shall be parallel to the web members.

SPECIFIED SNOW LOAD

The calculation of the Specified Snow Load (S) is determined using the following equation:

$$S = C_b \times S_s + S_r$$

Where:

S is the specified snow load
C_b is the basic snow load roof factor
S_s is the ground snow load
S_r is the associated rain load

Refer to the National Building Code of Canada or to your local building official for assistance in determining the specified snow load.

DESIGN STEPS

Using Tables B-2 and B-3:

Determine the truss span and slope from the design drawings. (Reminder: only slopes of 4 in 12 (1:3) and 3 in 12 (1:4) can be used.) For spans between or below values given in the tables, use the nailing schedule for the next largest span shown.

From the construction details determine if the raised or standard heel design will be used and determine if there are to be any cantilevers.

Determine the specified snow load (S) for the building location. Use a higher value of S for values between or below those given. Higher loads can use the equivalent S as noted in Table B-1 for reduced truss spacing.

Use Tables B-2 and B-3 to determine the number of nails required for each joint gusset plate. The truss joint number is shown on the respective construction details.

Use Tables B-2 and B-3 to determine the size of the chords–either 2 in. by 4 in. (38 x 89 mm), 2 in. by 6 in. (38 x 140mm) or a combination of both. All gusset plates shall be fastened with 3 in. (76 mm) common steel nails.

Use the construction details provided to layout patterns for the truss construction.

CONSTRUCTION STEPS

The following general steps are required to construct site-built trusses:

Select the best quality lumber for the top chord and the outer segments of the bottom chord - these are the areas of the highest stress.

Using the construction details, measure and cut chord material for one truss. Fit all pieces together to make sure that fit and dimensions are true, then use pieces as a pattern to mark and cut remaining members. Take care that all members butt tight and true at connections.

Using the construction details, measure and cut the plywood gussets. Insure that the face grain of the plywood runs parallel to the bottom chord, except for web members that have the grain running parallel to the web member. The larger dimensions are for larger plates that are used if any member at the joint is a 2 in. x 6 in. (38x 140mm) chord. Mark out the nailing pattern on one set of gussets. Use this pattern to layout the other similar gussets (see Figure B-4).

Nail truss connections on a solid, level surface. It is wise to place a piece of fiberboard sheathing or foam under the truss to accept the nail extensions. Note that nails must penetrate through both gussets and the member.

Flip the truss and clinch the nails perpendicular to the plywood grain.

Consider making a jig to make multiple trusses.

INSTALLATION DETAILS

The trusses shall be installed in a plumb position and each end shall be toe-nailed to the wall with three 3 1/4 in. (82 mm) nails or approved plates. The top chord shall be laterally supported by sheathing or by furring spaced at 18 in. (450 mm) on center or less.

Additional reinforcing is necessary when one or both ends of the truss are to be cantilevered (see Figure B-3).

Truss members shall not be notched, drilled or otherwise weakened to facilitate the installation of services such as plumbing, heating or electrical wiring or for any other reason.

Table B-1
Specified snow loads for site-built trusses

Truss spacing in. (mm)	Specified snow load					
	22.5 psf	1.08 kPa	30.1 psf	1.44 kPa	37.4 psf	1.79 kPa
24 (600)	22.5	1.08	30.1	1.44	37.4	1.79
20 (500)	30.1	1.44	40.1	1.92	49.9	2.39
18 (450)	33.8	1.62	45.1	2.16	56.2	2.69
16 (400)	37.6	1.8	50.1	2.4	62	2.97
12 (300)	45.1	2.16	60.1	2.88	74.8	3.58

Table B-2
Nailing schedules for 4 in 12 (1:3) roof slopes

Spans 16.3 to 36.3 feet (4,980 to 11,075 mm)
Gussets: 1/2 in. (12.5 mm) DFP plywood   Nailed "W" Truss

Top Chord Size	Nailing Schedule Bottom Chord Size	Specified Snow Load - S	Span	Number of Nails at Joint Locations on Figure B-1					
in (mm)	(in) mm	psf (kPa)	feet (mm)	1	2	3	4	5	6
2 x 4 (38 x 89)	2 x 4 (38 x 89)	22.6 psf (1.08 kPa)	16.3 (4980)	9	8	2	3	3	5
			18.3 (5590)	10	9	2	3	4	6
			20.3 (6200)	11	10	2	3	4	7
			22.3 (6810)	12	11	2	4	4	7
			24.3 (7415)	13	12	3	4	5	8
			26.3 (8025)	14	13	3	4	5	9
			28.3 (8635)	15	14	3	4	5	9
2 x 4 (38 x 89)	2 x 4 (38 x 89)	30.1 psf (1.44 kPa)	16.3 (4980)	12	11	2	4	4	7
			18.3 (5590)	13	12	3	4	5	8
			20.3 (6200)	15	13	3	4	5	9
			22.3 (6810)	16	14	3	5	6	10
			24.3 (7415)	17	16	4	5	6	11
			26.3 (8025)	19	17	4	6	7	11
			28.3 (8635)	20	18	4	6	7	12
2 x 4 (38 x 89)	2 x 4 (38 x 89)	37.4 psf (1.79 kPa)	16.3 (4980)	17	16	3	5	6	11
			18.3 (5590)	19	18	4	5	7	12
			20.3 (6200)	21	20	4	6	7	13
			22.3 (6810)	23	21	4	7	8	14
			24.3 (7415)	25	23	5	7	9	16
			26.3 (8025)	27	25	5	8	10	17
2 x 6 (38 x 140)	2 x 4 (38 x 89)	22.6 psf (1.08 kPa)	30 (9145)	15	14	3	4	5	10
2 x 6 (38 x 140)	2 x 4 (38 x 89)	30.1 psf (1.44 kPa)	30 (9145)	18	17	4	5	6	12
2 x 6 (38 x 140)	2 x 4 (38 x 89)	37.4 psf (1.79 kPa)	28.3 (8635)	21	20	5	6	7	14
			30 (9145)	22	21	5	6	7	15

Truss and gusset plate detailing nailed "W" truss
Roof slope 4 in 12 (1:3)

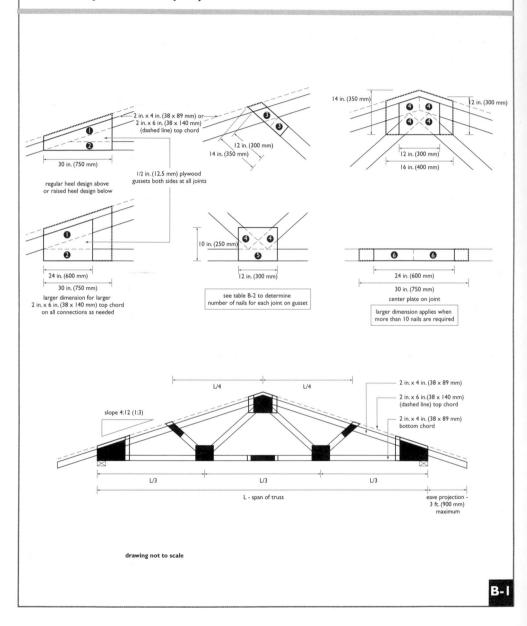

2 in. x 4 in. (38 x 89 mm) or
2 in. x 6 in. (38 x 140 mm)
(dashed line) top chord

30 in. (750 mm)

regular heel design above
or raised heel design below

1/2 in. (12.5 mm) plywood
gussets both sides at all joints

12 in. (300 mm)
14 in. (350 mm)

14 in. (350 mm)
12 in. (300 mm)

12 in. (300 mm)
16 in. (400 mm)

24 in. (600 mm)
30 in. (750 mm)

larger dimension for larger
2 in. x 6 in. (38 x 140 mm) top chord
on all connections as needed

10 in. (250 mm)

12 in. (300 mm)

see table B-2 to determine
number of nails for each joint on gusset

24 in. (600 mm)
30 in. (750 mm)
center plate on joint

larger dimension applies when
more than 10 nails are required

L/4   L/4

slope 4:12 (1:3)

2 in. x 4 in. (38 x 89 mm)

2 in. x 6 in. (38 x 140 mm)
(dashed line) top chord

2 in. x 4 in. (38 x 89 mm)
bottom chord

L/3   L/3   L/3

L - span of truss

eave projection -
3 ft. (900 mm)
maximum

drawing not to scale

B-1

Table B-3
Nailing schedules for 3 in 12 (1:4) roof slopes

Spans 16.3 to 36.3 feet (4,980 to 11,075 mm)

Gussets: 1/2 in. (12.5 mm) DFP plywood   Nailed "W" Truss

Nailing Schedule

Top Chord Size in(mm)	Bottom Chord Size in(mm)	Specified Snow Load - S psf (kPa)	Span feet (mm)	Number of Nails at Joint Locations on Figure B-2					
				1	2	3	4	5	6
2 x 4 (38 x 89)	2 x 4 (38 x 89)	22.6 psf (1.08 kPa)	16.3 (4980)	17	17	4	6	6	12
			18.3 (5590)	20	18	4	6	6	13
			20.3 (6200)	22	21	4	7	7	14
			22.3 (6810)	24	24	4	8	8	16
			24.3 (7415)	26	26	4	9	9	17
			26.3 (8025)	29	28	5	9	9	19
			28.3 (8635)	31	30	5	9	9	20
2 x 4 (38 x 89)	2 x 4 (38 x 89)	30.1 psf (1.44 kPa)	16.3 (4980)	21	21	4	7	7	14
			18.3 (5590)	24	23	4	7	7	16
			20.3 (6200)	27	26	5	8	8	17
			22.3 (6810)	29	29	5	9	9	19
			24.3 (7415)	32	31	5	10	10	21
			26.3 (8025)	35	34	6	11	11	23
2 x 6 (38 x 140)	2 x 4 (38 x 89)	22.6 psf (1.08 kPa)	16.3 (4980)	13	13	3	5	5	9
			18.3 (5590)	15	14	3	5	5	10
			20.3 (6200)	16	16	3	5	5	11
			22.3 (6810)	18	18	3	6	6	12
			24.3 (7415)	20	19	3	6	6	13
			26.3 (8025)	21	21	4	7	7	14
			28.3 (8635)	22	22	4	7	7	15
2 x 6 (38 x 140)	2 x 4 (38 x 89)	30.1 psf (1.44 kPa)	16.3 (4980)	16	16	3	5	5	11
			18.3 (5590)	18	17	3	5	5	12
			20.3 (6200)	20	19	4	6	6	13
			22.3 (6810)	22	22	4	7	7	14
			24.3 (7415)	24	23	4	8	8	16
			26.3 (8025)	26	25	5	8	8	17
			28.3 (8635)	27	27	5	8	8	18
2 x 6 (38 x 140)	2 x 4 (38 x 89)	37.4 psf (1.79 kPa2)	16.3 (4980)	18	18	4	6	6	12
			18.3 (5590)	21	20	4	6	6	14
			20.3 (6200)	24	23	5	7	7	15
			22.3 (6810)	26	25	5	8	8	17
			24.3 (7415)	28	27	5	9	9	18
			26.3 (8025)	30	30	6	10	10	20
2 x 6 (38 x 140)	2 x 6 (38 x 140)	22.6 psf (1.08 kPa)	30.3 (9245)	24	23	4	6	7	16
			32.3 (9855)	26	25	5	6	8	17
			34.3 (10 465)	28	27	6	7	9	18
			36.3 (11 075)	30	29	7	8	10	19
2 x 6 (38 x 140)	2 x 6 (38 x 140)	30.1 psf (1.44 kPa)	30.3 (9245)	30	29	6	7	9	20
			32.3 (9855)	32	31	6	7	10	21
			34.3 (10 465)	34	33	7	8	11	22
			36.3 (11 075)	36	35	8	9	12	23
2 x 6 (38 x 140)	2 x 6 (38 x 140)	37.4 psf (1.79 kPa)	30.3 (9245)	35	34	7	8	11	24
			32.3 (9855)	37	36	7	8	11	25
			34.3 (10 465)	39	38	8	9	12	26
			36.3 (11 075)	41	40	9	10	13	27

Truss and gusset plate detailing nailed "W" truss
Roof slope 3 in 12 (1:4)

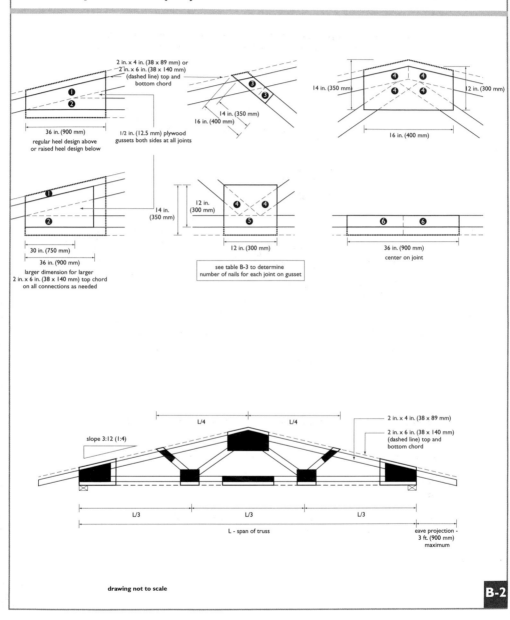

drawing not to scale

B-2

Cantilever detail nailed "W" truss with plywood gussets

The following design allows for the use of an additional web member Ⓐ
to relocate the bearing point away from the heel joint to create a cantilever

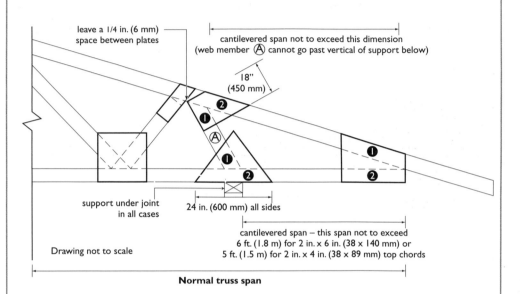

leave a 1/4 in. (6 mm)
space between plates

cantilevered span not to exceed this dimension
(web member Ⓐ cannot go past vertical of support below)

18"
(450 mm)

support under joint
in all cases

24 in. (600 mm) all sides

Drawing not to scale

cantilevered span – this span not to exceed
6 ft. (1.8 m) for 2 in. x 6 in. (38 x 140 mm) or
5 ft. (1.5 m) for 2 in. x 4 in. (38 x 89 mm) top chords

Normal truss span

Notes

1. Top and bottom chord sizes and nailing requirements are determined from tables B-2 and B-3.

2. The additional web member Ⓐ shall be the same size as the top chord.

3. If desired, both ends of the truss can be cantilevered using the above construction technique.

4. The nailing for the new gusset plates as per above to match heel joint. The size of gusset plates can be adjusted for member Ⓐ if space is restricted.

B-3

Method for fabricating joints

1. **Place fibreboard pad under joint and drive all nails from one side**

top chord

bottom chord

3 in. (75 mm) nail

1/2 in. (12.5 mm) plywood gusset

face grain parallel to bottom chord

staggered nails

3/4 in. (20 mm) fibreboard

2. **Flip truss. Remove fibreboard pads. Bend over projecting tips of nails at right angles to plywood face grain**

B-4

Index

INDEX

A

B

C

O

P

R

S

Canada Mortgage and Housing Corporation